EDEXCEL BIOLOGY 2

A-Level Year 2 **Student Workbook**

EDEXCEL BIOLOGY 2

A-Level Year 2 Student Workbook

Tracey
Senior Author

Meet the writing team

Tracey Greenwood
I have been writing resources for students since 1993. I have a Ph.D in biology, specialising in lake ecology and I have taught both graduate and undergraduate biology.

Lissa
Author

Lissa Bainbridge-Smith
I worked in industry in a research and development capacity for 8 years before joining BIOZONE in 2006. I have a M.Sc from Waikato University.

Kent
Author

Kent Pryor
I have a BSc from Massey University majoring in zoology and ecology and taught secondary school biology and chemistry for 9 years before joining BIOZONE as an author in 2009.

Richard
Founder & CEO

Richard Allan
I have had 11 years experience teaching senior secondary school biology. I have a Masters degree in biology and founded BIOZONE in the 1980s after developing resources for my own students.

Cover photograph
The veiled or cone head chameleon (*Chamaeleo calyptratus*) is native to the Arabian peninsula. Like all chameleons, they can change colouration in response to environment, social status, and stress. it is the most common species of chameleon in the pet trade as it is prolific breeder and is tolerant of a wide range of conditions.

 PHOTO: Science Photo Library
https://offset.com

Thanks to:
The staff at BIOZONE, including Mike Campbell and Holly Coon for design and graphics support, Paolo Curray and Malaki Toleafoa for IT support, Debbie Antoniadis and Arahi Hippolite for office handling and logistics, and the BIOZONE sales team.

First edition 2017
ISBN 978-1-927309-26-1

Purchases of this workbook may be made direct from the publisher:

BIOZONE

BIOZONE Learning Media (UK) Ltd.

Telephone local:	01283 530 366
Telephone international:	+44 1283 530 366
Fax local:	01283 831 900
Fax international:	+44 1283 831 900
Email:	sales@biozone.co.uk

www.**BIOZONE**.co.uk

Contents

Activity is marked: to be done;   when completed

Contents

Activity is marked:　　● to be done;　　✔ when completed

Using This Workbook

This first edition of Edexcel Biology 2 has been specifically written to meet the content and skills requirements of the second year of Edexcel A Level Biology. Learning outcomes in the introduction to each chapter provide you with a concise guide to the knowledge and skills requirements for each section of work. Each learning outcome is matched to the activity or activities addressing it. The eight core practicals at this level are identified in the chapter introductions by a flag and code (CP-#) and supported by activities designed to provide background and familiarity with apparatus, techniques, experimental design, and interpretation of results. Activities supporting specific mathematical skills (e.g. using a statistical test) are also identified with a similar flag (MATH). A range of activities will help you to build on what you already know, explore new topics, work collaboratively, and practise your skills in data handling and interpretation. We hope that you find the workbook valuable and that you make full use of its features.

▶ The outline of the chapter structure below will help you to navigate through the material in each chapter.

Introduction
- A check list of the knowledge and skills requirements for the chapter.
- A list of key terms.

Activities
- The KEY IDEA provides your focus for the activity.
- Annotated diagrams help you understand the content.
- Questions review the content of the page.

Review
- Create your own summary for review.
- Hints help you to focus on what is important.
- Your summary will consolidate your understanding of the content in the chapter.

Literacy
- Activities are based on, but not restricted to, the introductory key terms list.
- Several types of activities test your understanding of the concepts and biological terms in the chapter.

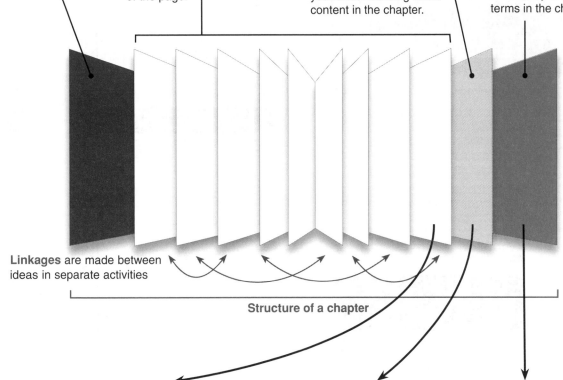

Linkages are made between ideas in separate activities

Structure of a chapter

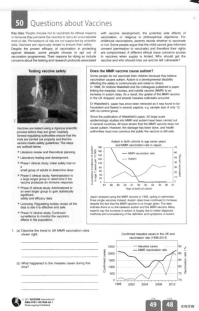

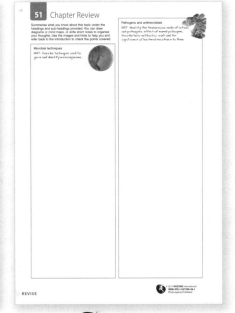

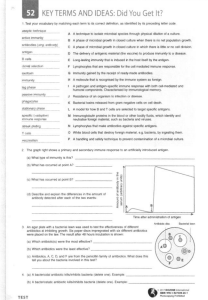

▶ Understanding the activity coding system and making use of the online material identified will enable you to get the most out of this resource. The chapter content is structured to build knowledge and skills but this structure does not necessarily represent a strict order of treatment. Be guided by your teacher, who will assign activities as part of a wider programme of independent and group-based work.

Look out for these features and know how to use them:

The **chapter introduction** provides you with a summary of the knowledge and skills requirements for the topic, phrased as learning outcomes. Flags identify the core practicals and mathematical skills. Use the check boxes to identify and mark off the points as you complete them. The chapter introduction also provides a list of key terms for the chapter, from which you can construct your own glossary.

The **activities** form most of this workbook. They are numbered sequentially and each has a task code identifying the skill emphasised. Each activity has a short introduction with a key idea identifying the main message of the page. Most of the information is associated with pictures and diagrams, and your understanding of the content is reviewed through the questions. Some of the activities involve modelling and group work.

Free response questions allow you to use the information provided to answer questions about the content of the activity, either directly or by applying the same principles to a new situation. In some cases, an activity will assume understanding of prior content.

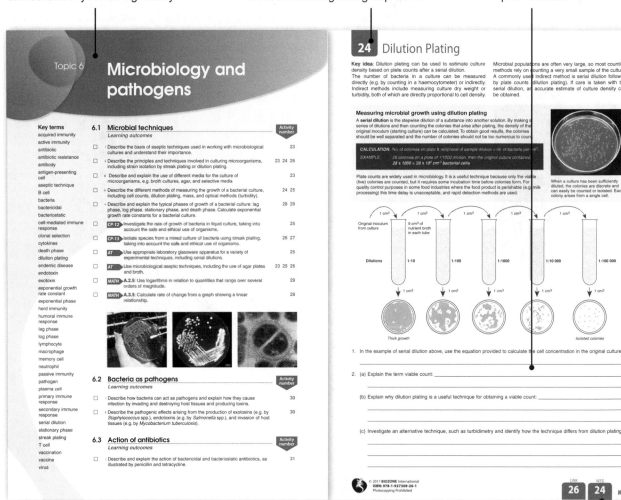

LINK tabs at the bottom of the activity page identify activities that are related in that they build on content or apply the same principles to a new situation.

WEB tabs at the bottom of the activity page alert the reader to the **Weblinks** resource, which provides external, online support material for the activity, usually in the form of an animation, video clip, photo library, or quiz. Bookmark the Weblinks page (see next page) and visit it frequently as you progress through the workbook.

A **TASK CODE** on the page tab identifies the type of activity. For example, is it primarily information-based (KNOW), or does it involve modelling or practical work (PRAC), or data handling (DATA)? A full list of codes is given on the following page but the codes themselves are relatively self-explanatory.

Using the Tab System

The tab system is a useful system for quickly identifying related content and online support. Links generally refer to activities that build on the information in the activity in depth or extent. In the example below, the weblink 24 provides a short video from BIORAD on serial dilution and plate counts. Activity 26 examines a related microbiological technique for colony isolation, streak plating, which supports core practical 13. Sometimes, a link will reflect on material that has been covered earlier as a reminder for important terms that have already been defined or for a formula that may be required to answer a question. The weblinks code is always the same as the activity number on which it is cited. On visiting the weblink page (below), find the number and it will correspond to one or more external websites providing a video or animation of some aspect of the activity's content. Occasionally, the weblink may access a reference paper or provide a bank of photographs where images are provided in colour, e.g. for plant and animal histology.

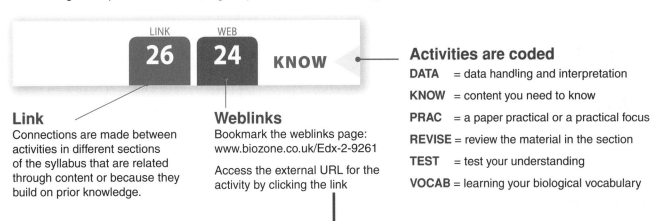

LINK	WEB	
26	**24**	**KNOW**

Link
Connections are made between activities in different sections of the syllabus that are related through content or because they build on prior knowledge.

Weblinks
Bookmark the weblinks page: www.biozone.co.uk/Edx-2-9261

Access the external URL for the activity by clicking the link

Activities are coded

DATA = data handling and interpretation

KNOW = content you need to know

PRAC = a paper practical or a practical focus

REVISE = review the material in the section

TEST = test your understanding

VOCAB = learning your biological vocabulary

www.biozone.co.uk/weblink/Edx-2-9261

This WEBLINKS page provides links to **external web sites** with supporting information for the activities. These sites are separate to those provided in the BIOLINKS area of BIOZONE's web site. Almost exclusively, they are narrowly focused animations and video clips directly relevant to the activity on which they are cited. They provide great support to aid student understanding of basic concepts, especially for visual learners.

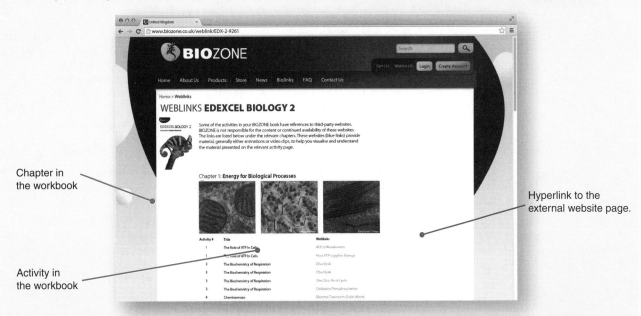

Chapter in the workbook

Activity in the workbook

Hyperlink to the external website page.

Bookmark weblinks by typing in the address: it is not accessible directly from BIOZONE's website
Corrections and clarifications to current editions are always posted on the weblinks page

Summary of Practical Skills for Edexcel AL

▶ The practical and mathematical skills for Edexcel A Level are outlined below and supported in the activities indicated. See Edexcel Biology 1 for the practical skills to be assessed in written papers and use of apparatus and techniques.

CP   A-Level core practical activities

Core practicals supported as indicated

		Activity number
☐	9 Investigate factors affecting the rate of respiration using a respirometer.	6
☐	10 Investigate the effects of different wavelengths of light on the rate of photosynthesis.	9
☐	11 Investigate the presence of different chloroplast pigments using chromatography.	10
☐	12 Investigate the rate of growth of bacteria in liquid culture.	25
☐	13 Isolate individual species from a mixed culture of bacteria using streak plating.	27
☐	14 Investigate the effect of gibberellin on the production of amylase in germinating cereals using a starch agar assay.	123
☐	15 Investigate the effect of different sampling methods on estimates of population size.	159
☐	16 Investigate the effect of one abiotic factor on the distribution or morphology of one species.	179

Practical skills for indirect assessment

Supported as indicated in Edexcel Biology 2 but also see Edexcel Biology 1

		Activity number
☐	a Independent thinking Solve problems in a practical context. Apply scientific knowledge to practical contexts.	75
☐	b Use and application of scientific methods and practices Comment on experimental design and evaluate scientific methods. Present data appropriately. Evaluate results and draw conclusions with reference to measurement uncertainties or errors. Identify variables, including those that must be controlled.	15 16 19
☐	c Numeracy and application of mathematical concepts in a practical context Plot and interpret graphs. Process and analyse data using appropriate mathematical skills. Consider margins of error, and accuracy and precision of data.	25 29 101 105
☐	d Instruments and equipment Know and understand how to use a wide range of experimental and practical instruments, equipment, and techniques appropriate the requirements of the specification.	23 24 26 54 71 155 157

Practical skills for direct assessment

Supported as indicated in Edexcel Biology 2 but also see Edexcel Biology 1

		Activity number
☐	a Independent thinking Apply investigative approaches and methods to practical work.	9 27 159
☐	b Use and apply of scientific methods and practices Safely and correctly use a range of practical equipment and materials and follow written instructions. Make and record observations. Keep appropriate records of experimental activities. Present information and data appropriately. Use appropriate software and tools to process data, carry out research, and report findings.	6 9 10 25 27 124
☐	c Research and referencing Use online and offline research skills, including websites, textbooks, and other printed scientific sources of information. Correctly cite sources of information.	EDX 1
☐	d Instruments and equipment Use a wide range of experimental and practical instruments, equipment, and techniques appropriate to the requirements of the specification.	6 10 25 27 124 159 180

Topic 5

Energy for biological processes

Key terms

absorption spectrum
accessory pigment
acetyl coA
action spectrum
alcoholic fermentation
anaerobic metabolism
ATP
ATP synthase
Calvin cycle
cellular respiration
chemiosmosis
chlorophyll
chloroplast
cristae
decarboxylation
dehydrogenation
electron transport chain
ethanol
FAD
fermentation
glucose
glycerate 3-phosphate
glycolysis
hexose sugar
Krebs cycle
lactic acid fermentation
light dependent reactions (phase)
light independent reactions (phase)
link reaction
matrix
mitochondrion
NAD / NADP
NAD / NADH
oxidative phosphorylation
photolysis
photophosphorylation
photosynthesis
photosystem
pyruvate
RuBisCo
RuBP
substrate level phosphorylation
triose phosphate

5.1 Aerobic respiration

Learning outcomes

Activity number

☐ i Know that cellular respiration yields ATP. Describe how ATP is used as a source of energy for metabolic reactions and explain why it also generates heat. — 1 7

☐ ii Know the different stages of cellular respiration and their the location in the cell. — 2

5.2 Glycolysis

Learning outcomes

Activity number

☐ i Explain the conversion of monosaccharides to pyruvate in glycolysis including:
• the phosphorylation of hexose molecules by ATP
• breakdown of glycerate 3-phosphate (GP)
• production of reduced coenzyme (NADH) and ATP — 3

Dartmouth College · Kristian Peters · Dartmouth College

5.3 Link reaction and Krebs cycle

Learning outcomes

Activity number

☐ i Recall that the link reaction and the Krebs cycle occur in the matrix of the mitochondria. — 2 3

☐ ii Explain how, during the complete oxidation of pyruvate via the link reaction and Krebs cycle, carbon atoms are removed to produce:
• carbon dioxide • reduced coenzyme (NADH) • ATP — 3

5.4 Oxidative phosphorylation

Learning outcomes

Activity number

☐ i Recall that the electron transport chain occurs in the inner membranes (cristae) of the mitochondria. — 2 3

☐ ii Explain the role of the electron transport chain in generating ATP through oxidative phosphorylation. — 3

☐ iii Explain the role of oxygen as the terminal electron acceptor in this process and identify the molecule formed. — 3

☐ iv Describe the generation of ATP by chemiosmosis. — 3 4

☐ v Explain the role of the mitochondrial membranes in chemiosmosis. — 3 4

5.5 Anaerobic metabolism in eukaryotes

Learning outcomes

Activity number

☐ i Understand that, in the absence of oxygen, eukaryotes can generate a limited yield of ATP through the partial breakdown of hexoses. — 5

☐ ii Explain the differences in ATP yield from one molecule of hexose sugar in aerobic compared with anaerobic conditions. — 3 5

☐ iii Explain how mammalian muscle produces lactate by lactic acid fermentation, including reference to the lactate shuttle. Describe the effect of lactate on muscle contraction (including the effect of low pH on enzyme activity).   5

☐ iv Explain how plant roots produce ethanol by alcoholic fermentation in anaerobic conditions.   5

☐ **CP-9** Investigate factors affecting the rate of aerobic respiration using a respirometer, taking into account safe and ethical use of organisms.   6

☐ **AT** Use appropriate apparatus to record a range of quantitative measurements.   6

☐ **AT** Safely and ethically use organisms to measure physiological functions.   6

☐ **MATH** **A.0.1**: Recognise and make use of appropriate units in calculations.   6

☐ **MATH** **A.3.2**: Plot two variables from experimental or other data.   6

5.6 Photosynthetic pigments
Learning outcomes

Activity number

☐ i Explain what is meant by the terms absorption spectrum and action spectrum with respect to light absorbing pigments.   8

☐ **CP-10** Investigate the effects of different wavelengths of light on the rate of photosynthesis.   9

☐ **AT** Use appropriate apparatus to record a range of quantitative measurements.   9

☐ **MATH** **A.0.1**: Recognise and make use of appropriate units in calculations.

☐ **MATH** **A.3.2**: Plot two variables from experimental or other data.

☐ ii Explain why plants have a variety of different photosynthetic pigments.   8

☐ **CP-11** Investigate the presence of different chloroplast pigments using chromatography.   10

☐ **AT** Separate biological compounds using thin layer/paper chromatography.   10

5.7 Photosynthesis
Learning outcomes

Activity number

☐ i Describe the structure of a chloroplast, including envelope, stroma, grana, and stroma lamellae. Identify the sites of the two stages of photosynthesis (light capture and carbon fixation).   11 12

Light dependent stage

☐ ii Explain the role of the thylakoid membranes in the light dependent stage of photosynthesis.   13

☐ iii Explain the cyclic and non-cyclic photophosphorylation including reference to the production of reduced NADP, ATP, and oxygen.   13

☐ **Light independent stage**

☐ iv Explain the role of the stroma in the light independent stage of photosynthesis.   14

☐ v Explain how carbon is fixed by combination with 5C ribulose bisphosphate (RuBP) to form glycerate-3-phosphate (GP) using the enzyme RUBISCO.   14

☐ vi Explain how reduced NADP and ATP from the light-dependent stage are used to: 14 15 16
   • synthesise glyceraldehyde 3-phosphate (also known as GALP, G3P, PGAL, or triose phosphate) from GP.
   • to regenerate 5C RuBP in the Calvin cycle.

☐ vii Explain how GALP is used as a raw material to produce monosaccharides, amino acids, and other molecules.   17

☐ viii Describe and explain the factors that limit photosynthesis including carbon dioxide, light intensity, and temperature.   18 19 20

☐ **AT** Use appropriate apparatus to record a range of quantitative measurements.   19

☐ **MATH** **A.0.1**: Recognise and make use of appropriate units in calculations.

☐ **MATH** **A.3.2**: Plot two variables from experimental or other data.

1 The Role of ATP in Cells

Key Idea: ATP transports chemical energy within the cell for use in metabolic processes.

All organisms require energy to be able to perform the metabolic processes required for them to function and reproduce. This energy is obtained by cellular respiration, a set of metabolic reactions which ultimately convert biochemical energy from 'food' into the nucleotide **adenosine triphosphate** (ATP). ATP is considered to be a universal energy carrier, transferring chemical energy within the cell for use in metabolic processes such as biosynthesis, cell division, cell signalling, thermoregulation, cell mobility, and active transport of substances across membranes.

Adenosine triphosphate (ATP)

The ATP molecule consists of three components; a purine base (**adenine**), a pentose sugar (**ribose**), and **three phosphate groups** which attach to the 5' carbon of the pentose sugar. The structure of ATP is described below.

The bonds between the phosphate groups contain electrons in a high energy state which store a large amount of energy. The energy is released during ATP hydrolysis. Typically, hydrolysis is coupled to another cellular reaction to which the energy is transferred. The end products of the reaction are adenosine diphosphate (ADP) and an inorganic phosphate (Pi).

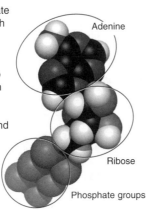

Adenine

Ribose

Phosphate groups

Note that energy is released during the formation of bonds during the hydrolysis reaction, not the breaking of bonds between the phosphates (which requires energy input).

The mitochondrion

Cellular respiration and ATP production occur in mitochondria. A mitochondrion is bounded by a double membrane. The inner and outer membranes are separated by an intermembrane space, compartmentalising the regions where the different reactions of cellular respiration take place. The folded inner membranes provide a large surface area for reactions.

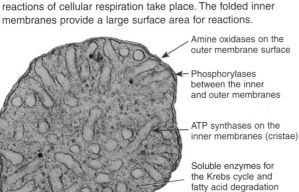

Amine oxidases on the outer membrane surface

Phosphorylases between the inner and outer membranes

ATP synthases on the inner membranes (cristae)

Soluble enzymes for the Krebs cycle and fatty acid degradation floating in the matrix

ATP powers metabolism

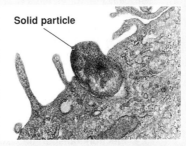

Solid particle

The energy released from the removal of a phosphate group of ATP is used to actively transport molecules and substances across the cellular membrane. Phagocytosis (left), which involves the engulfment of solid particles, is one such example.

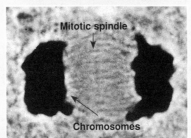

Mitotic spindle

Chromosomes

Cell division (mitosis), as observed in this onion cell, requires ATP to proceed. Formation of the mitotic spindle and chromosome separation are two aspects of cell division which require energy from ATP hydrolysis to occur.

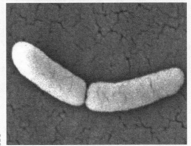

ATP is required when bacteria divide by binary fission (left). For example, ATP is required in DNA replication and to synthesise components of the peptidoglycan cell wall.

Maintaining body temperature requires energy. To maintain body heat, muscular activity increases (e.g. shivering). Cooling requires expenditure of energy too. For example, sweating is an energy requiring process involving secretion from glands in the skin.

1. Why do organisms need to respire? _____

_____

2. (a) Describe the general role of mitochondria in cell respiration: _____

_____

(b) Explain the importance of compartmentalisation in the mitochondrion: _____

_____

3. Explain why thermoregulation is associated with energy expenditure: _____

_____

_____

LINK   WEB
2   1

KNOW

2 ATP Production in Cells

Key Idea: Cellular respiration is the process by which the energy in glucose is transferred to ATP.

Cellular respiration can be **aerobic** (requires oxygen) or **anaerobic** (does not require oxygen). Some plants and animals can generate ATP anaerobically for short periods of time. Other organisms (anaerobic bacteria) use only anaerobic respiration and live in oxygen-free environments. Cellular respiration occurs in the cytoplasm and mitochondria. The overall process is summarised by the word equation:

glucose + oxygen → carbon dioxide + water + ATP.

An overview of ATP production in cells

Respiration involves three main stages plus a link reaction (summarised below). The first two stages are catabolic pathways, connected by a link reaction, which decompose glucose and other organic fuels. In the final stage, the electron transport chain accepts electrons from the earlier stages and passes these from one electron acceptor to another. The energy released at each transfer is used to make ATP. The final electron acceptor in this process is molecular oxygen.

1 **Glycolysis**. In the cytoplasm, glucose is broken down into two molecules of pyruvate.

2 **The link reaction**. In the mitochondrial matrix, pyruvate is split and added to coenzyme A.

3 **Krebs cycle**. In the mitochondrial matrix, a derivative of pyruvate is decomposed to CO_2.

4 **Electron transport and oxidative phosphorylation**. This occurs in the inner membranes of the mitochondrion and accounts for almost 90% of the ATP generated by respiration.

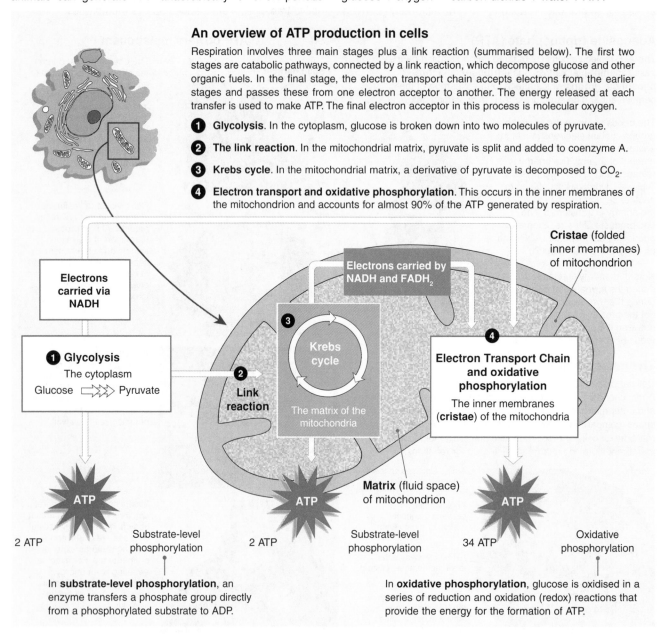

In **substrate-level phosphorylation**, an enzyme transfers a phosphate group directly from a phosphorylated substrate to ADP.

In **oxidative phosphorylation**, glucose is oxidised in a series of reduction and oxidation (redox) reactions that provide the energy for the formation of ATP.

1. Describe precisely in which part of the cell the following take place:

   (a) Glycolysis: _____

   (b) The link reaction: _____

   (c) Krebs cycle reactions: _____

   (d) Electron transport chain: _____

2. How does ATP generation in glycolysis and the Krebs cycle differ from ATP generation via the electron transport chain?

   _____

   _____

   _____

   _____

© 2017 **BIOZONE** International
ISBN: 978-1-927309-26-1
Photocopying Prohibited

3 The Biochemistry of Respiration

Key Idea: During cellular respiration, the energy in glucose is transferred to ATP in a series of enzyme controlled steps. The oxidation of glucose is a catabolic, energy yielding pathway. The breakdown of glucose and other organic fuels (such as fats and proteins) to simpler molecules releases energy for ATP synthesis. Glycolysis and the Krebs cycle supply electrons to the electron transport chain, which drives oxidative phosphorylation. Glycolysis nets two ATP. The conversion of pyruvate (the end product of glycolysis)

to acetyl CoA links glycolysis to the Krebs cycle. One "turn" of the cycle releases carbon dioxide, forms one ATP, and passes electrons to three NAD^+ and one FAD. Most of the ATP generated in cellular respiration is produced by oxidative phosphorylation when $NADH + H^+$ and $FADH_2$ donate electrons to the series of electron carriers in the electron transport chain. At the end of the chain, electrons are passed to molecular oxygen, reducing it to water. Electron transport is coupled to ATP synthesis.

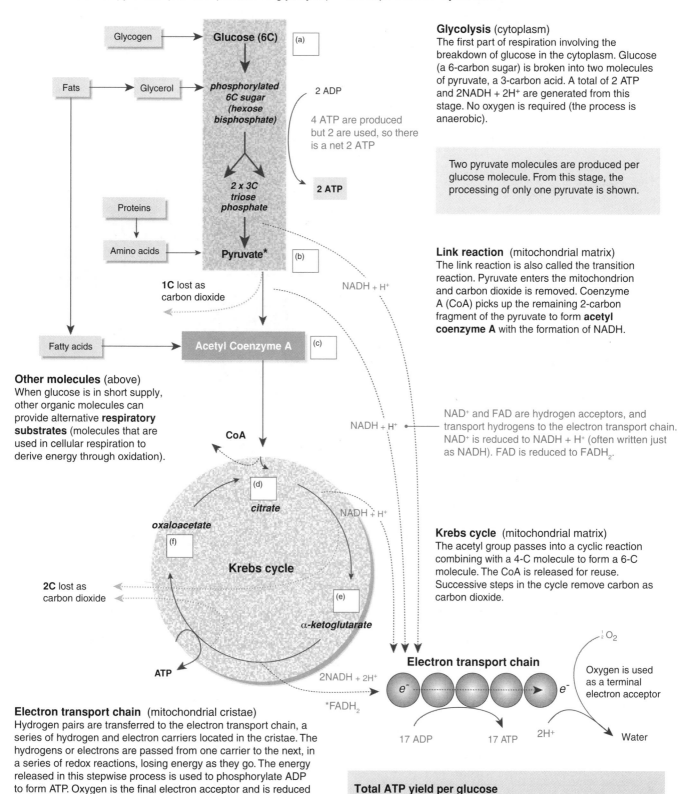

Glycolysis (cytoplasm)
The first part of respiration involving the breakdown of glucose in the cytoplasm. Glucose (a 6-carbon sugar) is broken into two molecules of pyruvate, a 3-carbon acid. A total of 2 ATP and $2NADH + 2H^+$ are generated from this stage. No oxygen is required (the process is anaerobic).

Two pyruvate molecules are produced per glucose molecule. From this stage, the processing of only one pyruvate is shown.

Link reaction (mitochondrial matrix)
The link reaction is also called the transition reaction. Pyruvate enters the mitochondrion and carbon dioxide is removed. Coenzyme A (CoA) picks up the remaining 2-carbon fragment of the pyruvate to form **acetyl coenzyme A** with the formation of NADH.

Other molecules (above)
When glucose is in short supply, other organic molecules can provide alternative **respiratory substrates** (molecules that are used in cellular respiration to derive energy through oxidation).

NAD^+ and FAD are hydrogen acceptors, and transport hydrogens to the electron transport chain. NAD^+ is reduced to $NADH + H^+$ (often written just as NADH). FAD is reduced to $FADH_2$.

Krebs cycle (mitochondrial matrix)
The acetyl group passes into a cyclic reaction combining with a 4-C molecule to form a 6-C molecule. The CoA is released for reuse. Successive steps in the cycle remove carbon as carbon dioxide.

Oxygen is used as a terminal electron acceptor

Electron transport chain (mitochondrial cristae)
Hydrogen pairs are transferred to the electron transport chain, a series of hydrogen and electron carriers located in the cristae. The hydrogens or electrons are passed from one carrier to the next, in a series of redox reactions, losing energy as they go. The energy released in this stepwise process is used to phosphorylate ADP to form ATP. Oxygen is the final electron acceptor and is reduced to water (hence **oxidative phosphorylation**).
Note FAD enters the electron transport chain at a lower energy level than NAD, and only 2ATP are generated per $FADH_2$.

Total ATP yield per glucose
Glycolysis: 2 ATP, *Krebs cycle*: 2 ATP, *Electron transport*: 34 ATP

LINK 4   LINK 2   WEB 3   **KNOW**

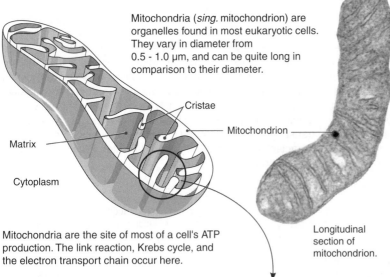

Mitochondria (*sing.* mitochondrion) are organelles found in most eukaryotic cells. They vary in diameter from 0.5 - 1.0 µm, and can be quite long in comparison to their diameter.

Cristae

Mitochondrion

Matrix

Cytoplasm

Mitochondria are the site of most of a cell's ATP production. The link reaction, Krebs cycle, and the electron transport chain occur here.

Longitudinal section of mitochondrion.

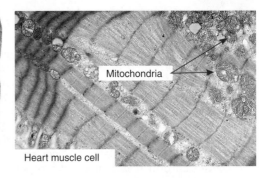

Mitochondria

Heart muscle cell

Cells that require a lot of ATP for cellular processes have a lot of mitochondria. Sperm cells contain a large number of mitochondria near the base of the tail. Liver cells have around 2000 mitochondria per cell, taking up 25% of the cytoplasmic space. Heart muscle cells (above) may have 40% of the cytoplasmic space taken up by mitochondria.

Location of cellular respiration

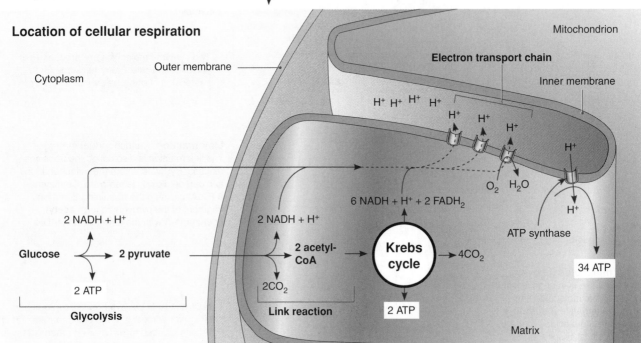

Mitochondrion

Outer membrane

Cytoplasm

Electron transport chain

Inner membrane

H^+ H^+ H^+ H^+

H^+ H^+ H^+

H^+

O_2 H_2O

6 NADH + H^+ + 2 FADH$_2$

ATP synthase

H^+

2 NADH + H^+

2 NADH + H^+

Glucose → 2 pyruvate

2 acetyl-CoA

Krebs cycle → 4CO$_2$

34 ATP

2 ATP

2CO$_2$

2 ATP

Glycolysis

Link reaction

Matrix

1. In the longitudinal section of a mitochondrion (above), label the matrix and cristae.

2. Explain the purpose of the link reaction: _____
   _____
   _____

3. On the diagram of cell respiration (previous page), state the number of carbon atoms in each of the molecules (a)-(f):

4. How many ATP molecules **per molecule of glucose** are generated during the following stages of respiration?

   (a) Glycolysis: _____ (b) Krebs cycle: _____ (c) Electron transport chain: _____ (d) Total: _____

5. Explain what happens to the carbon atoms lost during respiration: _____

6. Explain what happens during oxidative phosphorylation: _____
   _____
   _____
   _____
   _____
   _____

© 2017 **BIOZONE** International
ISBN: 978-1-927309-26-1
Photocopying Prohibited

4 Chemiosmosis

Key Idea: Chemiosmosis is the process in which electron transport is coupled to ATP synthesis.

Chemiosmosis occurs in the membranes of mitochondria, the chloroplasts of plants, and across the plasma membrane of bacteria. It involves establishing and using a proton gradient to drive ATP synthesis. Chemiosmosis has two key components: an **electron transport chain** sets up a proton gradient as electrons pass along it to a final electron acceptor, and an enzyme, **ATP synthase**, uses the proton

gradient to catalyse ATP synthesis. In respiration, electron carriers on the inner mitochondrial membrane oxidise NADH and FADH$_2$. The energy released from this process is used to move protons against their concentration gradient from the matrix into the intermembrane space. The return of protons to the matrix via ATP synthase is coupled to ATP synthesis. Similarly, in the chloroplasts of green plants, ATP is produced when protons pass from the thylakoid lumen to the chloroplast stroma via ATP synthase.

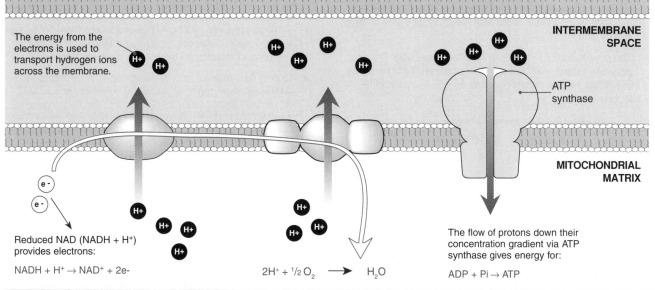

The energy from the electrons is used to transport hydrogen ions across the membrane.

INTERMEMBRANE SPACE

ATP synthase

MITOCHONDRIAL MATRIX

Reduced NAD (NADH + H$^+$) provides electrons:

$$NADH + H^+ \rightarrow NAD^+ + 2e-$$

$$2H^+ + \tfrac{1}{2} O_2 \rightarrow H_2O$$

The flow of protons down their concentration gradient via ATP synthase gives energy for:

$$ADP + Pi \rightarrow ATP$$

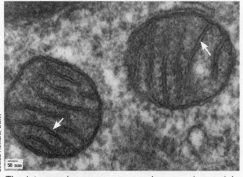

Louisa Howard, DEMF

50 nm

The intermembrane spaces can be seen (arrows) in this transverse section of mitochondria.

The evidence for chemiosmosis

The British biochemist Peter Mitchell proposed the chemiosmotic hypothesis in 1961. He proposed that, because living cells have membrane potential, electrochemical gradients could be used to provide the energy for ATP synthesis. The evidence for chemiosmosis from studies of isolated mitochondria and chloroplasts was extensive:

▶ The outer membranes of mitochondria were removed leaving the inner membranes intact. Adding protons to the treated mitochondria increased ATP synthesis.

▶ When isolated chloroplasts were illuminated, the medium in which they were suspended became alkaline.

▶ Isolated chloroplasts were kept in the dark and transferred first to a low pH medium (to acidify the thylakoid interior) and then to an alkaline medium (low protons). They then spontaneously synthesised ATP (no light was needed).

1. Summarise the process of chemiosmosis: _____

_____

_____

2. Why did the addition of protons to the treated mitochondria increase ATP synthesis?_____

_____

_____

3. Why did the suspension of isolated chloroplasts become alkaline when illuminated?_____

_____

4. (a) What was the purpose of transferring the chloroplasts first to an acid then to an alkaline medium? _____

_____

(b) Why did ATP synthesis occur spontaneously in these treated chloroplasts? _____

_____

© 2017 **BIOZONE** International
ISBN: 978-1-927309-26-1
Photocopying Prohibited

LINK
13

LINK
3

WEB
4

KNOW

5 Anaerobic Pathways

Key Idea: Glucose can be metabolised anaerobically to produce ATP. The ATP yield from anaerobic processes is much than from aerobic processes.

Aerobic respiration occurs in the presence of oxygen. Organisms can also generate ATP anaerobically (without oxygen) by using a molecule other than oxygen as the terminal electron acceptor for the pathway. In alcoholic fermentation, the electron acceptor is ethanal. In lactic acid fermentation, which occurs in mammalian muscle even when oxygen is present, the electron acceptor is pyruvate itself.

Lactic acid fermentation

▶ Mammalian skeletal muscle can produce ATP anaerobically using lactic acid fermentation. In this pathway, the electron acceptor is pyruvate, the end product of glycolysis. The pyruvate is reduced to lactic acid, which dissociates to form lactate and H+.

▶ The conversion of pyruvate to lactate is reversible. The pyruvate-lactate interconversion is catalysed by an enzyme (E) called lactate dehydrogenase. Hence it is called the lactate 'shuttle'.

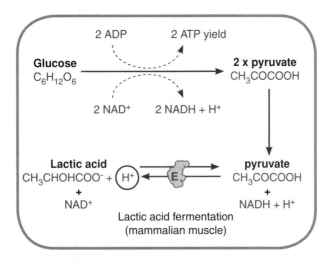

Lactic acid fermentation
(mammalian muscle)

▶ Importantly, this pathway operates alongside the aerobic system (even when oxygen is present) to enable greater intensity and duration of muscle activity. It is an important mechanism for balancing the distribution of substrates and waste products, especially when pyruvate is building up faster than it can be metabolised.

▶ Lactate can be metabolised in the muscle itself or it can enter the circulation and be taken up by the liver to replenish carbohydrate stores. It moves from its site of production to regions within and outside the muscle where it can be respired aerobically.

What causes muscle fatigue?

▶ At rest, muscles produce a surplus of ATP, which is stored as creatine phosphate (a short term energy supply molecule in muscle) and glycogen.

▶ During moderate activity, ATP requirements are met by the aerobic metabolism of glycogen and lipids and there is no proton accumulation in the muscle cells (lactate shuttle).

▶ During very intense activity, much more of the muscle's ATP needs are met by glycolysis. The effects of this are:

   • An increase in H+ (acidosis) because protons are not being removed via the mitochondrial electron transport system (circled in diagram left).
   • Lactate accumulates faster than it can be oxidised.
   • Accumulation of phosphate (Pi) from the breakdown of ATP and creatine phosphate.

▶ These metabolic changes lead to a fall in ATP production and impaired release of calcium stored within the muscle's endoplasmic reticulum. Calcium and ATP are needed for muscle contraction. The result is muscle fatigue, i.e. an impaired ability for contraction.

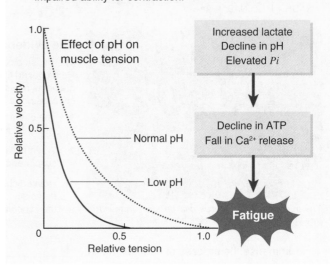

1. Describe the key difference between aerobic respiration and anaerobic pathways such as fermentation: _____

_____

2. What is the significance of the lactic acid fermentation pathway in mammalian muscle being reversible?

_____

_____

3. What ultimately causes muscle fatigue and how is it related to anaerobic metabolism? _____

_____

_____

_____

_____

© 2017 **BIOZONE** International
ISBN: 978-1-927309-26-1
Photocopying Prohibited

Alcoholic fermentation

▶ Organisms can generate ATP when oxygen is absent by using a molecule other than oxygen as the terminal electron acceptor for the pathway.

▶ In alcoholic fermentation, the electron acceptor is ethanal (acetaldehyde) which is reduced to ethanol in two steps with the release of CO_2. Enzymes (E) catalyse both steps.

▶ When oxygen is absent, especially when sugar is plentiful, they will use alcoholic fermentation to generate ATP. At ethanol levels >12-15%, the ethanol is toxic and this limits their ability to use this pathway indefinitely.

▶ The root cells of plants also use fermentation as a pathway when oxygen is unavailable but the ethanol must eventually be converted back to respiratory intermediates and respired aerobically.

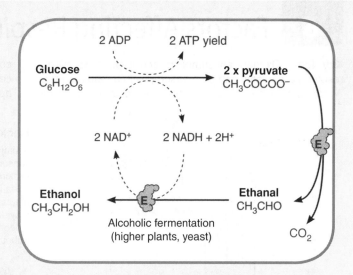

Alcoholic fermentation
(higher plants, yeast)

Tolerating anaerobic metabolism

Rice is grown in flooded rice paddies, which are low oxygen environments and reduce the amount of oxygen available to the rice plant's root cells. Rice root cells respire anaerobically, which produces ethanol. The ethanol is removed by the enzyme alcohol dehydrogenase. Additionally, the roots contain large air spaces (aerenchyma), which allow air to move between the stem and root cells, supplying oxygen from above the water surface.

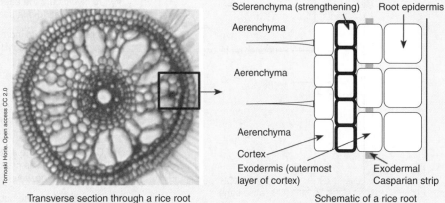

Tomoaki Horie. Open access CC 2.0

Transverse section through a rice root

Schematic of a rice root

Wintec

It was once thought that lactic acid was a toxic by-product of anaerobic metabolism in muscle and this caused fatigue. However, researchers now know that the causes of muscle fatigue are complex and most of the time lactate metabolism operates alongside the aerobic system to enable maximal muscle activity.

The alcohol and CO_2 produced from alcoholic fermentation in yeasts form the basis of the brewing and baking industries. In baking, the dough is left to ferment and the yeast metabolises sugars to produce ethanol and CO_2. The CO_2 causes the dough to rise.

Oxygen is generally scarce in waterlogged soils, so aerobic respiration is inhibited in the roots of plants in oxygen-poor soils. Carbohydrates are broken down by fermentation to produce ATP. Some plants (e.g. rice) are well adapted to low oxygen, flooded soils.

4. (a) Refer to page 6 and determine the efficiency of fermentation compared to aerobic respiration: _____ %

   (b) Why is the efficiency of these anaerobic pathways so low? _____

   _____

5. (a) When do root cells generate ATP anaerobically and why? _____

   _____

   (b) Why can't root cells metabolise anaerobically indefinitely? _____

   _____

   (c) Describe an adaptation in rice for growth in anaerobic conditions: _____

   _____

6 Factors Affecting Respiration Rate

Key Idea: Oxygen consumption and CO_2 production in respiring organisms can be measured with a respirometer. A respirometer can be used to measure the amount of oxygen consumed and the amount of carbon dioxide produced during cellular respiration. Respirometers are quite simple pieces of apparatus but can give accurate results if set up carefully.

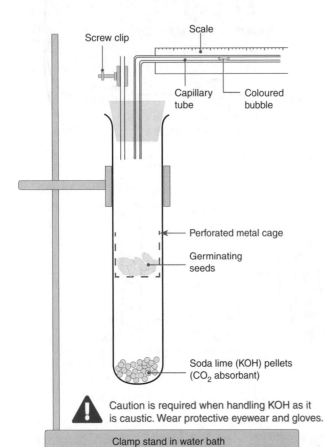

Screw clip
Scale
Capillary tube
Coloured bubble
Perforated metal cage
Germinating seeds
Soda lime (KOH) pellets (CO_2 absorbant)

Caution is required when handling KOH as it is caustic. Wear protective eyewear and gloves.

Clamp stand in water bath

Background

A simple respirometer (left) can be used to measure oxygen consumption during cellular respiration. Changes are measured by tracking the movement of a coloured bubble in the capillary tube. Soda lime or potassium hydroxide (KOH) is added to absorb any CO_2 produced during respiration. Measuring the movement of the bubble provides an estimate of how much oxygen is used. To determine the amount of CO_2 produced you would need to repeat the procedure without the KOH and determine the volume of by subtraction.

Aim and hypothesis

▶ To investigate the effect of temperature on the respiration rate of germinating pea seeds.

▶ If respiration rate increases with temperature then germinating seeds will use more oxygen at 25°C than at 10°C.

Method

▶ Five germinating pea seeds were placed into a perforated metal cage and suspended in a sealed respirometer chamber containing 5 g of KOH pellets (see left).

▶ Once in place, the screw clip was closed and the respirometer was placed into the waterbath with the capillary tube above the water level and equilibrated for 5 minutes.

▶ The position of the bubble was note at zero time (T= 0). Readings were then made every 5 minutes for 20 minutes. The capillary tube was calibrated to 20 µL per mm division.

▶ The experiment was carried out at 10°C and 25°C.

1. Why does the bubble in the capillary tube move? _____
   _____
   _____

2. The results from the student's experiment is shown in the table right.

   (a) Plot the results on the grid provided.

   (b) Calculate the rate of oxygen consumption at 10°C (give units):
   _____

   (c) Calculate the rate of oxygen consumption at 25°C (give units):
   _____

   (d) What effect did temperature have on respiration rate?
   _____
   _____
   _____

3. The students repeated the experiment using glass beads instead of peas. What was the purpose of this?
   _____
   _____

Time / minutes	Cumulative distance bubble moved / mm	
	10°C	25°C
0	0	0
5	0.3	0.6
10	0.4	0.8
15	0.5	0.9
20	0.5	1.0

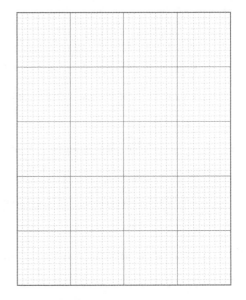

WEB
LINK

PRAC 6 3

7 Energy Transformations in Plant Cells

Key Idea: The energy from sunlight is captured and stored as glucose, which powers the production of ATP in the process of cellular respiration. Hydrolysis of ATP provides the energy for the chemical reactions in living systems.

Energy flow in the cell of an autotroph is shown below. Note that ATP has a central role in acting as an energy carrier to power metabolic reactions, releasing its energy quickly by

hydrolysis of the terminal phosphate. Some of the energy is lost as heat during these reactions. Recall that ATP hydrolysis is catalysed by the enzyme ATPase. Once ATP has released its energy, it becomes ADP (adenosine diphosphate), a low energy molecule that can be recharged by adding a phosphate. The energy to do this is supplied by the controlled breakdown of glucose in cellular respiration.

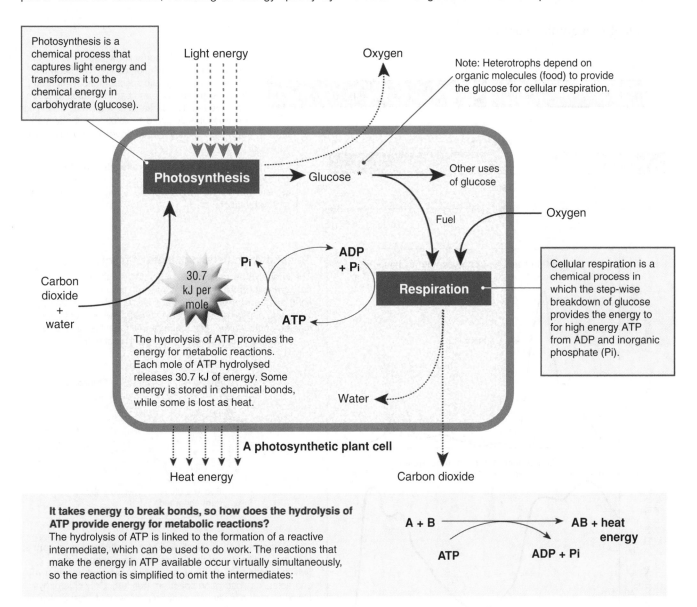

A photosynthetic plant cell

It takes energy to break bonds, so how does the hydrolysis of ATP provide energy for metabolic reactions?
The hydrolysis of ATP is linked to the formation of a reactive intermediate, which can be used to do work. The reactions that make the energy in ATP available occur virtually simultaneously, so the reaction is simplified to omit the intermediates:

1. How does ATP acts as a supplier of energy to power metabolic reactions? _____

_____

_____

_____

2. (a) What are the raw materials for photosynthesis? _____

   (b) What are the raw materials for respiration? _____

3. What is the immediate source of energy for reforming ATP from ADP? _____

4. What is the ultimate source of energy for plants? _____

5. What is the ultimate source of energy for animals? _____

8 Pigments and Light Absorption

Key Idea: Chlorophyll pigments absorb light of specific wavelengths and capture light energy for photosynthesis.

Substances that absorb visible light are called **pigments**, and different pigments absorb light of different wavelengths. The ability of a pigment to absorb particular wavelengths of light can be measured with a spectrophotometer. The light absorption vs the wavelength is called the **absorption**

spectrum of that pigment. The absorption spectrum of different photosynthetic pigments provides clues to their role in photosynthesis, since light can only perform work if it is absorbed. An **action spectrum** profiles the effectiveness of different wavelengths of light in fuelling photosynthesis. It is obtained by plotting wavelength against a measure of photosynthetic rate (e.g. O_2 production).

The electromagnetic spectrum

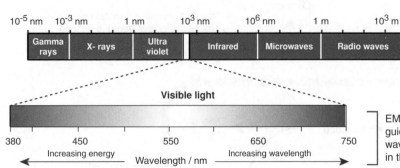

Light is a form of energy known as electromagnetic radiation (EMR). The segment of the electromagnetic spectrum most important to life is the narrow band between about 380 nm and 750 nm. This radiation is known as visible light because it is detected as colours by the human eye. It is visible light that drives photosynthesis.

EMR travels in waves, where wavelength provides a guide to the energy of the photons. The greater the wavelength of EMR, the lower the energy of the photons in that radiation.

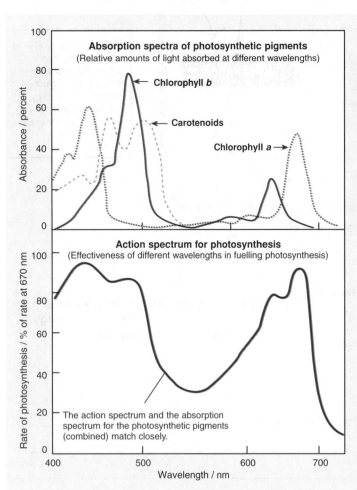

Absorption spectra of photosynthetic pigments
(Relative amounts of light absorbed at different wavelengths)

- Chlorophyll *b*
- Carotenoids
- Chlorophyll *a*

Action spectrum for photosynthesis
(Effectiveness of different wavelengths in fuelling photosynthesis)

The action spectrum and the absorption spectrum for the photosynthetic pigments (combined) match closely.

The photosynthetic pigments of plants

The photosynthetic pigments of plants fall into two categories: **chlorophylls** (which absorb red and blue-violet light) and **carotenoids** (which absorb strongly in the blue-violet and appear orange, yellow, or red). The pigments are located on the chloroplast membranes (the thylakoids) and are associated with membrane transport systems.

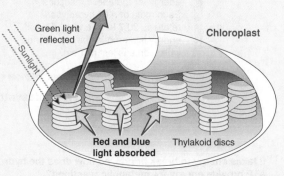

The pigments of chloroplasts in higher plants (above) absorb blue and red light, and the leaves therefore appear green (which is reflected). Each photosynthetic pigment has its own characteristic absorption spectrum (top left). Only chlorophyll *a* participates directly in the light reactions of photosynthesis, but the accessory pigments (chlorophyll *b* and carotenoids) can absorb wavelengths of light that chlorophyll *a* cannot and pass the energy (photons) to chlorophyll *a*, thus broadening the spectrum that can effectively drive photosynthesis.

Left: Graphs comparing absorption spectra of photosynthetic pigments compared with the action spectrum for photosynthesis.

1. What is meant by the absorption spectrum of a pigment? _____

_____

2. Why doesn't the action spectrum for photosynthesis exactly match the absorption spectrum of chlorophyll *a*? _____

_____

© 2017 **BIOZONE** International
ISBN: 978-1-927309-26-1
Photocopying Prohibited

9 How Does Wavelength Affect Photosynthesis?

Key Idea: The rate of photosynthesis varies with different wavelengths of visible light.

Photosynthetic pigments absorb specific wavelengths of light and capture the energy within it to drive photosynthesis.

However, some wavelengths are absorbed more strongly than others. The experiment described below investigates the effect of different wavelengths on the photosynthetic rate of a green plant.

Aim

To investigate the effect of wavelength on the photosynthetic rate of a green plant.

Method

▶ Select several green leaves of the same type. Avoiding areas with major leaf veins, use a hole punch to cut out 40 discs of a uniform size. Place the discs into a large syringe containing a 0.2% bicarbonate solution. Place a finger tightly over the tip of the syringe and slowly pull back on the plunger. Repeat until all the discs sink. Do not use any that remain floating. Keep the discs in a dark place until required.

▶ Label four 150 mL glass beakers as red, blue, green, and clear. To each beaker add 100 mL of 0.2% bicarbonate solution and 5 mL of detergent. Colour the solutions by adding 10 drops of the appropriate colour food colouring to the bicarbonate solution. No food colouring is added to the clear container.

▶ Place 10 leaf discs into the beaker, and place it 15 cm from a 100 watt light bulb. Start a timer immediately and record the time taken for all 10 leaf discs to float. Repeat with the remaining colours.

Background

Leaf disc assays are commonly used to investigate photosynthesis in the classroom because they are simple to perform and do not require any specialised equipment. The bicarbonate solution under pressure removes any oxygen in the leaf by replacing the air in the leaf air spaces and it also serves as a source of CO_2 during the experiment. As photosynthesis occurs, O_2 is produced and the leaf disks become buoyant and eventually float. The rate of flotation is an indirect measure of the rate of photosynthesis. The detergent is added to break down the water-repellent barrier on the leaf surface, allowing sodium bicarbonate to enter the leaf more easily.

1. Generate a brief hypothesis for this experiment: _____

_____

_____

_____

2. Why do the leaf discs float? _____

_____

_____

Results

The results from the experiment are shown below.

Light colour	Time taken for 10 discs to float / s
Blue	162
Red	558
Green	998
White	694

3. (a) Graph the results on the grid provided (right):

(b) Describe how photosynthesis was affected by light colour:

_____

_____

_____

_____

_____

4. Did the results support your hypothesis? Explain: _____

_____

_____

_____

_____

10 Separation of Pigments by Chromatography

Key Idea: Photosynthetic pigments can be separated from a mixture using chromatography.

Chromatography involves passing a mixture dissolved in a mobile phase (a solvent) through a stationary phase, which separates the molecules according to their specific characteristics (e.g. size or charge). In thin layer chromatography, the stationary phase is a thin layer of adsorbent material (e.g. silica gel or cellulose) attached to a solid plate. A sample is placed near the bottom of the plate which is placed in an appropriate solvent (the mobile phase).

Separation of photosynthetic pigments

The four primary pigments of green plants can be easily separated and identified using thin layer chromatography. The pigments from the leaves are first extracted by crushing leaves, together with acetone, using a mortar and pestle. The extract is dotted on to the chromatography plate. Acetone is used as the mobile phase (solvent). During thin layer chromatography, the pigments separate out according to differences in their relative solubilities. Two major classes of pigments are detected: the two greenish chlorophyll pigments and two yellowish carotenoid pigments.

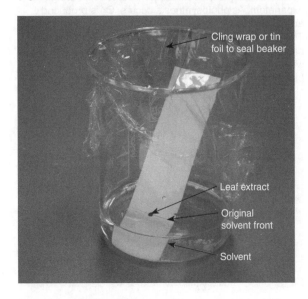

Cling wrap or tin foil to seal beaker

Leaf extract

Original solvent front

Solvent

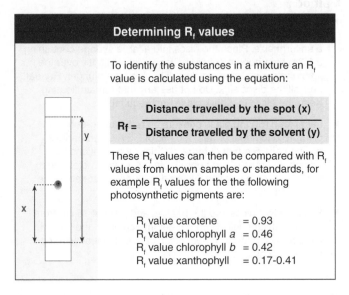

Determining R_f values

To identify the substances in a mixture an R_f value is calculated using the equation:

$$R_f = \frac{\text{Distance travelled by the spot (x)}}{\text{Distance travelled by the solvent (y)}}$$

These R_f values can then be compared with R_f values from known samples or standards, for example R_f values for the the following photosynthetic pigments are:

R_f value carotene	= 0.93
R_f value chlorophyll a	= 0.46
R_f value chlorophyll b	= 0.42
R_f value xanthophyll	= 0.17-0.41

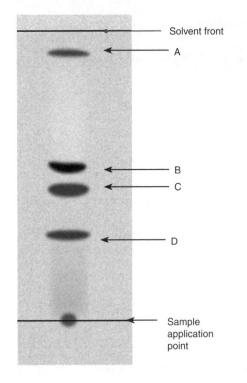

Solvent front

A

B

C

D

Sample application point

1. (a) Calculate the R_f values for the pigments A-D on the chromatography plate shown left.

   (b) Use the R_f values to identify the pigments:

   A: R_f value: _____

   Pigment: _____

   B: R_f value: _____

   Pigment: _____

   C: R_f value: _____

   Pigment: _____

   D: R_f value: _____

   Pigment: _____

2. A student carried out a chromatography experiment in class. The instructions said to leave the plate in the solvent for 30 minutes, but the student instead removed the plate after 20 minutes. How would this affect the R_f values and pigment separations obtained?

   _____

   _____

   _____

   _____

   _____

© 2017 **BIOZONE** International
ISBN: 978-1-927309-26-1
Photocopying Prohibited

11 Photosynthesis

Key Idea: Photosynthesis is the process by which light energy is used to convert CO_2 and water into glucose and oxygen.

Photosynthesis is of fundamental importance to living things because it transforms sunlight energy into chemical energy stored in molecules, releases free oxygen gas, and absorbs carbon dioxide (a waste product of cellular metabolism).

Photosynthetic organisms use special pigments, called **chlorophylls**, to absorb light of specific wavelengths and capture the light energy. Photosynthesis involves reduction and oxidation (redox) reactions. In photosynthesis, water is split and electrons are transferred together with hydrogen ions from water to CO_2, reducing it to sugar.

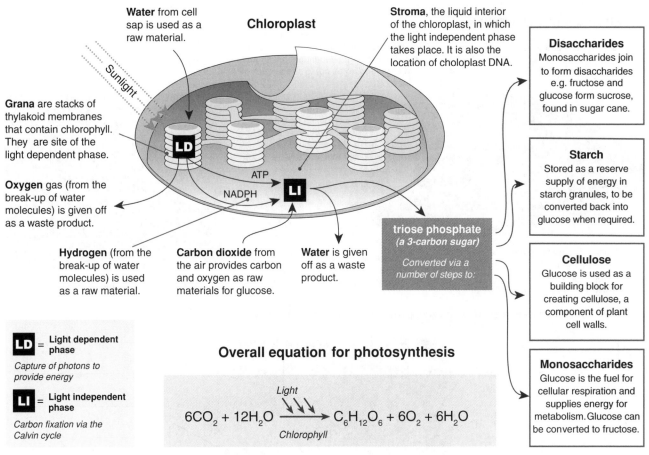

Water from cell sap is used as a raw material.

Chloroplast

Stroma, the liquid interior of the chloroplast, in which the light independent phase takes place. It is also the location of choloplast DNA.

Sunlight

Grana are stacks of thylakoid membranes that contain chlorophyll. They are site of the light dependent phase.

LD

ATP

Oxygen gas (from the break-up of water molecules) is given off as a waste product.

NADPH

LI

Hydrogen (from the break-up of water molecules) is used as a raw material.

Carbon dioxide from the air provides carbon and oxygen as raw materials for glucose.

Water is given off as a waste product.

triose phosphate *(a 3-carbon sugar)*

Converted via a number of steps to:

Disaccharides
Monosaccharides join to form disaccharides e.g. fructose and glucose form sucrose, found in sugar cane.

Starch
Stored as a reserve supply of energy in starch granules, to be converted back into glucose when required.

Cellulose
Glucose is used as a building block for creating cellulose, a component of plant cell walls.

Monosaccharides
Glucose is the fuel for cellular respiration and supplies energy for metabolism. Glucose can be converted to fructose.

LD = **Light dependent phase**
Capture of photons to provide energy

LI = **Light independent phase**
Carbon fixation via the Calvin cycle

Overall equation for photosynthesis

$$6CO_2 + 12H_2O \xrightarrow[\text{Chlorophyll}]{\text{Light}} C_6H_{12}O_6 + 6O_2 + 6H_2O$$

1. Distinguish between the two different regions of a chloroplast and describe the biochemical processes that occur in each:

   (a) _____

   _____

   _____

   (b) _____

   _____

   _____

2. State the origin and fate of the following molecules involved in photosynthesis:

   (a) Carbon dioxide: _____

   (b) Oxygen: _____

   (c) Hydrogen: _____

3. Discuss the potential uses for the end products of photosynthesis: _____

   _____

   _____

   _____

© 2017 **BIOZONE** International
ISBN: 978-1-927309-26-1
Photocopying Prohibited

LINK **14**   LINK **13**   LINK **12**   WEB **11** **KNOW**

12 Chloroplasts

Key Idea: Chloroplasts have a complicated internal membrane structure that provides the sites for the light dependent reactions of photosynthesis.

Chloroplasts are the specialised plastids in which photosynthesis occurs. A mesophyll leaf cell contains between 50-100 chloroplasts. The chloroplasts are generally aligned so that their broad surface runs parallel to the cell wall

to maximise the surface area available for light absorption. Chloroplasts have an internal structure characterised by a system of membranous structures called **thylakoids** arranged into stacks called **grana**. Special pigments, called **chlorophylls** and **carotenoids**, are bound to the membranes as part of light-capturing photosystems. They absorb light of specific wavelengths and thereby capture the light energy.

The structure of a chloroplast

Chloroplast is enclosed by a double membrane envelope (inner and outer membrane)

Thylakoid membranes provide a large surface area for light absorption. They are the site of the light dependent phase and are organised so as not to shade each other.

Liquid **stroma** contains the enzymes for the light independent phase. It also contains the chloroplast's DNA.

Starch granule

Lipid droplet

Grana (*sing.* granum) are stacks of thylakoids

Stroma lamellae connect the grana. They account for 20% of the thylakoid membrane.

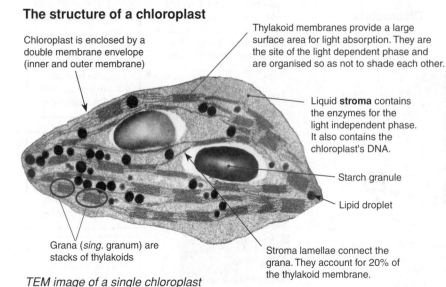
TEM image of a single chloroplast

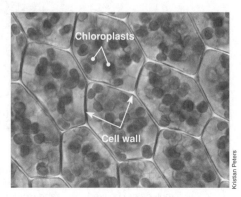
Chloroplasts

Cell wall

Kristian Peters

Chloroplasts visible in plant cells

1. Label the transmission electron microscope image of a chloroplast below:

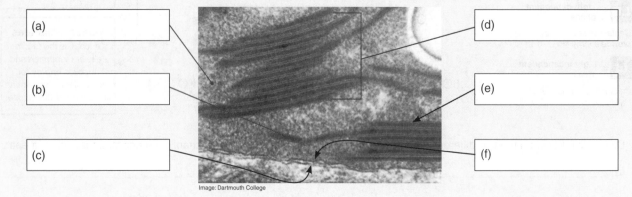

(a)

(b)

(c)

(d)

(e)

(f)

Image: Dartmouth College

2. (a) Where is chlorophyll found in a chloroplast? _____

_____

(b) Why is chlorophyll found there? _____

_____

_____

3. Explain how the internal structure of chloroplasts helps absorb the maximum amount of light: _____

_____

_____

_____

4. Explain why plant leaves appear green: _____

_____

_____

© 2017 **BIOZONE** International
ISBN: 978-1-927309-26-1
Photocopying Prohibited

13 Light Dependent Reactions

Key Idea: In light dependent reactions of photosynthesis, the energy from photons of light is used to drive the reduction of $NADP^+$ and the production of ATP.

Like cellular respiration, photosynthesis is a redox process, but in photosynthesis, water is split, and electrons and hydrogen ions, are transferred from water to CO_2, reducing it to sugar. The electrons increase in potential energy as they move from water to sugar. The energy to do this is provided by light. Photosynthesis has two phases. In the **light dependent**

reactions, light energy is converted to chemical energy (ATP and NADPH). In the **light independent reactions**, the chemical energy is used to synthesise carbohydrate. The light dependent reactions most commonly involve **non-cyclic phosphorylation**, which produces ATP and NADPH in roughly equal quantities. The electrons lost are replaced from water. In **cyclic phosphorylation**, the electrons lost from photosystem II are replaced by those from photosystem I. ATP is generated, but not NADPH.

Non-cyclic phosphorylation

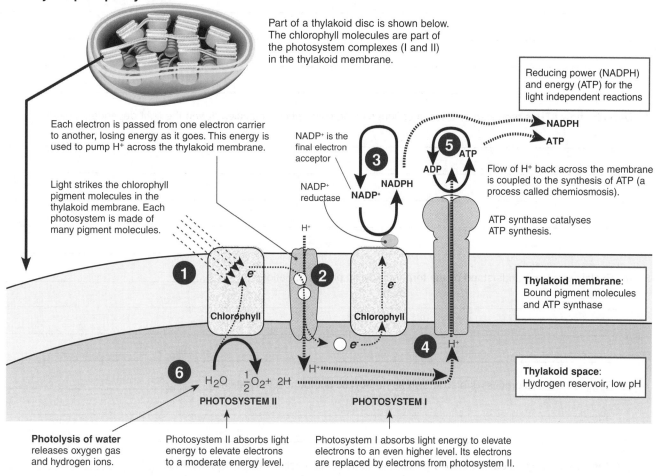

Part of a thylakoid disc is shown below. The chlorophyll molecules are part of the photosystem complexes (I and II) in the thylakoid membrane.

Reducing power (NADPH) and energy (ATP) for the light independent reactions

Each electron is passed from one electron carrier to another, losing energy as it goes. This energy is used to pump H^+ across the thylakoid membrane.

$NADP^+$ is the final electron acceptor

$NADP^+$ reductase

Flow of H^+ back across the membrane is coupled to the synthesis of ATP (a process called chemiosmosis).

Light strikes the chlorophyll pigment molecules in the thylakoid membrane. Each photosystem is made of many pigment molecules.

ATP synthase catalyses ATP synthesis.

Thylakoid membrane: Bound pigment molecules and ATP synthase

Thylakoid space: Hydrogen reservoir, low pH

$H_2O \quad \frac{1}{2}O_2 + 2H$

PHOTOSYSTEM II

PHOTOSYSTEM I

Photolysis of water releases oxygen gas and hydrogen ions.

Photosystem II absorbs light energy to elevate electrons to a moderate energy level.

Photosystem I absorbs light energy to elevate electrons to an even higher level. Its electrons are replaced by electrons from photosystem II.

Cyclic phosphorylation

Cyclic phosphorylation involves only photosystem I and NADPH is not generated. Electrons from photosystem I are shunted back to the electron carriers in the membrane. This pathway produces ATP only. The Calvin cycle uses more ATP than NADPH, so cyclic phosphorylation makes up the difference. It is activated when NADPH levels build up, and remains active until enough ATP is made to meet demand.

Electrons are cycled through a pathway that takes them away from $NADP^+$ reductase.

ATP is produced while NADPH production ceases.

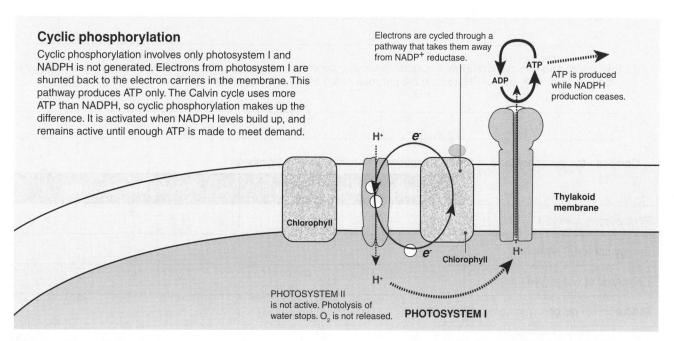

Thylakoid membrane

PHOTOSYSTEM II is not active. Photolysis of water stops. O_2 is not released.

PHOTOSYSTEM I

© 2017 **BIOZONE** International
ISBN: 978-1-927309-26-1
Photocopying Prohibited

1. Describe the role of the carrier molecule NADP in photosynthesis: _____

_____

2. Explain the role of chlorophyll molecules in photosynthesis: _____

_____

_____

_____

3. Summarise the events of the light dependent reactions and identify where they occur: _____

_____

_____

_____

_____

_____

4. Describe how ATP is produced as a result of light striking chlorophyll molecules during the light dependent phase:

_____

_____

_____

_____

_____

5. (a) Explain what you understand by the term non-cyclic phosphorylation: _____

_____

_____

_____

   (b) Suggest why this process is also known as non-cyclic photophosphorylation: _____

_____

_____

6. (a) Describe how cyclic photophosphorylation differs from non-cyclic photophosphorylation: _____

_____

_____

   (b) Both cyclic and non-cyclic pathways operate to varying degrees during photosynthesis. Since the non-cyclic pathway produces both ATP and NAPH, explain the purpose of the cyclic pathway of electron flow:

_____

_____

7. Complete the summary table of the light dependent reactions of photosynthesis

	Non-cyclic phosphorylation	Cyclic phosphorylation
Photosystem involved		
Energy carrier(s) produced		
Photolysis of water (yes / no)		
Production of oxygen (yes / no)		

© 2017 **BIOZONE** International
ISBN: 978-1-927309-26-1
Photocopying Prohibited

14 Light Independent Reactions

Key Idea: The light independent reactions of photosynthesis take place in the stroma of the chloroplast and do not require light to proceed.

In the **light independent reactions** (the **Calvin cycle**) hydrogen (H^+) is added to CO_2 and a 5C intermediate to make carbohydrate. The H^+ and ATP are supplied by the light dependent reactions. The Calvin cycle uses more ATP than NADPH, but the cell uses cyclic phosphorylation (which does not produce NADPH) when it runs low on ATP to make up the difference.

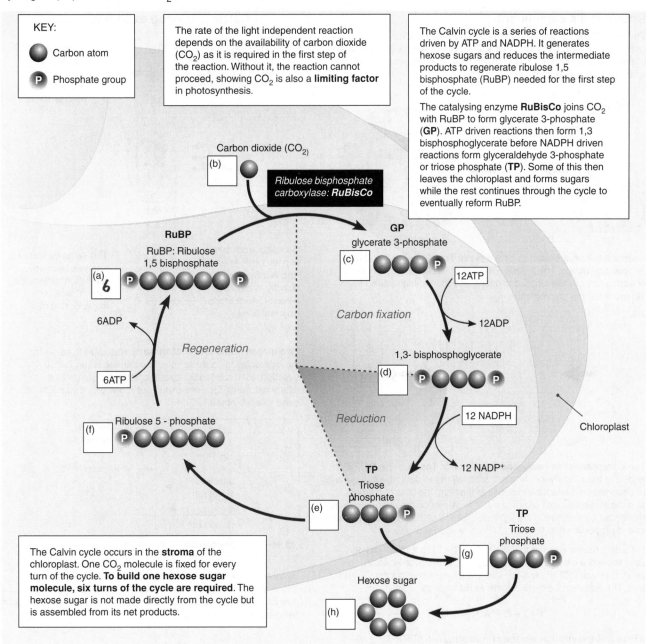

KEY:
- Carbon atom
- P Phosphate group

The rate of the light independent reaction depends on the availability of carbon dioxide (CO_2) as it is required in the first step of the reaction. Without it, the reaction cannot proceed, showing CO_2 is also a **limiting factor** in photosynthesis.

The Calvin cycle is a series of reactions driven by ATP and NADPH. It generates hexose sugars and reduces the intermediate products to regenerate ribulose 1,5 bisphosphate (RuBP) needed for the first step of the cycle.

The catalysing enzyme **RuBisCo** joins CO_2 with RuBP to form glycerate 3-phosphate (**GP**). ATP driven reactions then form 1,3 bisphosphoglycerate before NADPH driven reactions form glyceraldehyde 3-phosphate or triose phosphate (**TP**). Some of this then leaves the chloroplast and forms sugars while the rest continues through the cycle to eventually reform RuBP.

Carbon dioxide (CO_2)
(b)

Ribulose bisphosphate carboxylase: **RuBisCo**

RuBP
RuBP: Ribulose 1,5 bisphosphate
(a) **6**

GP
glycerate 3-phosphate
(c)
12ATP

Carbon fixation

12ADP

6ADP

Regeneration

6ATP

1,3- bisphosphoglycerate
(d)

12 NADPH

Chloroplast

Ribulose 5 - phosphate
(f)

Reduction

12 NADP⁺

TP
Triose phosphate
(e)

TP
Triose phosphate
(g)

Hexose sugar

(h)

The Calvin cycle occurs in the **stroma** of the chloroplast. One CO_2 molecule is fixed for every turn of the cycle. **To build one hexose sugar molecule, six turns of the cycle are required**. The hexose sugar is not made directly from the cycle but is assembled from its net products.

1. In the boxes on the diagram above, write the number of molecules formed at each step during the formation of **one hexose sugar molecule**. The first one has been done for you:

2. Explain the importance of RuBisCo in the Calvin cycle: _____

_____

3. Identify the actual end product on the Calvin cycle: _____

4. Write the equation for the production of one hexose sugar molecule from carbon dioxide: _____

_____

5. Explain why the Calvin cycle is likely to cease in the dark for most plants, even though it is independent of light: _____

_____

_____

15 Experimental Investigation of Photosynthesis

Key Idea: Hill's experiment using isolated chloroplasts and Calvin's "lollipop" experiment provided important information on the process of photosynthesis.

In the 1930s Robert Hill devised a way of measuring oxygen evolution and the rate of photosynthesis in isolated chloroplasts. During the 1950s Melvin Calvin led a team using radioisotopes of carbon to work out the steps of the light independent reactions (the Calvin cycle).

Robert Hill's experiment

The dye **DCPIP** (2,6-dichlorophenol-indophenol) is blue. It is reduced by H^+ ions and forms $DCPIPH_2$ (colourless). Hill made use of this dye to show that O_2 is produced during photosynthesis even when CO_2 is not present.

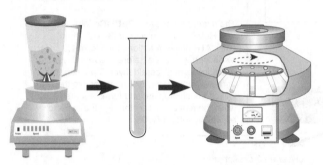

Leaves are homogenised to form a slurry. The slurry is filtered to remove any debris. The filtered extract is then centrifuged at low speed to remove the larger cell debris and then at high speed to separate out the chloroplasts.

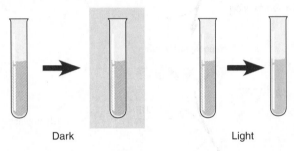

Dark	Light

The chloroplasts are resuspended in a buffer. The blue dye **DCPIP** is added to the suspension. In a test tube left in the dark, the dye remains unchanged. In a test tube exposed to the light, the blue dye fades and the test tube turns green again. The rate of colour change can be measured by measuring the light absorbance of the suspension. The rate is proportional to the rate at which oxygen is produced.

Hill's experiment showed that water must be the source of oxygen (and therefore electrons). It is split by light to produce H^+ ions (which reduce DCPIP) and O^{2-} ions (which combine to form O_2 and $2e^-$). The equation below summarises his findings:

$$H_2O + A \rightarrow AH_2 + \tfrac{1}{2} O_2$$

where A is the electron acceptor (*in vivo* this is NADP)

Calvin's lollipop experiment

Calvin and his colleges placed the algae *Chlorella vulgaris* in a thin bulb shaped flask to simulate a leaf (the lollipop).

Radioactive ^{14}C labelled CO_2 was bubbled into the flask at precise times.

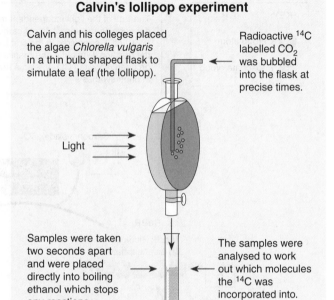

Samples were taken two seconds apart and were placed directly into boiling ethanol which stops any reactions.

The samples were analysed to work out which molecules the ^{14}C was incorporated into.

Two-dimensional chromatography was used to separate the molecules in each sample. The sample is run in one direction, then rotated 90 degrees and run again with a different solvent. This separates out molecules that might be close to each other.

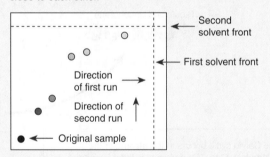

By identifying the order that the molecules incorporating the ^{14}C appeared it was possible to work out the steps of the now called Calvin cycle. This could only be done by taking samples only seconds apart.

---

1. Write an equation for the formation of $DCPIPH_2$ from DCPIP: _____

_____

2. What important finding about photosynthesis did Hill's experiment show? _____

_____

3. Why did the samples in Calvin's lollipop experiment need to be taken just seconds apart? _____

_____

_____

_____

© 2017 **BIOZONE** International
ISBN: 978-1-927309-26-1
Photocopying Prohibited

16 Investigating Enzymes in Photosynthesis

Key Idea: Replacing NADP+ with DCPIP as the electron acceptor allows the effect of light on the rate of the light dependent reactions to be measured indirectly.

NADP+ is the electron acceptor for the light dependent reaction. By substituting the dye DCPIP, which fades from blue to colourless as it accepts electrons, it is possible to indirectly measure the rate of the light dependent reactions and therefore the rate of enzyme activity during the reactions.

Background

Dehydrogenase enzymes play a role in the transport of electrons through the photosystem pathways of the light dependent reactions. The final acceptor of the electron is NADP+, forming NADPH. By substituting DCPIP to accept H+, the rate of enzyme activity can be measured.

The aim

To investigate the effect of light intensity on the rate of dehydrogenase activity in the light dependent reactions in isolated chloroplasts.

The method

Pieces of spinach leaf were blended using a standard food processor. The pulp was filtered through a muslin cloth into four centrifuge tubes kept in an ice bath. The filtered extract was spun down to produce a pellet and supernatant. The supernatant was discarded and each pellet resuspended with a medium of cold sucrose solution in a boiling tube. In tube 1 and 2 the dye DCPIP was added. In tube 3 DCPIP was added then the tube was covered in foil to exclude light. In tube 4 no DCPIP was added. In a fifth tube DCPIP and sucrose medium were added without any leaf extract. Tubes 1 and 3 were exposed to high intensity light. Tube 2 was exposed to a lower intensity light. The absorbance of all the tubes was measured using a colorimeter at time 0 and every minute for 15 minutes. The absorbance of tube 3 was measured at the beginning and end of the experiment only.

Results

Time / min	Tube number / absorbance				
	1	2	3	4	5
0	5.0	5.0	5.0	0.3	5.0
1	4.8	5.0	-	0.3	5.0
2	4.7	4.9	-	0.3	5.0
3	4.6	4.8	-	0.3	5.0
4	4.3	4.8	-	0.4	5.0
5	4.0	4.7	-	0.3	4.9
6	3.8	4.6	-	0.4	4.9
7	3.4	4.6	-	0.2	4.9
8	3.0	4.5	-	0.3	5.0
9	2.6	4.4	-	0.4	5.1
10	2.2	4.4	-	0.3	5.0
11	1.9	4.3	-	0.2	4.9
12	1.4	4.1	-	0.2	5.0
13	0.9	4.0	-	0.3	4.8
14	0.6	4.0	-	0.3	5.0
15	0.5	3.8	4.7	0.4	5.0

1. Write a brief hypothesis for this experiment:

_____

_____

_____

2. Use the grid below to draw a line graph of the change in absorbance over time of each of the tubes tested.

3. (a) What was the purpose of tube 4? _____

_____

_____

(b) What was the purpose of tube 5? _____

_____

_____

4. Why was the absorbance of tube 3 only measured at the start and end of the investigation? _____

_____

5. Why did the absorbance of tubes 4 and 5 vary? _____

_____

6. Write a conclusion for the investigation: _____

_____

17 The Fate of Triose Phosphate

Key Idea: The triose phosphate molecules produced in photosynthesis can be combined and rearranged to form monosaccharides such as glucose. Glucose is an important energy source and a precursor of many other molecules.

The triose phosphate molecules produced in photosynthesis can be combined and rearranged to form the hexose monosaccharide glucose. Glucose has three main fates:

immediate use to produce ATP molecules (available energy for work), storage for later ATP production, or for use in building other molecules. Plants use the glucose they make in photosynthesis to build all the molecules they require. Animals obtain their glucose by consuming plants or other animals. Other molecules (e.g. amino acids and fatty acids) are also obtained by animals this way.

The fate of glucose

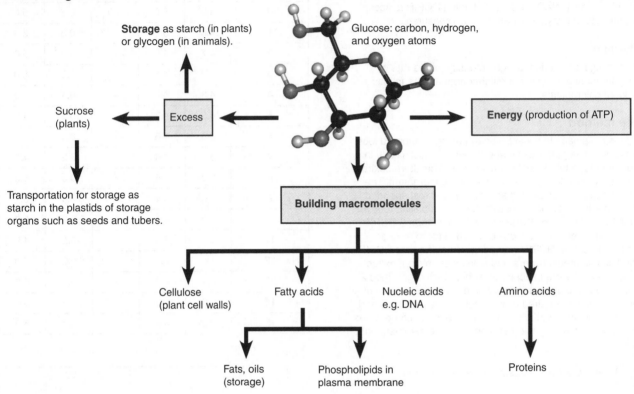

Storage as starch (in plants) or glycogen (in animals).

Glucose: carbon, hydrogen, and oxygen atoms

Sucrose (plants)

Excess

Energy (production of ATP)

Transportation for storage as starch in the plastids of storage organs such as seeds and tubers.

Building macromolecules

Cellulose (plant cell walls)

Fatty acids

Nucleic acids e.g. DNA

Amino acids

Fats, oils (storage)

Phospholipids in plasma membrane

Proteins

How do we know how glucose is used?

▶ Labelling the carbon atoms in a glucose molecule with isotopes shows how glucose is incorporated into other molecules.

▶ An isotope is an element (e.g. carbon) whose atoms have a particular number of neutrons in their nucleus. The different number of neutrons allows the isotopes to be identified by their density (e.g. a carbon atom with 13 neutrons is denser than a carbon atom with 12 neutrons).

▶ Some isotopes are radioactive. These radioactive isotopes can be traced using X-ray film or devices that detect the disintegration of the isotopes, such as Geiger counters.

The carbon atom

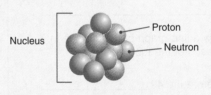

Nucleus

Proton

Neutron

The nucleus of an atom is made up of neutrons and protons. For any element, the number of protons remains the same, but the number of neutrons can vary. Electrons (not shown) are found outside the nucleus.

Naturally occurring C isotopes

^{12}C	^{13}C	^{14}C
6 protons	6 protons	6 protons
6 neutrons	7 neutrons	8 neutrons
Stable. 99.9% of all C isotopes.	Stable	Radioactive

1. How many triose phosphate molecules are used to form a glucose molecule?_____

2. What are the three main fates of glucose? _____

3. Identify a use for glucose in a plant that does not occur in animals: _____

4. How can isotopes of carbon be used to find the fate of glucose molecules? _____

_____

_____

© 2017 **BIOZONE** International
ISBN: 978-1-927309-26-1
Photocopying Prohibited

18 Factors Affecting Photosynthesis

Key Idea: Environmental factors, such as CO_2 availability and light intensity, affect the rate of photosynthesis.

The photosynthetic rate is the rate at which plants make carbohydrate. It is dependent on environmental factors, particularly the availability of light and carbon dioxide (CO_2). Temperature is important, but its influence is less clear

because it depends on the availability of the other two limiting factors (CO_2 and light) and the temperature tolerance of the plant. The relative importance of these factors can be tested experimentally by altering one of the factors while holding the others constant. The results for such an experiment are shown below.

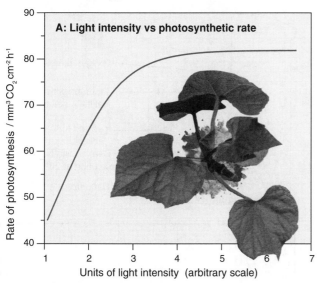

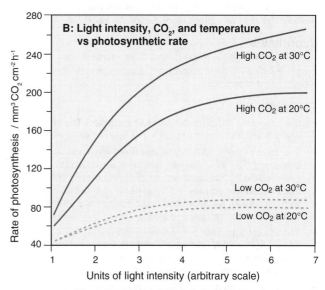

These figures illustrate the effect of different limiting factors on the rate of photosynthesis in cucumber plants. Figure A shows the effect of different light intensities when the temperature and carbon dioxide (CO_2) level are kept constant. Figure B shows the effect of different light intensities at two temperatures and two CO_2 concentrations. In each of these experiments, either CO_2 level or temperature was changed at each light intensity in turn.

1. Based on the figures above, summarise and explain the effect of each of the following factors on photosynthetic rate:

    (a) CO_2 concentration: _____

    _____

    (b) Light intensity: _____

    _____

    (c) Temperature: _____

    _____

2. Why does photosynthetic rate decline when the CO_2 level is reduced? _____

    _____

    _____

3. (a) In figure B, explain how the effects of CO_2 concentration were distinguished from the effects of temperature: _____

    _____

    (b) Which factor (CO_2 or temperature) had the greatest effect on photosynthetic rate: _____

    (c) How can you tell this from the graph? _____

    _____

4. How can glasshouses be used to create an environment in which photosynthetic rates are maximised? _____

    _____

    _____

    _____

5. Design an experiment to demonstrate the effect of temperature on photosynthetic rate. You should include a hypothesis, list of equipment, and methods. Staple your experiment to this page.

LINK
20

KNOW

19 Investigating Photosynthetic Rate

Key Idea: Measuring the production of oxygen provides a simple means of measuring the rate of photosynthesis.
The rate of photosynthesis can be investigated by measuring the substances involved in photosynthesis. These include measuring the uptake of carbon dioxide, the production of oxygen, or the change in biomass over time. Measuring the rate of oxygen production provides a good approximation of the photosynthetic rate and is relatively easy to carry out.

The aim

To investigate the effect of light intensity on the rate of photosynthesis in an aquatic plant, *Cabomba aquatica*.

Hypothesis

If photosynthetic rate is dependent on light intensity, more oxygen bubbles will be produced by *Cabomba* per unit time at higher light intensities.

The method

▶ 0.8-1.0 grams of *Cabomba* stem were weighed. The stem was cut and inverted to ensure a free flow of oxygen bubbles.

▶ The stem was placed into a beaker filled with a solution containing 0.2 mol L^{-1} sodium hydrogen carbonate (to supply carbon dioxide). The solution was at approximately 20°C. A funnel was inverted over the *Cabomba* and a test tube filled with the sodium hydrogen carbonate solution was inverted on top to collect any gas produced.

▶ The beaker was placed at distances (20, 25, 30, 35, 40, 45 cm) from a 60W light source and the light intensity measured with a lux meter at each interval. One beaker was not exposed to the light source (5 lx).

▶ Before recording data, the *Cabomba* stem was left to acclimatise to the new light level for 5 minutes. Because the volumes of oxygen gas produced are very low, bubbles were counted for a period of three minutes at each distance.

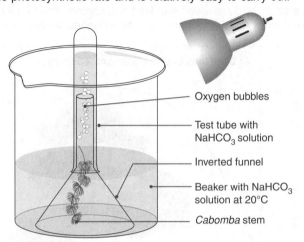

Oxygen bubbles

Test tube with NaHCO$_3$ solution

Inverted funnel

Beaker with NaHCO$_3$ solution at 20°C

Cabomba stem

The results

Light intensity / lx (distance)	Bubbles counted in three minutes	Bubbles per minute
5	0	
13 (45 cm)	6	
30 (40 cm)	9	
60 (35 cm)	12	
95 (30 cm)	18	
150 (25 cm)	33	
190 (20 cm)	35	

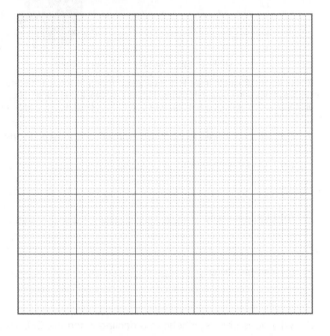

1. Complete the table by calculating the rate of oxygen production (bubbles of oxygen gas per minute):

2. Use the data to draw a graph of the bubble produced per minute vs light intensity:

3. Although the light source was placed set distances from the *Cabomba* stem, light intensity in lux was recorded at each distance rather than distance *per se*. Explain why this would be more accurate:

_____

_____

_____

4. The sample of gas collected during the experiment was tested with a glowing splint. The splint reignited when placed in the gas. What does this confirm about the gas produced?

_____

_____

5. What could be a more accurate way of measuring the gas produced in the experiment? _____

_____

_____

© 2017 **BIOZONE** International
ISBN: 978-1-927309-26-1
Photocopying Prohibited

20 Overcoming Limiting Factors in Photosynthesis

Key Idea: The growth of plants in glasshouses can be increased by manipulating abiotic factors.

Manipulating abiotic (physical) factors can maximise crop yields for economic benefit. For example, covering the soil with black plastic reduces weed growth and increases soil temperature and so boosts production. A more complete control of the abiotic conditions is achieved by growing crops in a controlled-environment system such as a greenhouse.

Temperature, carbon dioxide concentration, and light intensity may be optimised to maximise the rate of photosynthesis and therefore growth. Glasshouses also allow specific abiotic factors to be manipulated to trigger a change in the growing behaviour of some crops (e.g. flowering). Carbon dioxide enrichment dramatically increases the growth of glasshouse crops providing that other important abiotic factors (such as mineral nutrients) are not limiting.

The growing environment can be controlled or modified to varying degrees. Black plastic sheeting can be laid over the soil to control weeds and absorb any excess solar heat. Tunnel enclosures (such as those above) may be used to reduce light intensity and airflow, prevent frost damage, and reduce damage by pests.

Large, commercial glasshouses have elaborate computer-controlled watering systems linked to sensors that measure soil moisture, air temperature, and humidity. Coupled with a timer, they deliver optimal water conditions for plant growth by operating electric solenoid valves attached to the irrigation system.

Air flow through a glasshouse is essential to providing a homogeneous air temperature. Air flow also ensures an even distribution of carbon dioxide gas throughout the enclosure. A general airflow from one end of the enclosure to the other is maintained by a large number of fans all blowing in the same direction.

Carbon dioxide enrichment

Carbon dioxide (CO_2) is a raw material used in photosynthesis. If the supply of carbon dioxide is cut off or reduced, plant growth and development are curtailed. The amount of CO_2 in air is normally 0.03% (250-330 ppm). Most plants will stop growing when the CO_2 level falls below 150 ppm. Even at 220 ppm, a slow-down in plant growth is noticeable (see graph right).

Controlled CO_2 atmospheres, which boost the CO_2 concentration to more than 1000 ppm, significantly increase the rate of formation of dry plant matter and total yield (e.g. of flowers or fruit). Extra carbon dioxide can be generated (at a cost) by burning hydrocarbon fuels, using compressed, bottled CO_2 or dry ice, or by fermentation or decomposition of organic matter.

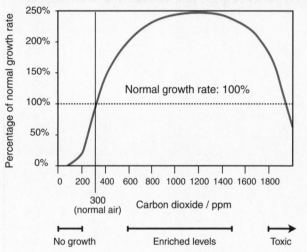

The effect of CO_2 concentration on plant growth

Normal growth rate: 100%

Percentage of normal growth rate (y-axis): 0%, 50%, 100%, 150%, 200%, 250%

Carbon dioxide / ppm (x-axis): 0, 200, 400, 600, 800, 1000, 1200, 1400, 1600, 1800

300 (normal air)

No growth — Enriched levels — Toxic

1. Explain why **CO₂ enrichment** has the capacity to radically increase crop production: _____

_____

_____

2. Explain why air flow needs to be controlled in a glasshouse: _____

_____

_____

3. List the abiotic factors that are controlled in a glasshouse environment: _____

_____

_____

21 Chapter Review

Summarise what you know about this topic under the headings and sub-headings provided. You can draw diagrams or mind maps, or write short notes to organise your thoughts. Use the images and hints to help you and refer back to the introduction to check the points covered:

Aerobic cellular respiration

HINT: Name the stages in aerobic respiration, where they occur, and the ATP yield of each. Write the overall equation for cellular respiration

Glycolysis

HINT: Describe glycolysis, including inputs and outputs.

Anaerobic metabolism

HINT: Summarise lactic acid fermentation in mammalian muscle and alcoholic fermentation in plants.

The link reaction and Krebs cycle

HINT: Describe the role of the link reaction. Describe the inputs and outputs of the Krebs cycle.

Oxidative phosphorylation

HINT: Describe how the electron transport chain generates ATP.

REVISE

© 2017 BIOZONE International
ISBN: 978-1-927309-26-1
Photocopying Prohibited

Photosynthetic pigments

HINT: Why do plants have different pigments? Define absorption and action spectra.

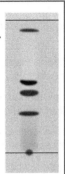

Photosynthesis: light dependent reactions

HINT: Summarise the events of the light dependent reactions. Distinguish cyclic and non-cyclic phosphorylation.

Photosynthesis: inputs and outputs

HINT: State the general equation for photosynthesis. Outline the location and inputs and outputs of the light dependent and light independent reactions.

Photosynthesis: light independent reactions

HINT: Summarise the events of the Calvin cycle including the role of enzymes. Describe the fate of triose phosphate.

© 2017 **BIOZONE** International
ISBN: 978-1-927309-26-1

22 KEY TERMS AND IDEAS: Did You Get It?

1. Match each term to its definition, as identified by its preceding letter code.

absorption spectrum ....

alcoholic fermentation ....

Calvin cycle ....

cellular respiration ....

electron transport chain ....

glycolysis ....

grana ....

Krebs cycle ....

light dependent phase ....

link reaction ....

matrix ....

mitochondria ....

oxidative phosphorylation ....

pyruvate ....

ribulose bisphosphate ....

A A series of anaerobic reactions that convert glucose into pyruvate. The energy released is used to produce ATP.

B The process in cellular respiration which involves the oxidation of glucose by a series of redox reactions that provide the energy for the formation of ATP.

C Organelles responsible for producing the cell's ATP. They appear oval in shape with an outer double membrane and a convoluted interior membrane.

D The stage in cellular respiration where pyruvate enters the mitochondrion and carbon dioxide is removed.

E An anaerobic pathway in yeasts and plants where ethanal acts as the electron acceptor and the end product is ethanol.

F The stacks of thylakoids within the chloroplasts of plants.

G The phase in photosynthesis when light energy is converted to chemical energy.

H The term to describe the light absorption of a pigment vs the wavelength of light.

I The phase in photosynthesis where chemical energy is used for the synthesis of carbohydrate. Also called the light independent phase.

J Also known as the citric acid cycle. Part of a metabolic pathway involved in the chemical conversion of carbohydrates, fats and proteins to CO_2 and water to generate a form of usable energy (ATP).

K The catabolic process in which the chemical energy in complex organic molecules is coupled to ATP production.

L A product of glycolysis. An important intermediate in many metabolic pathways.

M A 5-carbon molecule which acts as the primary CO_2 acceptor in photosynthesis.

N Series of protein complexes, which pass electrons from high to low redox potentials and couple this to the transfer of H^+ across a membrane and the generation of ATP.

O The region of the mitochondrion enclosed by the inner mitochondrial membrane.

2. Complete the diagram of cellular respiration below by filling in the boxes below:

No. ATP (a)

No. ATP (b)

No. ATP (c)

Glycolysis

Link reaction

(d)

(e)

Input (f)

Waste CO_2 **Waste** (g)

Waste (h)

3. (a) Write the process of photosynthesis as a chemical equation: _____

   (b) Where does photosynthesis occur? _____

4. Label the following features of a chloroplast on the diagram below: granum, stroma, thylakoid disc, stroma lamellae

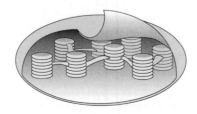

 © 2017 **BIOZONE** International
ISBN: **978-1-927309-26-1**
Photocopying Prohibited

TEST

Topic 6

Microbiology and pathogens

6.1 Microbial techniques

Learning outcomes

Activity number

☐ i Describe the basis of aseptic techniques used in working with microbiological cultures and understand their importance. — 23

☐ ii Describe the principles and techniques involved in culturing microorganisms, including strain isolation by streak plating or dilution plating. — 23 24 26

☐ iii Describe and explain the use of different media for the culture of microorganisms, e.g. broth cultures, agar, and selective media — 23

☐ iv Describe the different methods of measuring the growth of a bacterial culture, including cell counts, dilution plating, mass, and optical methods (turbidity). — 24 25

☐ v Describe and explain the typical phases of growth of a bacterial culture: lag phase, log phase, stationary phase, and death phase. Calculate exponential growth rate constants for a bacterial culture. — 28 29

☐ **CP-12** Investigate the rate of growth of bacteria in liquid culture, taking into account the safe and ethical use of organisms. — 25

☐ **CP-13** Isolate species from a mixed culture of bacteria using streak plating, taking into account the safe and ethical use of organisms. — 26 27

☐ **AT** Use appropriate laboratory glassware apparatus for a variety of experimental techniques, including serial dilutions. — 25

☐ **AT** Use microbiological aseptic techniques, including the use of agar plates and broth. — 23 25 26

☐ **MATH** A.2.5: Use logarithms in relation to quantities that range over several orders of magnitude. — 29

☐ **MATH** A.3.5: Calculate rate of change from a graph showing a linear relationship. — 28

6.2 Bacteria as pathogens

Learning outcomes

Activity number

☐ i Describe how bacteria can act as pathogens and explain how they cause infection by invading and destroying host tissues and producing toxins. — 30

☐ ii Describe the pathogenic effects arising from the production of exotoxins (e.g. by *Staphylococcus* spp.), endotoxins (e.g. by *Salmonella* spp.), and invasion of host tissues (e.g. by *Mycobacterium tuberculosis*). — 30

6.3 Action of antibiotics

Learning outcomes

Activity number

☐ i Describe and explain the action of bactericidal and bacteriostatic antibiotics, as illustrated by penicillin and tetracycline. — 31

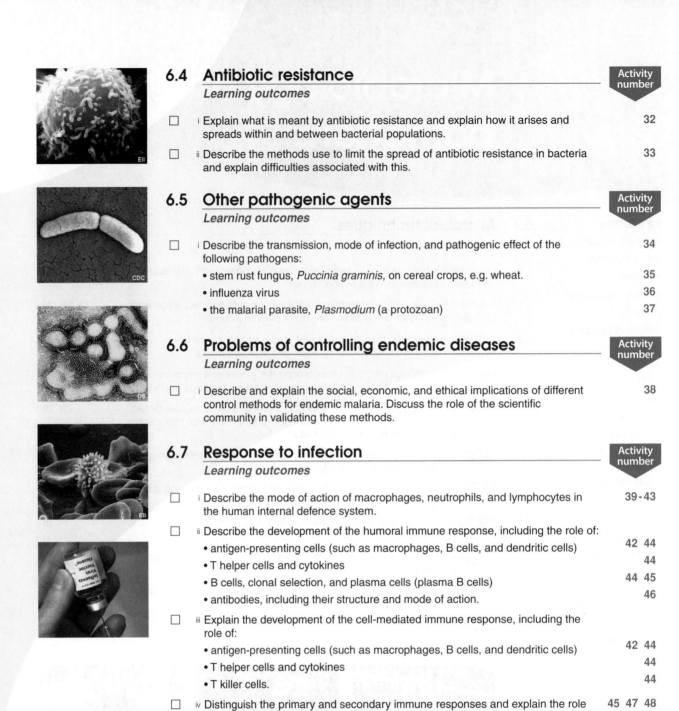

6.4　Antibiotic resistance

Learning outcomes

6.5　Other pathogenic agents

Learning outcomes

6.6　Problems of controlling endemic diseases

Learning outcomes

6.7　Response to infection

Learning outcomes

23 Culturing Microorganisms

Key Idea: A variety of culture media can be used to grow microbes in the laboratory. The use of aseptic technique to reduce microbial contamination is an important skill.

Microorganisms have very specific requirements that must be met in order for them to grow. In the laboratory, microbes are grown using specific media and culture conditions chosen to meet their particular metabolic requirements (see below). Introducing a microbe to a culture medium is called **inoculation**. Care must be taken during inoculation to prevent cross contamination by unwanted microbes. Contamination is minimised by using **aseptic techniques**, a set of procedures designed to reduce the probability of contamination.

Conditions for the culture of bacteria and fungi

Fungi

Medium: Fungi are commonly grown on solid agar. Few microbes can digest agar, so the medium is not used up during growth.

Temperature: Most fungi have an optimum temperature for growth of 25°C, but most are adapted to survive between 5 and 35°C.

pH: Fungi prefer a neutral (pH 7) growing environment, although most species can tolerate slightly acidic conditions.

Nutrients: Fungi need a source of carbon and nitrogen to produce protein, and a supply of trace elements such as potassium, phosphorus, and magnesium.

Water potential: Fungi are 85-90% water by mass. Water is constantly lost from the hyphae via evaporation and must be replaced through absorption from the media. To aid water uptake, media have a water potential that is less negative than that of the fungal tissue.

Gaseous environment: The majority of fungi are aerobic and very few species can tolerate anaerobic conditions. This is why fungi always grow on the surface of a culture medium, not inside it.

Bacteria

Medium: Agar, a gelatinous seaweed extract is commonly used as a medium for microbial culture. Bacteria can grown on solid agar plates (below) or in agar broths.

Temperature: Most bacteria cultured in the school laboratory are classified as **mesophiles**, which grow best between 20°C and 40°C.

pH: Most bacteria grow optimally in media with a pH between 6 and 8. Very few bacteria can grow in very acidic conditions.

Nutrients: Bacteria need a source of carbon, nitrogen, and mineral salts as raw ingredients for cellular growth. Magnesium, zinc, copper, and iron are essential trace elements.

Water potential: All bacteria require water for growth. To prevent cell lysis or dehydration, the water potential of the medium must be such that net water fluxes into and out of the bacterial cell are minimised.

Gaseous environment: Aerobic bacteria will grow only in oxygenated environments, whereas obligate anaerobes (e.g. *Clostridium*) do not tolerate oxygen. Microaerophilic species, which grow in low concentrations of oxygen, sometimes require an environment rich in carbon dioxide.

Types of growth media

Solid nutrient agar plate containing TCBS agar

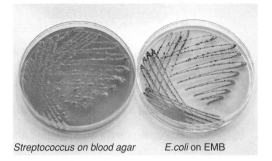

Streptococcus on blood agar   *E.coli* on EMB

Liquid agar media (above) are often called nutrient broths, and are used when the number of bacteria in the inoculum is low or to grow large numbers of bacteria. Unlike solid media, which allow individual colonies to be identified, bacteria grown in liquid media must be subcultured onto a solid medium for identification and to ensure pure (uncontaminated) cultures. Some agar media are designed to grow a wide variety of microbes, whereas selective media are manipulated to only allow certain types to grow.

When grown on a solid agar plate, microbial colonies can be easily isolated for further study or isolation. The type of nutrients and growth substances added to the agar varies depending on the specific metabolic needs of the microbe being isolated. This plate has a TCBS **selective medium** to encourage the growth of the gram negative pathogen *Vibrio cholerae*. The high pH medium inhibits the growth of gram positive bacteria, provides a carbohydrate source easily utilised by *Vibrio*, and also contains indicators to detect pH changes.

Selective media contain substances that will enhance the growth of certain bacteria while inhibiting the growth of others. Selective media are often used in medical diagnosis to determine if a specific pathogen (disease-causing agent) is present. Selective media may include a specific sugar required for metabolism, salts, antibiotics, or metabolic inhibitors. **Differential media** are similar to selective media but contain dyes or chemicals that enable closely related microbes to be distinguished. Eosin methylene blue (EMB) is both a selective and a differential medium. It contains dyes toxic to gram positive bacteria, and bile salts which kill all gram negative bacteria except coliforms. Blood agar is an enriched differential medium for streptococcal species that cause lysis of red blood cells.

Aseptic technique

Aseptic technique is a fundamental skill in microbiology as it prevents unwanted microorganisms contaminating a laboratory culture. The technique involves the use of heat (a flame) and sometimes alcohol to sterilise the tools used to transfer a microbial inoculum to the growth medium.

Exposure of the culture media to the environment is limited to reduce the risk of contamination from the environment. For this reason, the lid of an agar plate or screw cap of a liquid broth are only partially opened for as little time as possible to inoculate the media. Aseptic technique also minimises the risk of microbes being released into the environment. This is especially important when dealing with pathogenic microbes. The example provided on the right shows the inoculation of an agar plate using aseptic technique.

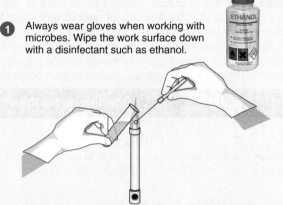

1 Always wear gloves when working with microbes. Wipe the work surface down with a disinfectant such as ethanol.

Sources of contamination

Sources of contamination include:

- ▶ Airborne microbes
- ▶ Contamination from the researcher's body
- ▶ Dirty (unsterilised) equipment or bench top
- ▶ Contaminated culture media

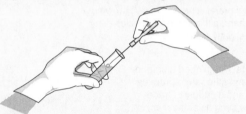

2 Hold the inoculating loop in the flame until it glows red hot. Remove the lid from the culture broth and pass the neck of the bottle through the flame.

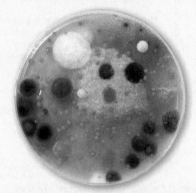

The environment contains many microbes that could potentially contaminate an inoculum if correct aseptic technique is not followed. The agar plate above was left exposed in a laboratory for one hour and then incubated. Many different types of microbes have grown on it.

3 Dip the cool inoculating loop into the broth. Flame the neck of the bottle again and replace the lid.

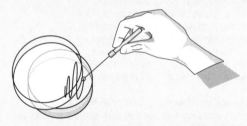

4 Raise the lid of the plate just enough to allow the loop to streak the plate. Streak the surface of the media. Seal the plate with tape and incubate upside down.

1. (a) What is a selective growth medium? _____
   _____

   (b) When might the use of selective growth media be important? _____
   _____
   _____

   (c) How do selective media achieve their effect?_____
   _____
   _____

2. Why is it important to use aseptic technique when growing microbial cultures? _____
   _____
   _____

3. What would happen if you did not cool the inoculation loop before you dipped it into the culture broth? _____
   _____
   _____

© 2017 **BIOZONE** International
ISBN: 978-1-927309-26-1
Photocopying Prohibited

24 Dilution Plating

Key Idea: Dilution plating can be used to estimate culture density based on plate counts after a serial dilution.

The number of bacteria in a culture can be measured directly (e.g. by counting in a haemocytometer) or indirectly. Indirect methods include measuring culture dry weight or turbidity, both of which are directly proportional to cell density.

Microbial populations are often very large, so most counting methods rely on counting a very small sample of the culture. A commonly used indirect method is serial dilution followed by plate counts (dilution plating). If care is taken with the serial dilution, an accurate estimate of culture density can be obtained.

Measuring microbial growth using dilution plating

A **serial dilution** is the stepwise dilution of a substance into another solution. By making a series of dilutions and then counting the colonies that arise after plating, the density of the original inoculum (starting culture) can be calculated. To obtain good results, the colonies should be well separated and the number of colonies should not be too numerous to count.

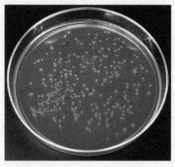

Madprime cc 3.0

CALCULATION: No. of colonies on plate X reciprocal of sample dilution = no. of bacteria per cm^3.

EXAMPLE: *28 colonies on a plate of 1/1000 dilution, then the original culture contained:*
$$28 \times 1000 = 28 \times 10^3 \ cm^{-3} \ bacterial \ cells$$

Plate counts are widely used in microbiology. It is a useful technique because only the viable (live) colonies are counted, but it requires some incubation time before colonies form. For quality control purposes in some food industries where the food product is perishable (e.g. milk processing) this time delay is unacceptable, and rapid detection methods are used.

When a culture has been sufficiently diluted, the colonies are discrete and can easily be counted or isolated. Each colony arises from a single cell.

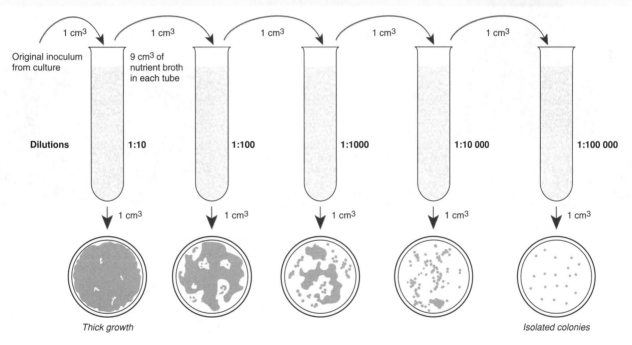

Thick growth — *Isolated colonies*

1. In the example of serial dilution above, use the equation provided to calculate the cell concentration in the original culture:

_____

2. (a) Explain the term viable count: _____

_____

(b) Explain why dilution plating is a useful technique for obtaining a viable count: _____

_____

_____

(c) Investigate an alternative technique, such as turbidimetry and identify how the technique differs from dilution plating:

_____

_____

_____

25 Investigating Bacterial Growth

Key Idea: Bacterial growth can be measured over time using a spectrophotometer.

Bacteria divide and increase their cell numbers by a process called binary fission. The rate of cell division varies between species; some divide rapidly (every 20 minutes) while others can take days to divide. The increase in cell numbers can be measured in the laboratory with a spectrophotometer as an increase in culture turbidity. The experiment below describes how students investigated bacterial growth in *E.coli* on two different growth media.

The aim

To investigate the growth rate of *E.coli* in two different liquid cultures, a minimal growth medium and a nutrient enriched complex growth medium.

The method

Using aseptic technique, the students added 0.2 mL of a pre-prepared *E.coli* culture to two test tubes. One test tube contained 5.0 mL of a minimal growth medium and the second contained 5.0 mL of a complex medium. Both samples were immediately mixed, and 0.2 mL samples removed from each and added to a cuvette. The absorbance of the sample was measured using a spectrophotometer at 660 nm. This was the 'time zero' reading. The test tubes were covered with parafilm, and placed in a 37°C water bath. Every 30 minutes, the test tubes were lightly shaken and 0.2 mL samples were taken from each so the absorbance could be measured. The results are presented in the table (right).

A spectrophotometer (left) is an instrument used to measure transmittance of a solution and so can be used to quantify bacterial growth where an increase in cell numbers results in an increase in turbidity.

In this experiment, students measured the absorbance of the solution. Absorbance measures the amount of light absorbed by the sample. Often, transmission (the amount of light that passes through a sample) is used to measure cell growth.

All bacteria should be treated as pathogenic and strict hygiene practices should be followed. These include wearing gloves, using aseptic techniques, not consuming food or drink in the laboratory, washing all surfaces with disinfectant afterwards, and hand washing. These precautions prevent the accidental introduction of the bacteria into the environment, and prevent accidental infection.

Results

| Incubation time / min | Absorbance at 660 nm | |
	Minimal medium	Complex medium
0	0.021	0.014
30	0.022	0.015
60	0.025	0.019
90	0.034	0.033
120	0.051	0.065
150	0.078	0.124
180	0.118	0.238
210	0.179	0.460
240	0.273	0.698
270	0.420	0.910
300	0.598	1.070

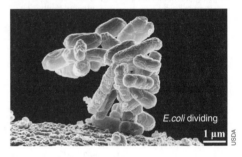

E.coli dividing
1 μm
USDA

1. Why is it important to follow strict hygiene precautions when working with bacteria?

_____

_____

_____

2. (a) On the grid (right) plot the results for *E.coli* growth on the two media:

(b) What is the absorbance measuring? _____

_____

(c) Describe the effect of the complex medium on *E.coli* growth:

_____

_____

_____

3. Another group of students wanted to calculate the number of cells in each sample. Explain how this could be achieved:

_____

_____

_____

© 2017 **BIOZONE** International
ISBN: 978-1-927309-26-1
Photocopying Prohibited

26 Strain Isolation

Key Idea: Streak plating is a simple method to isolate individual bacterial colonies for further study.

The most common way of separating bacterial cells on the agar surface is the **streak plate method**. This method dilutes the sample by mechanical means. After incubation, the area at the beginning of the streak pattern will show confluent growth (growth as a continuous sheet), while the area at the end of the streak will show individual colonies. Isolated colonies can be removed using aseptic techniques, and transferred to a sterile medium. After incubation, assuming aseptic techniques have been used, all organisms in the new culture will be descendants of the same organism (i.e. a pure culture). The organism can then be identified and studied (e.g. for sensitivity to particular antibiotics).

The streaking starts here. Streaks are made in the order indicated by the numbers on the plate. The first streak is made from the initial bacterial mixture.

In each streak, the loop picks up bacteria from the previous series, diluting the number of cells each time.

Individual colonies (arising from one cell) should be obtained here. These can be removed and then cultured separately.

Latex gloves ensure no contamination from either bacteria or fungi on the hands.

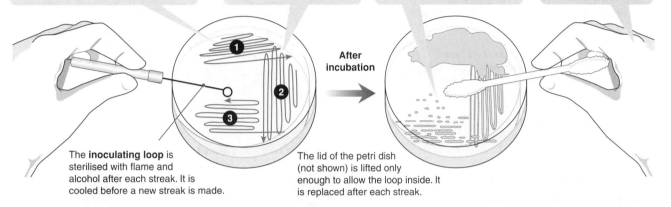

After incubation

The **inoculating loop** is sterilised with flame and alcohol after each streak. It is cooled before a new streak is made.

The lid of the petri dish (not shown) is lifted only enough to allow the loop inside. It is replaced after each streak.

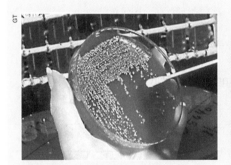

Colonies become visible when approximately 10 to 100 million bacterial cells are present. Note the well-isolated colonies in the photo above. A single colony may be removed for further investigation.

A swab containing a single strain of bacteria is used to inoculate additional nutrient plates to produce pure cultures of bacteria.

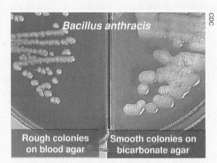

Bacillus anthracis

Rough colonies on blood agar   **Smooth colonies on bicarbonate agar**

To test purity, a sample of a culture can be grown on a selective medium that promotes the growth of a single species. A selective medium may contain a nutrient specific to a particular species.

1. What is the purpose of streak plating? _____

2. Outline the process of streak plating: _____

   _____

   _____

   _____

3. Why is the lid only partially removed during streaking? _____

   _____

4. (a) How would you know your streak plating had been effective?_____

   _____

   (b) What could you do to test that all your colonies were the same species? _____

   _____

LINK **27**   LINK **23**   WEB **26**   **KNOW**

27 Isolating a Bacterial Species

Key Idea: Individual bacterial species can be isolated from a mixed culture using streak plating. Their appearance can be used to help distinguish the colonies.

In nature, bacteria exist as mixed assemblages. To study individual species, they must exist as pure cultures, in which all organisms are the same species. Streak plating can be used to separate cells, which will give rise to distinct colonies. Differences in colony shape, colour, size, and elevation profile can then be used to distinguish the different species. In this activity you will use your knowledge of microbiological techniques and the information given to demonstrate how you would obtain a pure culture from a mixed bacterial population.

Background

Students were provided with a culture containing three species of bacteria. Using an aseptic streak plating technique, they plated the mixed culture on to a general growth agar plate. The plate was incubated at 37°C for two days.

Three distinct colony types grew. All three colony types were white/cream in colour but had distinctive appearances (below right).
For clarity, on the diagram:
Colony type 1 is shown as black.
Colony type 2 is shown as grey.
Colony type 3 is shown as blue.

Closer inspection of the agar plate revealed that there were several, well isolated colonies of types 1 and 2. However, only one colony of the third type formed, and it overlapped a type 1 colony.

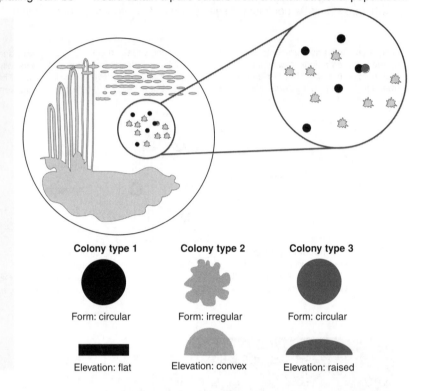

Colony type 1	Colony type 2	Colony type 3
Form: circular	Form: irregular	Form: circular
Elevation: flat	Elevation: convex	Elevation: raised

1. Colony types 1 and 3 overlapped each other. They were both the same colour and formed circular colonies. How could the students tell that organisms growing in colony type 1 and 3 were different?

_____

_____

2. (a) Describe what steps the students would take next to produce pure cultures of each colony: _____

_____

_____

_____

(b) What extra steps might be needed to isolate colony type 3? _____

_____

_____

_____

(c) Explain why these steps may be needed: _____

_____

_____

3. One student's agar plate was very contaminated with fungi (right). How could this have happened?

_____

_____

_____

© 2017 **BIOZONE** International
ISBN: 978-1-927309-26-1
Photocopying Prohibited

28 Microbial Growth Curve

Key Idea: Microbial growth in a closed culture consists of lag, log, stationary and death phases. The exponential growth rate constant can be determined from the growth curve.

In a closed system (like a test tube), a population of bacterial cells exhibits a very specific growth pattern. Microbial growth curves consist of four phases (lag, log, stationary, and death phases). A typical growth curve is shown below. From the growth curve it is possible to calculate generation times (how long it takes for the population to double) and exponential growth rate constants.

Typical microbial growth curve

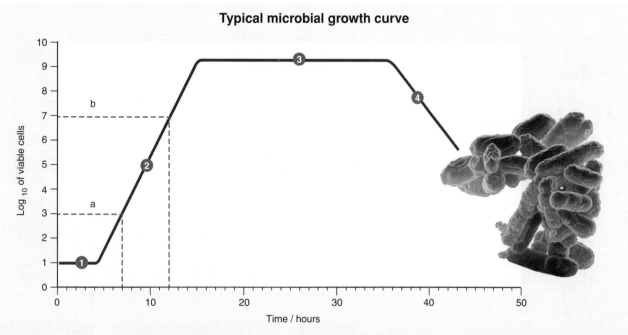

Time / hours

① **Lag phase**: Cells increase in size and synthesise enzymes, but there is little or no cell division. Cell numbers are relatively constant.

② **Log phase**: The phase of exponential growth. In conditions optimal for microbial growth, the cells begin multiplying at an exponential rate, due to high metabolic activity and cellular reproduction. Cells are most vulnerable to adverse conditions and anti-microbial agents.

③ **Stationary phase**: In a closed culture system no new nutrients are added and waste products are not removed. Microbial growth slows as the nutrients become depleted and waste products build up. The growth rate equals the death rate, so there is no net growth in the microbial population, and numbers stabilise.

④ **Death phase**: Microbial numbers decrease as the death rate exceeds growth rate. This is the result of a lack of nutrients and build up of toxic metabolites.

1. Why is there an initial lag in the growth of a microorganism placed into a new culture? _____
_____
_____

2. (a) Identify the phase where growth is fastest: _____

   (b) Explain why this growth rate cannot be maintained in a closed system: _____
   _____
   _____

3. What causes the death phase? _____

4. Use the formulae (right) to calculate the exponential growth constant (μ) and the generation time (g) for the two points (a and b) on the microbial growth curve plotted above.

   Definitions are given in the blue box far right.

$$\mu = \frac{2.303\ (\log_{10}N_x - \log_{10}N_0)}{(t_x - t_0)}$$

$$g = \frac{(\log_{10}N_x - \log_{10}N_0)}{(\log_{10}2)}$$

2.303 conversion factor ($\log_e$ to $\log_{10}$)

$\log_{10}N_x = \log_{10}$ viable cells at 12 hours

$\log_{10}N_0 = \log_{10}$ viable cells at 7 hours

$t_x - t_0$ = time period of exponential growth

$\log_{10}2 = 0.301$

μ: _____   g: _____

LINK
29

WEB
28

KNOW

29 Plotting Microbial Growth

Key Idea: Microbial growth can be plotted on a graph and used to predict microbial cell numbers at a set time.

Bacteria reproduce by a **binary fission**, a simple cell division that is preceded by cell elongation and involves one cell dividing in two. The time required for a cell to divide is the **generation time** and it varies between species and with environmental conditions such as temperature. When actively growing bacteria are inoculated into a liquid growth medium and the population is counted at intervals, a line can be plotted to show the growth of the cell population over time. You can simulate this for a hypothetical bacterial population with a generation time of 20 minutes.

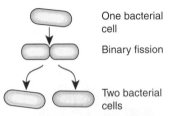

One bacterial cell

Binary fission

Two bacterial cells

Time / min	Number of cells
0	1
20	2
40	4
60	8
80	
100	
120	
140	
160	
180	
200	
220	
240	
260	
280	
300	
320	
340	
360	

1. Complete the table above by doubling the number of bacteria for every 20 minute interval.

2. State how many bacteria were present after: 1 hour: _____ 3 hours: _____ 6 hours: _____

3. Graph the results on the grid above. Make sure that you choose suitable scales and labels for each axis.

4. (a) Predict the number of cells present after 380 minutes: _____

   (b) Plot this value on the graph above:

5. Why is a log graph used to plot microbial growth? _____

_____

_____

© 2017 **BIOZONE** International
ISBN: 978-1-927309-26-1
Photocopying Prohibited

30 Bacterial Pathogens

Key Idea: Bacterial pathogens are bacteria that cause disease, invading the host and causing a range of symptoms. **Pathogens** are disease-causing agents. Bacterial pathogens are responsible for a wide range of diseases and are highly successful pathogens. To be successful, a pathogen must multiply and spread between hosts before being detected by the host's immune system. The bacteria causes harm when it infects the body and begins to multiply. Host harm may occur through physical damage to the host's cells as a result of rapid reproduction of the bacteria, disruption of the host's cellular functions, a hypersensitivity reaction in the host (a strong response by the immune system), or through the production of toxins that damage or destroy cells and disrupt the host's immune system.

How bacteria enter the body

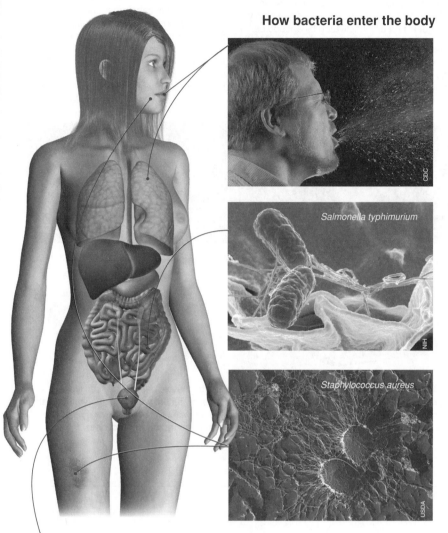

Salmonella typhimurium

Staphylococcus aureus

Respiratory tract
The mouth and nose are major entry points for pathogens which are inhaled from the expelled mucus of other people. Tuberculosis (TB) is a respiratory disease caused by the bacterium *Mycobacterium tuberculosis*. The bacterium is spread through the air when infectious people cough (left), sneeze, talk, or spit and the infectious particles are inhaled. 5700 cases of TB were reported in England in 2015.

Gastrointestinal tract
Food and water contaminated with pathogenic bacteria can cause a range of diseases with symptoms from mild to fatal. Ingestion of some strains of *Salmonella* is a common cause of a type of food poisoning called salmonellosis. The bacteria produce endotoxins which cause harm to the host when released from the bacterial cell. In 2015, 8500 cases of salmonellosis were reported in the UK.

Breaking the skin surface
The skin provides an effective barrier to most pathogens, but cuts and abrasions allow pathogens to enter the body. There are over 40 species of *Staphylcoccus* bacteria, many of which colonise the skin and nose of humans with no ill effect. However, if the bacteria infect deeper into the body they can cause serious harm, including death. Entry is through ingestion of contaminated food or via cuts in the skin. *Staphylococcus* produce a range of exotoxins that cause damage to the host.

Urinogenital openings
Urinogenital openings provide entry points for the pathogens responsible for urinogenital infections, including sexually transmitted infections (STIs). Gonorrhoea, caused by the bacterium *Neisseria gonorrhoeae* is an example of an STI.

1. What is a pathogen? _____

_____

2. Describe some common ways for pathogenic bacteria to enter the human body and give examples of each: _____

_____

_____

_____

_____

_____

_____

© 2017 **BIOZONE** International
ISBN: 978-1-927309-26-1
Photocopying Prohibited

LINK
31

WEB
30

KNOW

How bacteria cause disease

Invasion of host tissue

Some bacteria cause damage by invading and directly damaging the host tissue. When *Mycobacterium tuberculosis* is inhaled, bacilli reach the lungs, where they are ingested by alveolar macrophages. Usually the macrophages destroy the bacteria, but some bacilli can stay hidden from the immune system and multiply within the macrophages. More macrophages are attracted to the area and a tubercle (nodule) forms.

Tuberculosis may then become dormant or the tubercle may rupture, releasing bacilli into the bronchioles. Affected tissue is replaced by scarring (fibrosis) and cavities filled with cheese-like white necrotic material.

Production of exotoxins

Exotoxins are highly toxic proteins produced and secreted primarily by gram positive bacteria as part of their normal growth and metabolism. The exotoxins help the bacteria to colonise the host. Due to their solubility, they are easily transported around the body. They may act locally or (more commonly) produce widespread systemic effects, damaging membranes, interfering with cellular metabolism, and causing massive inflammatory reactions. Exotoxins are highly antigenic and are inactivated by antibodies.

Staphylcoccus aureus produces a variety of exotoxins. Some are enzymatic and convert the host's tissue into nutrients for bacterial growth. Others inhibit the immune response allowing *S. aureus* to multiply and spread.

Production of endotoxins

Endotoxins are lipopolysaccharides (LPS) associated with the membrane forming the outermost layer of the cell wall in gram negative bacteria. They are released from the outer membrane when the cell dies.

Endotoxins act in the vicinity of the bacteria. They are less toxic than exotoxins and are heat stable. While the dose required to produce symptoms is relatively high, the immune system cannot neutralise them with antibodies. Endotoxins are associated with fever in the host and can produce a range of symptoms including shock. In the human gut, lysis of *Salmonella* cells releases LPS, which damage the intestinal cells, impairing fluid absorption, and causing diarrhoea. If untreated, severe dehydration follows.

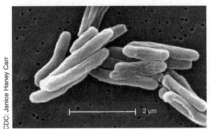

Gram positive cell, e.g. *Staphylococcus*

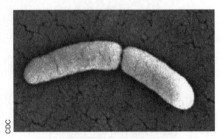

Gram negative cell, e.g. *Salmonella*

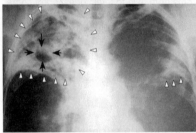

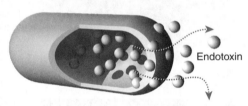

LPS

Endotoxin

X-ray of lungs affected by TB. The white triangles show congested airspaces and the dark arrows show a cavity, from which infective material is coughed up.

Exotoxins are unstable and can usually be destroyed by heat. Heat inactivated exotoxins (toxoids) are used in vaccinations because they are so potently antigenic.

Endotoxins are released by cell lysis. However, recent work has shown they can also be exported from live cells as part of membrane transport processes.

3. For each of the following describe their pathogenic effect on their host:

(a) *Mycobacterium tuberculosis*: _____

_____

_____

(b) *Salmonella* spp: _____

_____

_____

(c) *Staphylcoccus* spp: _____

_____

_____

4. Distinguish between exotoxins and endotoxins: _____

_____

_____

5. (a) Identify a pathogen associated with the production of exotoxins: _____

(b) Identify a pathogen associated with the production of endotoxins: _____

31 Antibiotics

Key Idea: Antibiotics are chemicals that kill bacteria (bactericidal) or inhibit their growth (bacteriostatic).

Antibiotics are chemicals that act against bacterial infections by either killing the bacteria (**bactericidal** action) or preventing them from growing (**bacteriostatic** action). Antibiotics interfere with bacterial growth by disrupting key aspects of bacterial metabolism (below). Antibiotics are

ineffective against viruses because viruses lack the structure and metabolic machinery that antibiotics target. Antibiotics are produced naturally by bacteria and fungi to kill or inhibit competitors or pathogens, but most modern antibiotics are semi-synthetic modifications of these natural compounds. The action of two commonly used antibiotics, penicillin and tetracycline, are described below.

How antibiotics work

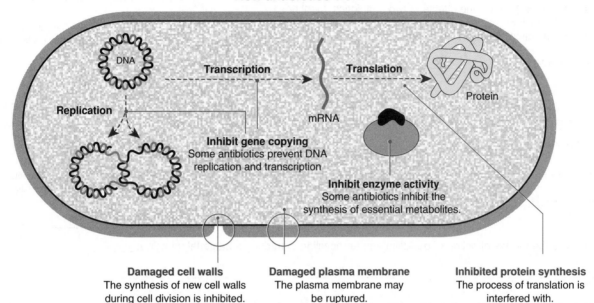

Inhibit gene copying
Some antibiotics prevent DNA replication and transcription

Inhibit enzyme activity
Some antibiotics inhibit the synthesis of essential metabolites.

Damaged cell walls
The synthesis of new cell walls during cell division is inhibited.

Damaged plasma membrane
The plasma membrane may be ruptured.

Inhibited protein synthesis
The process of translation is interfered with.

Penicillin and tetracycline: modes of action

Penicillins are a group of bactericidal antibiotics produced by species of *Penicillium* fungi. When bacteria divide they must synthesise a new cell wall. Penicillin interferes with the normal cell wall synthesis in gram positive bacteria, preventing the formation of the peptidoglycan cross-links in the cell wall. It does this by inhibiting the enzyme that forms the cross links. Without cross links, the cell wall lacks the strength to enclose the cell contents. Pressure inside the cell becomes too much and the cell surface membrane ruptures, killing the cell (right). Gram negative bacteria are less sensitive to penicillins because their cell wall contains less peptidoglycan and it lies inside an outer membrane of lipopolysaccharide.

The antibiotic tetracycline has a bacteriostatic action and inhibits protein synthesis. Tetracycline reversibly binds to the 30S subunit of the bacterial ribosome and prevents transfer RNA (tRNA) attaching and adding its amino acid to the polypeptide chain. Tetracycline is a broad spectrum antibiotic meaning it is used against many different bacterial pathogens.

Tetracycline inhibits protein synthesis

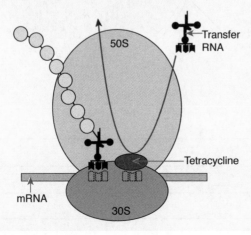

Penicillin interferes with cell wall synthesis

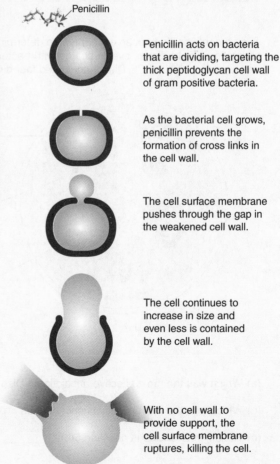

Penicillin acts on bacteria that are dividing, targeting the thick peptidoglycan cell wall of gram positive bacteria.

As the bacterial cell grows, penicillin prevents the formation of cross links in the cell wall.

The cell surface membrane pushes through the gap in the weakened cell wall.

The cell continues to increase in size and even less is contained by the cell wall.

With no cell wall to provide support, the cell surface membrane ruptures, killing the cell.

LINK **33** LINK **32** WEB **31** KNOW

42

1. Why are viruses not affected by antibiotics? _____
_____
_____

2. Distinguish between bacteriostatic and bactericidal: _____
_____
_____

3. The graph (right) shows the effects of two antibiotics. Identify the antibiotic with a bacteriostatic action and the antibiotic with a bactericidal action. Explain your choice:

Bacteriostatic: _____
_____
_____

Bactericidal: _____
_____
_____

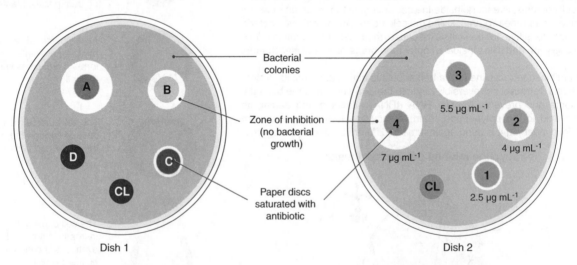

4. Compare the modes of action of penicillin and tetracycline in treating a bacterial infection: _____
_____
_____
_____
_____

5. Two students carried out an experiment to determine the effect of antibiotics on bacteria. They placed discs saturated with antibiotic on petri dishes evenly coated with bacterial colonies. Dish 1 contained four different antibiotics labelled A to D and a control labelled CL. Dish 2 contained four different concentrations of a single antibiotic and a control labelled CL.

Bacterial colonies

A   B

Zone of inhibition (no bacterial growth)

D   C

CL

Paper discs saturated with antibiotic

Dish 1

3
5.5 µg mL⁻¹

4   2
7 µg mL⁻¹   4 µg mL⁻¹

CL   1
2.5 µg mL⁻¹

Dish 2

(a) Which was the most effective antibiotic on Dish 1? _____

(b) Which was the most effective concentration on Dish 2? _____

(c) Explain your choice in question 5(b): _____
_____

32 The Evolution of Antibiotic Resistance

Key Idea: Bacteria can develop resistance to antibiotics and can pass this on to the next generation and to other populations. **Antibiotic resistance** arises when a genetic change allows bacteria to tolerate levels of antibiotic that would normally inhibit growth. This resistance may arise spontaneously by mutation or copying error, or by transfer of genetic material between microbes. Genomic analyses from 30 000 year old permafrost sediments show that the genes for antibiotic resistance have long been present in the bacterial genome. Modern use of antibiotics has simply provided the selective environment for their proliferation. Many bacterial strains have even acquired resistance to multiple antibiotics.

The evolution of antibiotic resistance in bacteria

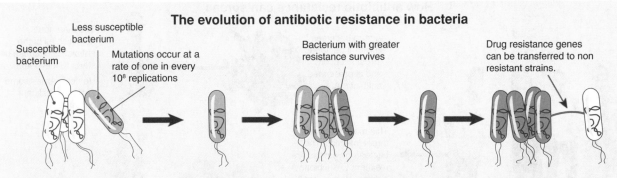

Susceptible bacterium

Less susceptible bacterium

Mutations occur at a rate of one in every 10^8 replications

Bacterium with greater resistance survives

Drug resistance genes can be transferred to non resistant strains.

Any population, including bacterial populations, includes variants with unusual traits, in this case reduced sensitivity to an antibiotic. These variants arise as a result of mutations in the bacterial chromosome. Such mutations are well documented and some are ancient.

When a person takes an antibiotic, only the most susceptible bacteria will die. The more resistant cells remain and continue dividing. Note that the antibiotic does not create the resistance; it provides the environment in which selection for resistance can take place.

If the amount of antibiotic delivered is too low, or the course of antibiotics is not completed, a population of resistant bacteria develops. Within this population too, there will be variation in susceptibility. Some will survive higher antibiotic levels.

A highly resistant population has evolved. The resistant cells can exchange genetic material with other bacteria (via horizontal gene transmission), passing on the genes for resistance. The antibiotic initially used against this bacterial strain will now be ineffective.

The bacterium responsible for TB, *Mycobacterium tuberculosis*, has developed resistance to several drugs.

Today, one in seven new TB cases is resistant to the two drugs most commonly used as treatments and 5% of these patients die. Some strains have evolved resistance to more than one drug. Multi-drug resistant TB (MDR TB) is the most common, but extensively drug resistant (XDR) strains are unaffected by most of the TB drugs.

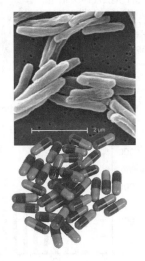

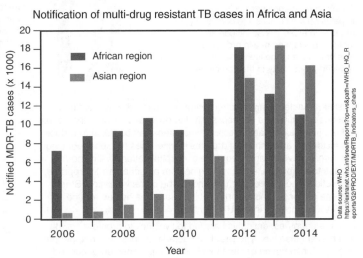

Notification of multi-drug resistant TB cases in Africa and Asia

- African region
- Asian region

Notified MDR-TB cases (x 1000)

Year

Data source: WHO
https://extranet.who.int/sree/Reports?op=vs&path=/WHO_HQ_Reports/G2/PROD/EXT/MDRTB_Indicators_charts

1. Describe two ways in which antibiotic resistance can become widespread:

   (a) _____

   (b) _____

2. Genomic evidence indicates that the genes for antibiotic resistance are ancient:

   (a) How could these genes have arisen in the first place? _____

   _____

   (b) Explain why these genes are proliferating now: _____

   _____

3. (a) Describe the trend in MDR TB over the last decade: _____

   (b) Why are the MDR and XDR strains of MTB so worrying? _____

   _____

33 The Implications of Antibiotic Resistance

Key Idea: Antibiotic resistance makes it harder to treat and eliminate the causes of bacterial disease.

Antibiotic resistance makes it difficult to treat and control some bacterial diseases. Patients with infections caused by drug-resistant bacteria are more likely to suffer medical complications and death. Some bacteria have evolved resistance to multiple antibiotics. The infections they cause are very difficult to treat and are more easily spread through the population. It is very likely that, in the near future, there will be no effective antibiotics against some pathogens. New discoveries of effective antibiotics are rare, only four new antibiotics have been approved for use since 2000.

How antibiotic resistance can spread

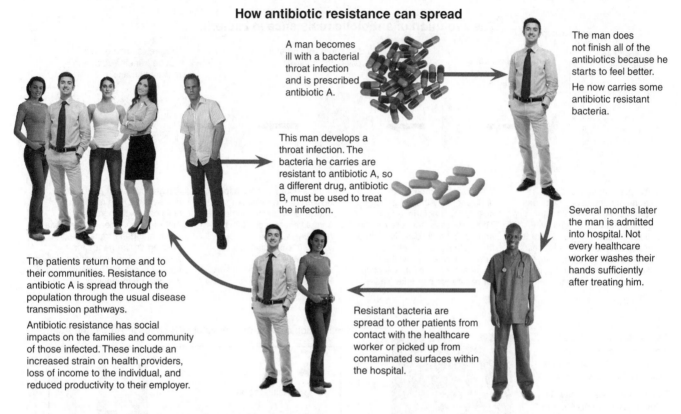

A man becomes ill with a bacterial throat infection and is prescribed antibiotic A.

The man does not finish all of the antibiotics because he starts to feel better.

He now carries some antibiotic resistant bacteria.

This man develops a throat infection. The bacteria he carries are resistant to antibiotic A, so a different drug, antibiotic B, must be used to treat the infection.

Several months later the man is admitted into hospital. Not every healthcare worker washes their hands sufficiently after treating him.

The patients return home and to their communities. Resistance to antibiotic A is spread through the population through the usual disease transmission pathways.

Antibiotic resistance has social impacts on the families and community of those infected. These include an increased strain on health providers, loss of income to the individual, and reduced productivity to their employer.

Resistant bacteria are spread to other patients from contact with the healthcare worker or picked up from contaminated surfaces within the hospital.

Resistant bacterial strains often occur because patients have been prescribed antibiotics unnecessarily, the dose is too low, or the patient did not finish all the antibiotics. Several steps can be taken to reduce the incidence and impact of drug resistance. These include reducing the spread in vulnerable people (e.g. hospital patients), limiting the access to antibiotics, and ensuring doctors prescribe an appropriate antibiotic at the correct strength and for the correct duration. Strict hygiene protocols and reporting of infections has helped reduce MRSA transmission in the UK (right).

In some countries, antibiotics are fed to livestock to promote growth and prevent disease. The resistant bacteria are passed on to people through consumption of meat that has not been handled or cooked properly, or from eating produce where animal faecal material containing the resistant bacteria has been used as fertiliser.

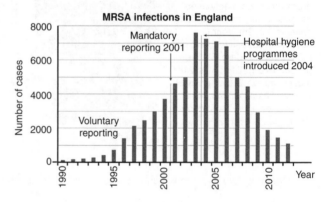

MRSA infections in England

Mandatory reporting 2001

Hospital hygiene programmes introduced 2004

Voluntary reporting

Number of cases

Year

1. Describe some of the biological and social consequences of antibiotic resistance: _____

_____

_____

_____

_____

2. Using the example of MRSA in the UK, explain how the incidence and spread of resistant strains can be reduced:

_____

_____

_____

_____

LINK 32

© 2017 **BIOZONE** International
ISBN: 978-1-927309-26-1
Photocopying Prohibited

34 Fungi, Viruses, and Protozoan Pathogens

Key Idea: Microorganisms such as fungi and protozoa, and infectious agents such as viruses, cause a range of diseases. In addition to bacteria, many other types of microbes and infectious agents can be pathogenic (cause disease). Viruses, some protozoans, and some fungi are responsible for a wide range of diseases in humans. Some diseases are relatively harmless, while others can be have serious effects or even be fatal. The pathways and mechanism of infection varies greatly between each group, this means some pathogenic infections can be more easily prevented and treated than others.

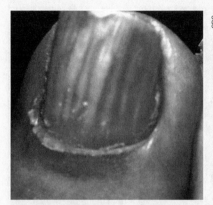

Ten percent of the adult population suffer from toenail infections caused by fungi.

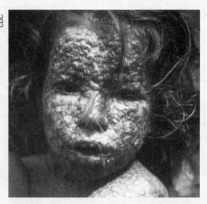

Photo: Bangladeshi girl with smallpox (1973). Smallpox was declared eradicated in 1980.

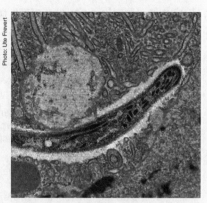

Malaria sporozoite in the gut epithelia. The parasite is carried by a mosquito vector.

Pathogenic **fungi** are a common cause of plant disease, but they also cause disease in animals. Fungal infections are long lasting and hard to treat because the fungi grow slowly. Infections commonly occur in the skin, hair, nails, genitals, and pharynx, but they can affect internal organs too.

Viruses are non-cellular obligate, intracellular parasites and need living host cells in order to multiply. Antibiotics, which target bacterial cells only, are ineffective against viruses, but viral diseases can be effectively controlled, or even eradicated, through vaccination programmes.

Eukaryotic pathogens include fungi, algae, protozoa, and parasitic worms. Many are highly specialised parasites with a number of hosts, e.g. the malaria parasite has a mosquito and a human host. Certain life stages reside within the host's cells, making them (like viruses) hard to treat.

Pathogen success and failure

▶ In general, a host's immune system quickly recognises an invading pathogen as foreign, usually on the basis of its surface proteins (antigens) or the toxins it produces. This recognition triggers an immune (defensive) response in the host that destroys the pathogen. To be successful, a pathogen must avoid the host's immune system for long enough to infect a new host.

▶ Different pathogens use different strategies to avoid detection and infect other hosts. They may multiply rapidly and spread before the immune system can react (e.g. common cold, right) or they may produce a slower chronic infection that is more difficult for the immune system to overcome (e.g. HIV/AIDS).

▶ Pathogens that kill the host before being able to spread are not successful. In high density populations, diseases with a high mortality (death rate) such as Bubonic plague, Ebola, and smallpox, can spread successfully (witness the 2014 Ebola outbreaks in western African countries). However, in low density areas, pathogens that kill their host quickly have poor transmission, as too few hosts can be infected during the infectious period.

One method a pathogen can use to spread between hosts is to cause an irritation in the throat that produces a cough. The cough spreads infected droplets to other hosts.

1. What must a pathogen do to be successful? _____

_____

2. Why is a killing the host too quickly a disadvantage to the pathogen? _____

_____

_____

3. Why do some outbreaks of infectious disease "burn out" quickly: _____

_____

_____

© 2017 **BIOZONE** International
ISBN: 978-1-927309-26-1
Photocopying Prohibited

LINK **37**   LINK **36**   LINK **35**   KNOW

35 Stem Rust Fungus

Key Idea: Stem rust fungal disease infects commercially important cereal crops and can cause significant losses. Thousands of fungal species are plant pathogens. Many important food crops are susceptible to fungal disease, so prevention and treatment is very important to maintain food security. Fungi are spread by spores which may be dispersed long distances by air or water, or be present in the soil. Many fungal plant diseases can be controlled by crop rotation and the use fungicides if a disease is present. Stem rust (described below) is one example of a fungal pathogen.

Puccinia graminis causes stem rust in wheat

▶ Stem rust disease is named after the rust coloured pustules/blisters that develop on infected plants. The disease is caused by a type of rust fungus called *Puccinia graminis*.

▶ *P. graminis* is an obligate parasite, it requires a living host to survive and reproduce.

▶ *P. graminis* is an economically important disease because it can infect many important food crops such as wheat, barley, oats, and rye, and affect food supply through significant crop losses.

▶ Stem rust disease has infected wheat crops throughout the history of wheat cultivation. This has been partially overcome by producing rust-resistance wheat plants using genetic engineering. The first of these were in use during the 1950s. However, mutations (DNA changes) to the *P. graminis* genome have resulted in the evolution of new strains of the fungus to which even genetically modified wheat is susceptible.

▶ More traditional controls of the fungus include chemical spraying (fungicides) and removal of nearby barberry plants, which are necessary for the successful completion of the stem rust life cycle.

Wheat infected with stem rust disease (above, left) and healthy wheat plant (above, right).

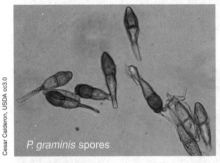
P. graminis spores

Infected wheat stems

Testing disease resistant wheat crops in Kenya

Transmission

P. graminis has a complicated life cycle involving several spore stages and two hosts (barberry and wheat). This makes the disease difficult to control and treat. Infection occurs when spores are carried by wind or splashes of water from an infected plant to a new plant.

Mode of infection

In favourable (warm and wet) conditions, the transferred spores germinate and infect the plant by penetrating the leaf stomata or the outer layers of the stalk. Eventually a mycelium (a mass of thread-like hyphae) is produced and the fungus absorbs nutrients that the wheat plant would otherwise utilise.

Pathogenic effect

The infection weakens the stem and plants may fall over as a result. A reduction in nutrients available to the wheat plant results in smaller, deformed wheat grains and reduces grain yield. Stomatal infection can disrupt control of transpiration and may lead to desiccation.

1. Why is stem rust disease a significant disease to humans? _____

_____

_____

2. Describe the transmission and mode of infection of *P. graminis*: _____

_____

_____

3. Describe the pathogenic effect and economic significance of stem rust disease on wheat crops: _____

_____

_____

_____

_____

LINK
34

© 2017 **BIOZONE** International
ISBN: 978-1-927309-26-1
Photocopying Prohibited

36 The Influenza Virus

Key Idea: Viruses are infectious agents and are responsible for a large number of diseases including influenza (the flu). Viruses are responsible for many human diseases including the respiratory disease influenza (the flu). Influenza is a highly contagious disease caused by the *Influenzavirus*. It is highly contagious, spreading from person to person by touching virus infected surfaces or by breathing in droplets expelled when an infected person talks, sneezes, or coughs.

Once contracted influenza is difficult to treat and is usually are left to run its course. Recovery from infection is usually associated with the host's immune system combating the infection. Immunisation provides the best protection against influenza (the vaccine is 75% effective). However, because the *Influenzavirus* virus constantly undergoes genetic changes, people must be vaccinated each season with the most recently circulating influenza viruses to stay protected.

Transmission, action, and pathogenic effect of *Influenzavirus*

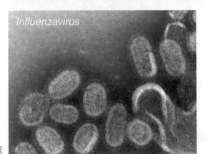

Influenzavirus

CDC

Transmission

Most commonly, influenza is spread when a person inhales airborne droplets from an infected patient. The transmission rate is extremely high because the virus can survive outside of the body for up to 24 hours, and high numbers of viral particles are transmitted coughs and sneezes. Each year around 500 000 people die from the flu and millions are people are infected.

Mode of infection

The virus binds to surface receptors on respiratory cells and are transported into the cell by endocytosis (infolding of the cell membrane). Components of the virus are transported to the nucleus and take over the cell's metabolic machinery so that thousands of copies of the virus are made (replicated). The new viral particles are transported to the cell membrane and bud off to infect other cells.

Pathogenic effect

The effects of *Influenzavirus* are varied in their severity and can be fatal in some instances. Infection causes a fever and inflammation (particularly of the respiratory cells) as the body tries to kill off the virus. Some people develop complications affecting their respiratory system (e.g. pneumonia), lung damage, sinus or ear infections, blood poisoning or even brain damage.

The *Influenzavirus* mutates

Three strains of *Influenzavirus* affect humans, *Influenzavirus* A, B, and C. The most effective protection against the flu is vaccination. However, because the *Influenzavirus* constantly mutates the annual vaccine must be adjusted each year to protect against the most recent strains. Mutation can occur in two ways:

▶ **Antigenic drifts** are small changes in the virus that happen continually over time. Updated vaccines can help to counteract these alterations.

▶ **Antigenic shift** occurs when two or more different viral strains (or different viruses) combine to form a new subtype (below). The changes are large and sudden and most people lack immunity to the new subtype and are susceptible.

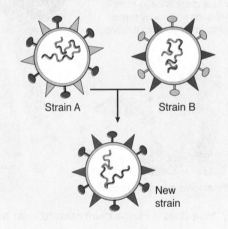

Strain A   Strain B

New strain

1. Why is the flu so contagious? _____

_____

_____

2. How does the *Influenzavirus* infect a host and replicate new viral particles? _____

_____

_____

3. Why is the *Influenzavirus* so difficult to prevent by vaccination? _____

_____

_____

_____

_____

© 2017 **BIOZONE** International
ISBN: 978-1-927309-26-1
Photocopying Prohibited

37 Malaria

Key Idea: Malaria is caused by parasitic protozoa. The protozoa are carried by the *Anopheles* mosquito and are transmitted to humans when they are bitten by the mosquito. Malaria is a disease caused by protozoan parasites of the genus *Plasmodium*. The plasmodia have a life cycle involving two hosts, *Anopheles* mosquitoes and humans. Humans become infected when bitten by mosquitoes infected with the protozoans. In their human host, the plasmodia infect red

blood cells (RBCs) and multiply inside the cells by asexual reproduction. Four *Plasmodium* species can cause malaria, ranging in severity from relatively mild to fatal. *Falciparum* malaria is the most severe because it affects red blood cells of all ages. Destruction of the RBCs results in a condition called haemolytic anaemia (loss of RBCs through lysis). The infected blood cells also become sticky and block blood vessels to vital organs such as the kidneys and the brain.

Transmission and effects of malaria

1. Transmission

A mosquito infected with *Plasmodium* bites a human. The parasite completes the sexual part of its life cycle in the mosquito before being transferred to the human host.

2. Mode of infection

The parasite travels through the blood to the liver where it reproduces rapidly within the liver cells. After a short period (~ 48 hours) parasites infect red blood cells and continue to multiply (although some may remain dormant for years in the liver).

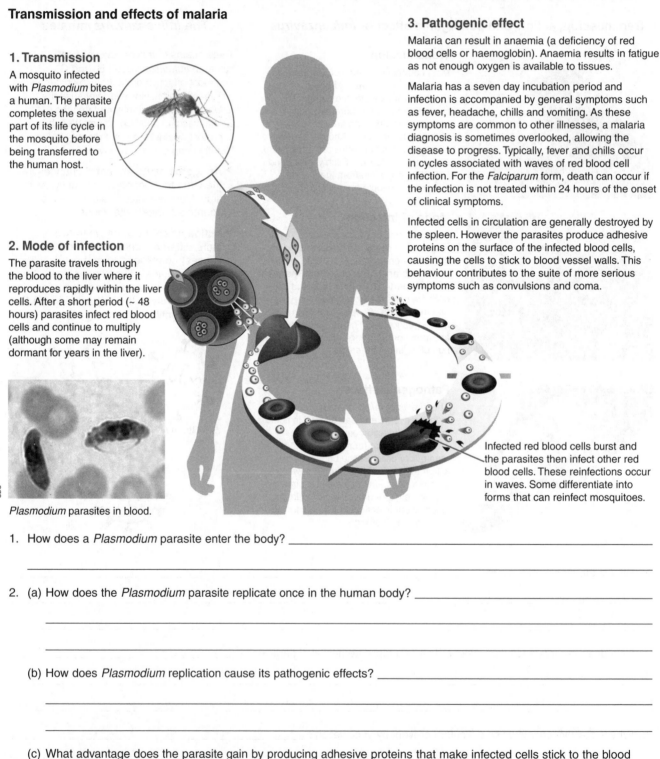

Plasmodium parasites in blood.

3. Pathogenic effect

Malaria can result in anaemia (a deficiency of red blood cells or haemoglobin). Anaemia results in fatigue as not enough oxygen is available to tissues.

Malaria has a seven day incubation period and infection is accompanied by general symptoms such as fever, headache, chills and vomiting. As these symptoms are common to other illnesses, a malaria diagnosis is sometimes overlooked, allowing the disease to progress. Typically, fever and chills occur in cycles associated with waves of red blood cell infection. For the *Falciparum* form, death can occur if the infection is not treated within 24 hours of the onset of clinical symptoms.

Infected cells in circulation are generally destroyed by the spleen. However the parasites produce adhesive proteins on the surface of the infected blood cells, causing the cells to stick to blood vessel walls. This behaviour contributes to the suite of more serious symptoms such as convulsions and coma.

Infected red blood cells burst and the parasites then infect other red blood cells. These reinfections occur in waves. Some differentiate into forms that can reinfect mosquitoes.

1. How does a *Plasmodium* parasite enter the body? _____

_____

2. (a) How does the *Plasmodium* parasite replicate once in the human body? _____

_____

_____

   (b) How does *Plasmodium* replication cause its pathogenic effects? _____

_____

_____

   (c) What advantage does the parasite gain by producing adhesive proteins that make infected cells stick to the blood vessel walls? How does contribute to their pathogenicity?

_____

_____

_____

© 2017 **BIOZONE** International
ISBN: 978-1-927309-26-1
Photocopying Prohibited

38 Malaria is Endemic in Some Countries

Key Idea: Environmental, social, and economic factors make it difficult to eradicate malaria from some countries.

Malaria occurs in over 90 countries, but is considered endemic (always present) in certain regions such as Sub-Saharan Africa and Papua New Guinea. Environmental conditions, social factors (e.g. education), public health care capability, and economic status all contribute to a country's ability to eradicate malaria. For example, 90% of malaria cases and deaths occur in Sub-Saharan Africa, a region with environmental conditions well suited to survival of the *Anopheles* mosquito vector. It is also an economically poor and socially undeveloped region, and has few resources at its disposal to control the spread of malaria. The scientific community has an important role to play in improving the treatment and prevention of malaria, and ultimately in eradicating the disease altogether.

The distribution and control of malaria

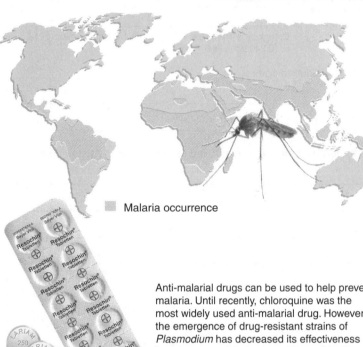

Malaria occurrence

▶ Malaria occurs in tropical and subtropical areas (left) where temperature, humidity, and rainfall are suitable for the survival and reproduction of the *Anopheles* mosquitoes, which the malaria parasites need to complete their life cycle. The highest transmission occurs in Africa (south of the Sahara) and in parts of Oceania such as Papua New Guinea.

▶ Malaria is a leading cause of death and disease in many developing countries, where pregnant women and children are most affected. More than 200 million people contract malaria every year and the disease kills hundreds of thousands annually. Its economic cost is estimated at US$12 billion per year.

Why is malaria difficult to eradicate?

Anti-malarial drugs can be used to help prevent malaria. Until recently, chloroquine was the most widely used anti-malarial drug. However the emergence of drug-resistant strains of *Plasmodium* has decreased its effectiveness in some areas. It is now used in combination with other antimalarial drugs (left) to extend its effective usage.

Malaria disproportionately affects low income populations and economically disadvantaged countries. Therefore it is important that the companies developing new drugs and insecticides sell them at a price that makes them accessible to even the poorest countries.

▶ Several factors make malaria a very difficult disease to control. The *Plasmodium* parasite has two different hosts and a complex life cycle, making it very difficult to target with drugs. The parasite has also evolved resistance to anti-malarial drugs, allowing it to continue to spread and, in some cases, re-emerge in areas where it had previously been eradicated. Likewise, mosquitoes are evolving insecticide resistance and their numbers are remaining high, allowing a greater transmission of the *Plasmodium* parasite.

▶ Vigilant monitoring and reporting on insecticide resistance is an important step in eliminating malaria. Once resistance is identified, new strategies (e.g. the use of more than one insecticide) or use of new insecticides can be used to control the mosquito vector.

Control and prevention of malaria

Spraying insecticide to kill mosquitoes

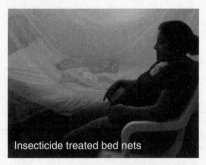

Insecticide treated bed nets

An integrated approach is used to control and prevent the spread of malaria. These include physical methods such using insecticide treated nets to stop mosquitoes biting a person while they are sleeping, drug treatments, especially for pregnant women and infants, and residual pesticide spraying (indoors and outdoors) to kill mosquitoes.

Social and economic factors have a significant role in the spread of malaria. People living in poor rural populations often cannot afford the bed nets that would protect them from mosquitoes. The governments of malaria-endemic countries often lack financial resources and do not have adequate equipment, medicine, or trained staff to treat malaria.

Larvae of the *Anopheles* mosquito can breed in diverse habitats, many of which are created as a result of human activity. For example, small pools of water in ditches, water troughs, containers (above), or rice fields are all potential breeding sites for mosquitoes. Mosquito numbers can be reduced by eliminating as many potential breeding sites as possible.

Monitoring the effect of insecticide spraying

▶ Monitoring allows scientists to know if a preventive strategy, such as insecticide spraying, is effective in reducing malaria cases. Recommendations (e.g. changing the frequency or type of insecticide used) can then be made based on solid scientific analysis.

▶ A commonly used monitoring method is to compare the **incidence** (the rate of new cases) of malaria in a community before and after insecticide spraying. If the spraying is effective, the incidence of malaria in the community will decrease. An ineffective programme will see no change (or even an increase) in the number of malaria cases reported.

▶ Ethiopia is an African country in which 70% of the population is at risk of contracting malaria. In the East Shoa region, 22 villages were sprayed with DDT insecticide. The incidence of malaria before and after insecticide spraying were compared. The results from six villages are shown in the table (right).

Table 1. Comparison of the incidence of malaria before and after DDT spraying.

Village	Malaria incidence / % of population	
	Before spraying	After spraying
Bagaya	7.7	4.7
Dambi	8.7	5.1
Fulxino	8.1	3.8
Godino	4.3	2.7
Wajitu	4.0	2.4
Yatu	6.5	2.5

Data source: Hamusse, S.D. *et.al*, Global Heath Action 2012; 5: 10.3402/gha.v5i0.11619.

1. What aspects of the biology of *Plasmodium* make malaria difficult to control? _____

_____

_____

2. Describe how social and economic factors contribute to how well malaria is controlled in Sub-Saharan African countries:

_____

_____

_____

3. (a) On the grid right plot the incidence of malaria in the six Ethiopian villages shown in Table 1 before and after DDT spraying.

   (b) State (with reasons) if insecticide spraying was an effective preventative measure in the villages studied:

   _____

   _____

   _____

   _____

   (c) Predict what would happen to the results if *Anopheles* mosquitoes in the region evolved DDT resistance?

   _____

   _____

   _____

   _____

4. Discuss the ethical considerations associated with developing and providing controls for endemic malaria:

_____

_____

_____

_____

_____

39 The Body's Defences

Key Idea: The human body has a tiered system of defences that provides resistance against disease.

The body has a suite of physical, chemical, and biological defences against pathogens, collectively called **resistance**. The first line of defence consists of external barriers to prevent pathogen entry. If this fails, a second line of defence targets any foreign bodies that enter. Lastly, the specific immune response provides targeted defence against the pathogen. The defence responses of the body fall into two broad categories, the innate and the adaptive immune responses. The **innate** (non-specific) response (the first and second lines of defence) protects against a broad range of non-specific pathogens. It involves blood proteins (e.g. complement) and phagocytic white blood cells. The **adaptive** (or specific) immune response (the third line of defence) is specific to identified pathogens. It involves defence by specific T cells (**cellular immunity**) as well as antibodies, which neutralise foreign antigens (**humoral immunity**).

Most microorganisms find it difficult to get inside the body. If they succeed, they face a range of other defences.

The natural populations of harmless microbes living on the skin and mucous membranes inhibit the growth of most pathogenic microbes

Microorganisms are trapped in sticky mucus and expelled by cilia (tiny hairs that move in a wavelike fashion).

1st line of defence

The skin provides a physical barrier to the entry of pathogens. Healthy skin is rarely penetrated by microorganisms. Its low pH is unfavourable to the growth of many bacteria and its chemical secretions (e.g. sebum, antimicrobial peptides) inhibit growth of bacteria and fungi. Tears, mucus, and saliva also help to wash bacteria away.

2nd line of defence

A range of defence mechanisms operate inside the body to inhibit or destroy pathogens. These responses react to the presence of any pathogen, regardless of which species it is. White blood cells are involved in most of these responses. It includes the **complement system** whereby plasma proteins work together to bind pathogens and induce inflammation to help fight infection.

3rd line of defence

Once the pathogen has been identified by the immune system, **lymphocytes** launch a range of specific responses to the pathogen, including the production of defensive proteins called **antibodies**. Each type of antibody is produced by a B-cell clone and is specific against a particular antigen.

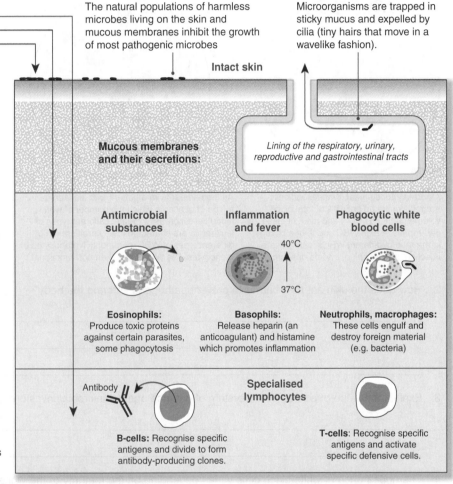

Intact skin

Mucous membranes and their secretions:

Lining of the respiratory, urinary, reproductive and gastrointestinal tracts

Antimicrobial substances

Eosinophils: Produce toxic proteins against certain parasites, some phagocytosis

Inflammation and fever

40°C

37°C

Basophils: Release heparin (an anticoagulant) and histamine which promotes inflammation

Phagocytic white blood cells

Neutrophils, macrophages: These cells engulf and destroy foreign material (e.g. bacteria)

Antibody

Specialised lymphocytes

B-cells: Recognise specific antigens and divide to form antibody-producing clones.

T-cells: Recognise specific antigens and activate specific defensive cells.

Helena Paffen CC3.0

Intact skin (above) provides a physical barrier to stop pathogens entering the body. Cuts or abrasions allow pathogens to enter.

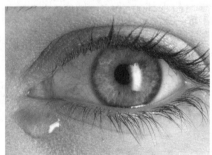

Antimicrobial chemicals are present in many bodily secretions, including tears. Tears also wash away contaminants from the eyes.

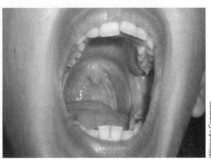

Wikimedia Commons

Harmless microbes colonise certain areas of the body (e.g. skin, gut, mouth, nose and throat) and prevent pathogens establishing.

1. Distinguish between specific and non-specific resistance: _____

_____

_____

_____

_____

© 2017 **BIOZONE** International
ISBN: 978-1-927309-26-1
Photocopying Prohibited

LINK 44   LINK 41   LINK 40   WEB 39

KNOW

WBC counts can be diagnostic

White blood cells (WBCs) or leucocytes (right) play an important role in protecting the body against pathogens. In a healthy person, WBCs occur in predictable ratios. Infection results in elevated numbers of WBCs, particularly neutrophils, whereas a change in the relative proportions of different WBCs can be diagnostic of specific diseases. An analysis of the relative proportions of the different types of WBCs is called a **differential white cell count**.

Most common →→→→→→→ Least common

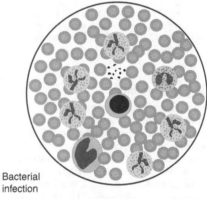

| | Light staining granules | Smaller, rounder, agranular | Agranular, lobed nucleus | Stains dark pink | Stains dark purple |

Platelets · Erythrocyte · Neutrophil · Lymphocyte · Monocyte · Eosinophil · Basophil

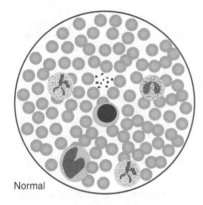

Normal

A normal blood smear. White blood cells normally make up only 1% of total blood volume (4-11 × 10⁹ L⁻¹) and most of these are neutrophils. A high WBC count, or a change in the ratio of different WBCs, can indicate infection, inflammation, trauma or allergy.

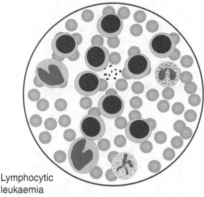

Lymphocytic leukaemia

A blood smear from a patient with leukaemia, a type of cancer in which the number of white blood cells increases greatly. Different types of leukaemia are characterised by proliferation of different types of WBC, commonly lymphocytes or monocytes. The WBCs are often non-functional.

Bacterial infection

A blood smear from someone with a bacterial infection. The body produces more WBCs to fight off the invading pathogen. Specifically a person with an infection will have higher levels of mature neutrophils and band neutrophils (an immature form of a neutrophil).

2. How does the skin act as a barrier to prevent pathogens entering the body? _____

_____

_____

_____

3. Explain the value of a three tiered system of defence against microbial invasion: _____

_____

_____

4. The appearance of white blood cells varies depending on the maturity of the white blood cell. For example, in band neutrophils, which are a common indicator of infection, the nucleus is curved, rather than lobular. Study the blood smears and answer the following questions.

(a) Identify the main type of white blood cell present in photo A:

_____

(b) What does this blood smear tell you about the health of the person it was taken from?

_____

_____

(c) Study the blood smear labelled B. State whether you think the slide is normal or abnormal:

_____

(d) Give a reason for the answer you gave in (c):

_____

_____

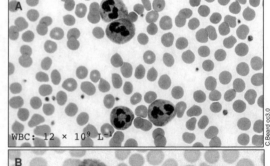

A

WBC: 12 × 10⁹ L⁻¹

C.Beard cc3.0

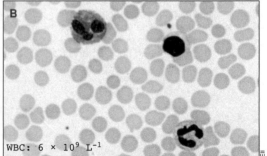

B

WBC: 6 × 10⁹ L⁻¹

© 2017 **BIOZONE** International
ISBN: 978-1-927309-26-1
Photocopying Prohibited

40 The Innate Immune Response

Key Idea: The innate immune response provides a rapid response to contain and destroy pathogens. Inflammation is an important part of the response.

The innate immune system provides protection against a pathogen, even if it has never encountered it before. The innate response is very fast and provides general protection (it is not antigen specific), but does not provide long lasting immunity. Many different cells and processes are involved. The primary outcome is to destroy and remove the cause of infection. This is achieved through containing the infection through inflammation and then recruitment of immune cells to destroy the pathogen. During this process a series of biochemical reactions (the complement system) are activated to destroy the pathogen and recruit immune cells to the site.

Phagocytic cells of the innate immune system

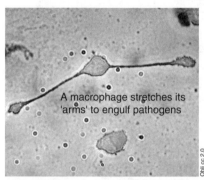
A macrophage stretches its 'arms' to engulf pathogens
Obli cc 2.0

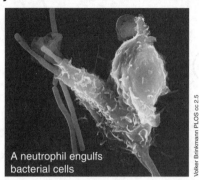
A neutrophil engulfs bacterial cells
Volker Brinkmann PLOS cc 2.5

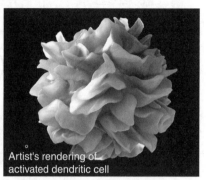
Artist's rendering of activated dendritic cell

Macrophage

Macrophages are very large and are highly efficient phagocytes. They are found throughout the body and move using an amoeboid movement (above) to hunt down and destroy pathogens. Macrophages also have a role in recruiting other immune cells to an infection site.

Neutrophil

Neutrophils are the most abundant type of phagocyte and are usually the first cells to arrive at the site of an infection. They contain toxic substances that kill or inhibit the growth of bacteria and fungal pathogens. Neutrophils release cytokines which amplify the immune response and recruit other cells to the infection site.

Dendritic cell

Dendritic cells are present in tissue that are in contact with the external environment (e.g. skin, and linings of the nose, lungs, and digestive tract). They act as messengers between the innate and adaptive immune system by presenting antigen materials to the T cells of the immune system.

Other cells and processes of the innate immune response

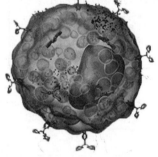

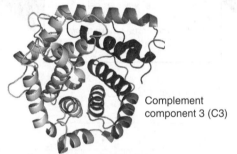
Complement component 3 (C3)

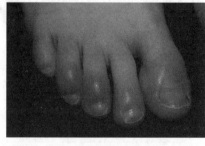

Mast cells

Mast cells contain a lot of histamine, a chemical involved in both inflammation and allergic responses. When activated, histamine is released from the mast cell causing the blood vessels to dilate and become leaky. The increased permeability allows phagocytes to reach the site of infection.

Complement proteins

The complement system comprises a number of different proteins. The proteins circulate as inactive precursors until they are activated. Complement proteins have three main roles: phagocytosis, attracting macrophages and neutrophils to the infection site, and rupturing the membranes of foreign cells.

The process of inflammation

The inflammatory process is a protective response to pathogen invasion. It has several functions: (1) to destroy the cause of the infection and remove it and its products from the body; (2) if this fails, to limit the effects on the body by confining the infection to a small area; (3) replacing or repairing tissue damaged by the infection.

1. Outline the role of the following phagocytes in the innate immune response:

(a) Macrophages: _____

_____

(b) Neutrophils: _____

_____

(c) Dendritic cells: _____

_____

The inflammatory response

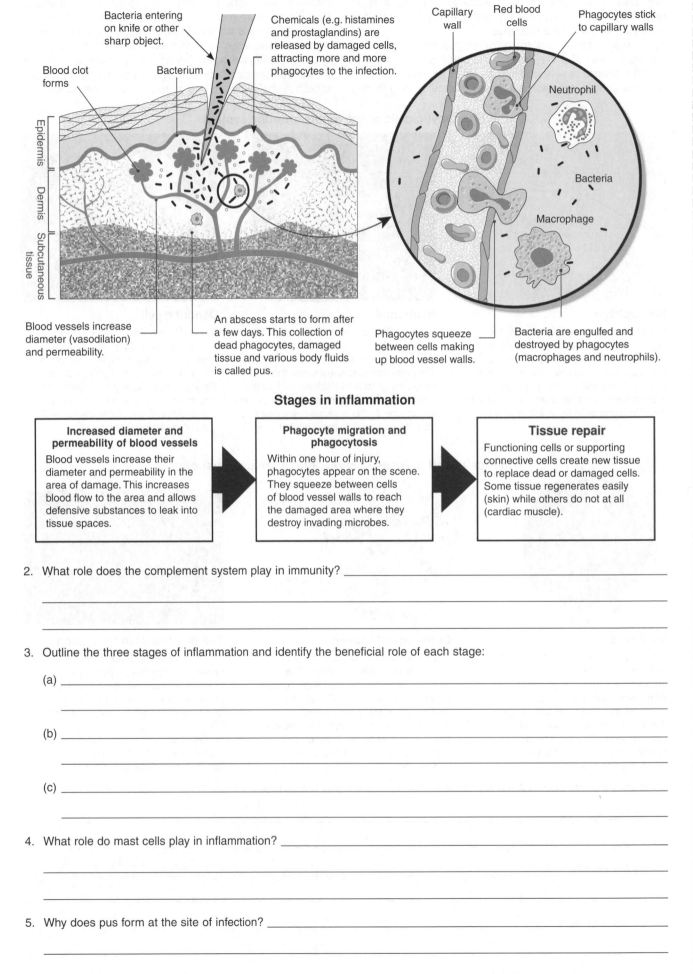

Bacteria entering on knife or other sharp object.

Chemicals (e.g. histamines and prostaglandins) are released by damaged cells, attracting more and more phagocytes to the infection.

Capillary wall

Red blood cells

Phagocytes stick to capillary walls

Blood clot forms

Bacterium

Neutrophil

Epidermis

Dermis

Subcutaneous tissue

Bacteria

Macrophage

Blood vessels increase diameter (vasodilation) and permeability.

An abscess starts to form after a few days. This collection of dead phagocytes, damaged tissue and various body fluids is called pus.

Phagocytes squeeze between cells making up blood vessel walls.

Bacteria are engulfed and destroyed by phagocytes (macrophages and neutrophils).

Stages in inflammation

Increased diameter and permeability of blood vessels

Blood vessels increase their diameter and permeability in the area of damage. This increases blood flow to the area and allows defensive substances to leak into tissue spaces.

Phagocyte migration and phagocytosis

Within one hour of injury, phagocytes appear on the scene. They squeeze between cells of blood vessel walls to reach the damaged area where they destroy invading microbes.

Tissue repair

Functioning cells or supporting connective cells create new tissue to replace dead or damaged cells. Some tissue regenerates easily (skin) while others do not at all (cardiac muscle).

2. What role does the complement system play in immunity? _____

_____

_____

3. Outline the three stages of inflammation and identify the beneficial role of each stage:

(a) _____

_____

(b) _____

_____

(c) _____

_____

4. What role do mast cells play in inflammation? _____

_____

_____

5. Why does pus form at the site of infection? _____

_____

© 2017 **BIOZONE** International
ISBN: 978-1-927309-26-1
Photocopying Prohibited

41 Phagocytes and Phagocytosis

Key Idea: Phagocytes are mobile white blood cells that ingest microbes and digest them by phagocytosis.

All types of phagocytes (e.g. neutrophils, dendritic cells, and macrophages) are white blood cells. These specialised cells have receptors on their surfaces that can detect antigenic material, such as microbes. They then ingest the microbes and digest them by phagocytosis. As well as destroying microbes, phagocytes also release cytokines that help to coordinate the overall response to an infection. Macrophages and dendritic cells also play a role in antigen presentation in processing and presenting antigens from ingested microbes to other cells of the immune system (opposite).

1 **Detection and interaction**
Microbe coated in opsonins is detected by the phagocyte and attaches to it. Opsonins are molecules in the blood that coat foreign material (e.g. a bacterial cell), marking it as a target for phagocytosis.

2 **Engulfment**
The opsonin markers trigger engulfment of the microbe by the phagocyte. The microbe is taken in by endocytosis.

3 **Phagosome forms**
A phagosome forms, enclosing the microbe in a membrane.

4 **Fusion with lysosome**
Phagosome fuses with a lysosome containing powerful antimicrobial proteins. The fusion forms a phagolysosome.

5 **Digestion**
The microbe is broken down into its chemical constituents.

6 **Discharge**
Indigestible material is discharged from the phagocyte.

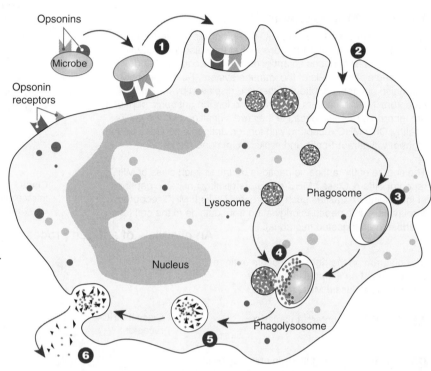

The interaction of microbes and phagocytes

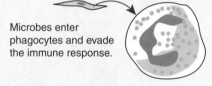

Some microbes kill phagocytes.

Microbes enter phagocytes and evade the immune response.

Dormant microbes may hide inside phagocytes.

Some microbes kill phagocytes

Some microbes produce toxins that can actually kill phagocytes, e.g. toxin-producing staphylococci and the dental plaque-forming bacteria *Actinobacillus*.

Microbes evade immune system

Some microbes can evade the immune system by entering phagocytes. The microbes prevent fusion of the lysosome with the phagosome and multiply inside the phagocyte, almost filling it. Examples include *Chlamydia*, *Mycobacterium tuberculosis*, *Shigella*, and malarial parasites.

Dormant microbes hide inside

Some microbes can remain dormant inside the phagocyte for months or years at a time. Examples include the microbes that cause brucellosis and tularemia.

1. Identify the white blood cells capable of phagocytosis: _____

2. Explain the role of opsonins and phagocyte receptors in enhancing phagocytosis: _____

_____

_____

3. Explain how some microbes can overcome phagocytic cells and use them to their advantage: _____

_____

_____

_____

42 Processing Antigens

Key Idea: Antigen processing prepares and displays antigens for presentation to the T-cells of the immune system.

Antigen presenting cells (APCs) process and present antigens for recognition by T-cells. During antigen processing, the APC digests the foreign antigen into smaller peptide fragments. These fragments are then displayed on the surface of the APC by MHC receptors. The immune response evoked by the T-cells depends on which MHC receptor (MHCI or MHCII) is activated. Antigen presentation is necessary for T-cells to recognise infection or abnormal growth and activate other cells of the immune system. Dendritic cells, macrophages, and B-cells are APCs.

The role of MHC receptors

Recall there are two types of MHC receptors, class I and class II (right). Both have similar functions in that they display antigenic peptides on cell surfaces so antigens can be recognised and processed by the T-cells of the immune system. T-cells can only recognise antigenic peptides if they are displayed by the MHC receptors. MHC receptors presenting no foreign antigenic peptides are ignored by T-cells, because they are signalling that the cell is healthy. Only MHC receptors with foreign antigenic peptides bound to them will attract T-cells and evoke an immune response.

The source of the antigenic peptides bound to each class of MHC receptor differs. Class I MHC receptors display antigenic peptides of intracellular parasites such as viruses. Class II MHC receptors display antigenic peptides originating from outside of the cell (such as those from ingested microbes).

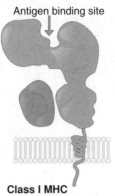

Antigen binding site

Class I MHC
Intracellular antigens, e.g. viral proteins

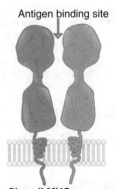

Antigen binding site

Class II MHC
Extracellular antigens, e.g. proteins from phagocytosed microbes

An overview of antigen processing

The diagram on the right represents antigen processing of an extracellular peptide antigen via a class II MHC receptor.

1 An APC encounters an antigen.

2 The antigen is engulfed via phagocytosis and digested into short peptide fragments.

3 Class II MHC receptors bind the fragments and form a MHC-antigen complex.

4 The MHC-antigen complex is displayed on the surface of the APC.

5 A receptor on the T helper cell recognises the peptide as foreign. It binds and a series of events stimulate the adaptive immune response.

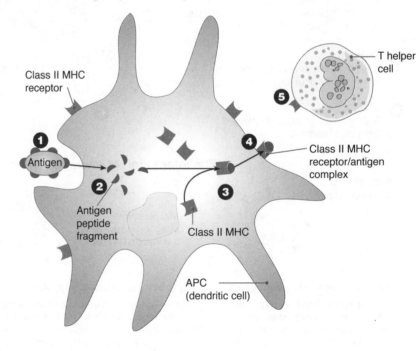

1. What is the purpose of antigen processing? _____

_____

_____

2. Why do MHC receptors with no antigenic peptide bound not cause an immune response?_____

_____

_____

3. Describe the differences between class I and class II MHC receptors: _____

_____

_____

_____

© 2017 **BIOZONE** International
ISBN: 978-1-927309-26-1
Photocopying Prohibited

43 The Lymphatic System

Key Idea: Defensive white blood cells are transported in lymph through the lymphatic system and are concentrated in the lymph nodes.

The lymphatic system is a network of tissues and organs that collects the tissue fluid leaked from the blood vessels and returns it to the heart. The lymphatic system has an important role in immunity because the fluid transported around the body by the lymphatic system (lymph) is rich in infection-fighting white blood cells. The thymus is a primary lymphoid organ and the site of T cell maturation. Secondary lymphoid tissues (spleen and lymph nodes) are important as the site of lymphocyte (T and B cell) activation.

Tonsils
A collection of secondary lymphoid tissues in the throat. They provide defence against ingested or inhaled pathogens and produce activated B and T cells.

Thymus
A primary lymphoid organ located above the heart. It is large in infants and shrinks after puberty to a fraction of its original size. Important for maturation of **T-cells**.

Spleen
The largest mass of lymphatic tissue in the body. It stores and releases blood in case of demand (e.g. in severe bleeding), produces mature B-cells and antibodies and removes antibody-coated antigenic material.

Lymph nodes
Ovoid masses of lymph tissue where lymphocytes are concentrated. Each node receives lymph through several narrow afferent (entry) vessels and exits via wider efferent (exit) vessels.

Red bone marrow
A primary lymphoid tissue where all the different kinds of blood cells (including white blood cells) are produced by cellular differentiation from stem cells. B cells also mature here.

Lymphatic vessels
When the fluid leaking from capillaries is picked up by lymph capillaries, it is called **lymph**. The lymph, carrying leukocytes, flows in lymphatic vessels through the secondary lymphoid tissues.

The lymphatic system and immunity

The fluid circulating through the lymphatic system passes through the secondary lymphoid tissues, including the **lymph nodes**. These are ovoid organs, which are present throughout the lymphatic system. Lymph nodes receive lymph via incoming (afferent) vessels and are the site of lymphocyte activation.

Lymphocytes in circulation are constantly moving between sites where antigens may be encountered. These antigens are presented to T cells in the secondary lymphoid tissues. Recognition of the antigen leads to activation and proliferation of both T and B cells, vastly increasing the number of lymphocytes. After several days, antigen-activated lymphocytes begin leaving the lymphoid tissue.

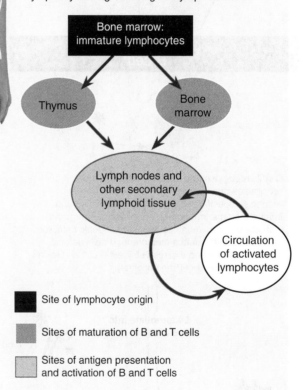

Bone marrow: immature lymphocytes

Thymus

Bone marrow

Lymph nodes and other secondary lymphoid tissue

Circulation of activated lymphocytes

■ Site of lymphocyte origin

■ Sites of maturation of B and T cells

□ Sites of antigen presentation and activation of B and T cells

1. What is the general role of the lymphatic system in immunity? _____

_____

_____

2. (a) What is the role of the secondary lymphoid tissue, e.g. lymph nodes, in the immune response? _____

_____

_____

(b) Why do you think lymph nodes become swollen when someone has an infection? _____

_____

© 2017 **BIOZONE** International
ISBN: 978-1-927309-26-1
Photocopying Prohibited

44 The Adaptive Immune System

Key Idea: Antigens, such as the cell walls of microbial cells, presented on the surface of macrophages help activate cells of the immune system against specific pathogens.

There are two main components of the adaptive immune system: the humoral and the cell-mediated responses. They work separately and together to protect against disease. The **humoral immune response** is associated with the serum (the non-cellular part of the blood) and involves the action of antibodies secreted by B cells (B lymphocytes). Antibodies are found in extracellular fluids including lymph, plasma, and mucus secretions and protect against viruses, and bacteria and their toxins. The **cell-mediated immune response** is associated with the production of specialised lymphocytes called **T cells**. Antigens are recognised by T cells only after antigen processing. The antigen is first engulfed by a macrophage, which processes the antigen and presents it on its surface. T helper cells can then recognise the antigen and activate other cells of the immune system.

Lymphocytes and their functions

Bone marrow
B cells mature in the bone marrow in the shaft of the long bones (e.g. the femur). They migrate from here to the lymphatic organs.

Stem cell
Stem cells in the bone marrow and fetal liver give rise to T cells and B cells.

Thymus gland
The thymus gland is located above the heart. It is large in infants but regresses with age. Immature T cells move to the thymus to mature before migrating to other lymphatic organs.

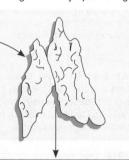

B cell

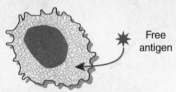

Free antigen

B cells recognise and bind antigens. Each B cell recognises one specific antigen. Helper T cells recognise specific antigens on B cell surfaces and induce their maturation and proliferation. A mature B cell may carry as many as 100 000 antigenic receptors embedded in its surface membrane. B cells defend against bacteria and viruses outside the cell and toxins produced by bacteria (free antigens).

T cell

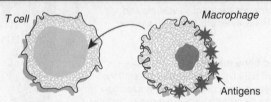

T cell   *Macrophage*

Antigens

T cells respond only to antigen fragments that have been processed and presented by infected cells or macrophages (phagocytic cells) (see opposite). They defend against:
- Intracellular bacteria and viruses
- Protozoa, fungi, flatworms, and roundworms
- Cancerous cells and transplanted foreign tissue

Differentiate into two kinds of cells

Antibody

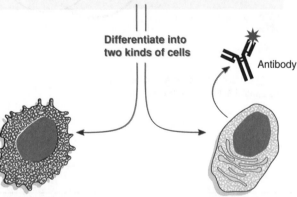

Memory cells

Some B cells differentiate into long-lived memory cells (see Clonal Selection). When these cells encounter the same antigen again (even years or decades later), they rapidly differentiate into antibody-producing plasma cells.

Plasma cells

When stimulated by an antigen (see Clonal Selection), some B cells differentiate into plasma cells, which secrete **antibodies** into the bloodstream. The antibodies then inactivate the circulating antigens.

Differentiate into various kinds of cells:

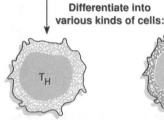

T_H

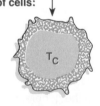

T_C

T helper cell
activates T cytotoxic cells and other helper T cells. They are needed for B cell activation.

T cytotoxic cell destroys target cells on contact. Recognises tumour or virus-infected cells by their surface markers. Also called T killer cells.

There are also other types of T cells:
T memory cells have encountered specific antigens before and can respond quickly and strongly when the same antigen is encountered again.
T regulator cells control immune response by turning it off when no more antigen is present. They are important in the development of self tolerance.

© 2017 **BIOZONE** International
ISBN: 978-1-927309-26-1
Photocopying Prohibited

Dendritic cells stimulate the activation and proliferation of lymphocytes

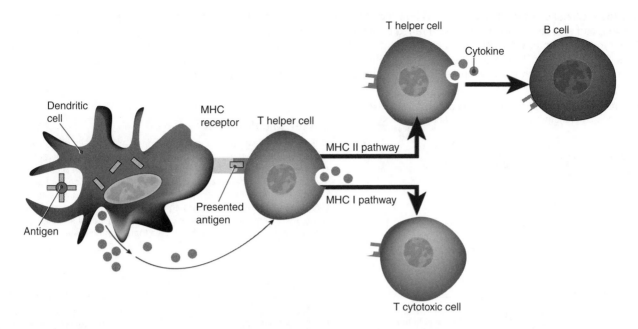

Immature dendritic cells (DCs) originate in the bone marrow and migrate throughout the body. Once they have processed an antigen they begin to mature. They migrate to lymph nodes and, through antigen presentation and secretion of cytokines, stimulate the activation and proliferation of T cells. DCs exhibiting MHC I receptors stimulate the production of T cytotoxic cells. DCs exhibiting MHC II receptors stimulate the production of T helper cells. These in turn go on to stimulate the production of antibody-producing B cells.

1. Where do B cells and T cells originate (before maturing)?_____

2. (a) Where do B cells mature? _____

   (b) Where do T cells mature? _____

3. Describe the nature and general action of the two major divisions in the immune system:

   (a) Humoral immune system: _____

   _____

   _____

   (b) Cell-mediated immune system: _____

   _____

   _____

4. Explain how an antigen causes the activation and proliferation of T cells and B cells, including the role of dendritic cells:

   _____

   _____

   _____

   _____

5. In what way do dendritic cells act as messengers between the innate and the adaptive immune systems?

   _____

   _____

6. Describe the function of each of the following cells in the immune system response:

   (a) T helper cells: _____

   (b) T cytotoxic cells: _____

© 2017 **BIOZONE** International
ISBN: 978-1-927309-26-1
Photocopying Prohibited

45 Clonal Selection

Key Idea: Clonal selection theory explains how lymphocytes can respond to a large and unpredictable range of antigens. The **clonal selection theory** explains how the immune system can respond to the large and unpredictable range of potential antigens in the environment. The diagram below describes clonal selection after antigen exposure for B cells. In the same way, a T cell stimulated by a specific antigen will multiply and develop into different types of T cells. Clonal selection and differentiation of lymphocytes provide the basis for **immunological memory.**

Five (a-e) of the many B cells generated during development. Each one can recognise only one specific antigen.

Clonal selection theory

Millions of B cells form during development. Antigen recognition is randomly generated, so collectively they can recognise many antigens, including those that have never been encountered. Each B cell has receptors on its surface for specific antigens and produces antibodies that correspond to these receptors. When a B cell encounters its antigen, it responds by proliferating and producing many clones that produce the same kind of antibody. This is called clonal selection because the antigen selects the B cells that will proliferate.

This B cell encounters and binds an antigen. It is then stimulated to proliferate.

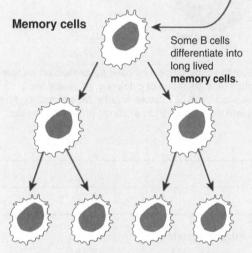

Memory cells

Some B cells differentiate into long lived **memory cells**.

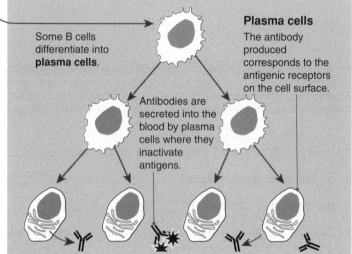

Plasma cells

The antibody produced corresponds to the antigenic receptors on the cell surface.

Some B cells differentiate into **plasma cells**.

Antibodies are secreted into the blood by plasma cells where they inactivate antigens.

Some B cells differentiate into long lived **memory cells**. These are retained in the lymph nodes to provide future immunity (**immunological memory**). In the event of a second infection, memory B cells react more quickly and vigorously than the initial B cell reaction to the first infection.

Plasma cells secrete antibodies specific to the antigen that stimulated their development. Each plasma cell lives for only a few days, but can produce about 2000 antibody molecules per second. Note that during development, any B cells that react to the body's own antigens are selectively destroyed in a process that leads to **self tolerance** (acceptance of the body's own tissues).

1. Describe how clonal selection results in the proliferation of one particular B cell clone: _____

_____

_____

_____

2. (a) What is the function of the plasma cells in the immune system response? _____

_____

(b) What is the significance of B cells producing antibodies that correspond to (match) their antigenic receptors?

_____

_____

3. (a) Explain the basis of immunological memory: _____

_____

(b) Why are B memory cells able to respond so rapidly to an encounter with an antigen long after an initial infection?

_____

© 2017 **BIOZONE** International
ISBN: 978-1-927309-26-1
Photocopying Prohibited

46 Antibodies

Key Idea: Antibodies are large, Y-shaped proteins, made by plasma cells, which destroy specific antigens.

Antibodies and antigens play key roles in the response of the immune system. **Antigens** are foreign molecules which promote a specific immune response. Antigens include pathogenic microbes and their toxins, as well as substances such as pollen grains, blood cell surface molecules, and the surface proteins on transplanted tissues. **Antibodies** (or immunoglobulins) are proteins made in response to antigens. They are secreted from B cells into the plasma where they can recognise, bind to, and help destroy antigens. There are five classes of antibodies, each plays a different role in the immune response. Each type of antibody is specific to only one particular antigen.

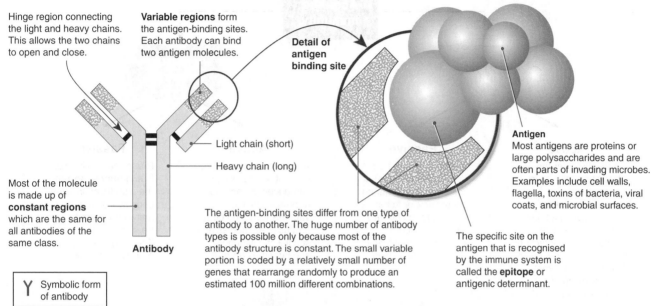

Hinge region connecting the light and heavy chains. This allows the two chains to open and close.

Variable regions form the antigen-binding sites. Each antibody can bind two antigen molecules.

Detail of antigen binding site

Light chain (short)

Heavy chain (long)

Most of the molecule is made up of **constant regions** which are the same for all antibodies of the same class.

Antibody

Y Symbolic form of antibody

The antigen-binding sites differ from one type of antibody to another. The huge number of antibody types is possible only because most of the antibody structure is constant. The small variable portion is coded by a relatively small number of genes that rearrange randomly to produce an estimated 100 million different combinations.

Antigen
Most antigens are proteins or large polysaccharides and are often parts of invading microbes. Examples include cell walls, flagella, toxins of bacteria, viral coats, and microbial surfaces.

The specific site on the antigen that is recognised by the immune system is called the **epitope** or antigenic determinant.

How antibodies inactivate antigens

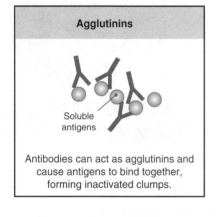

Agglutinins

Soluble antigens

Antibodies can act as agglutinins and cause antigens to bind together, forming inactivated clumps.

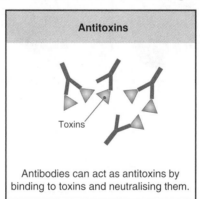

Antitoxins

Toxins

Antibodies can act as antitoxins by binding to toxins and neutralising them.

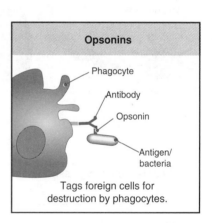

Opsonins

Phagocyte

Antibody

Opsonin

Antigen/ bacteria

Tags foreign cells for destruction by phagocytes.

1. Describe the structure of an antibody, identifying the specific features of its structure that contribute to its function:

_____

_____

_____

2. Explain how the following actions by antibodies enhance the immune systems ability to stop infections:

(a) Acting as agglutinins: _____

_____

(b) Acting as antitoxins: _____

_____

(c) Working with opsonins: _____

_____

LINK 44   LINK 41   WEB 46

KNOW

47 Acquired Immunity

Key Idea: Acquired immunity is a resistance to specific pathogens acquired over the life-time of an organism.

We are born with natural or **innate resistance** which provides non-specific immunity to certain illnesses. In contrast, **acquired immunity** is protection developed over time to specific antigens. **Active immunity** develops after the immune system responds to being exposed to microbes or foreign substances. **Passive immunity** is acquired when antibodies are transferred from one person to another. Immunity may also be naturally acquired, through natural exposure to microbes, or artificially acquired as a result of medical treatment (below).

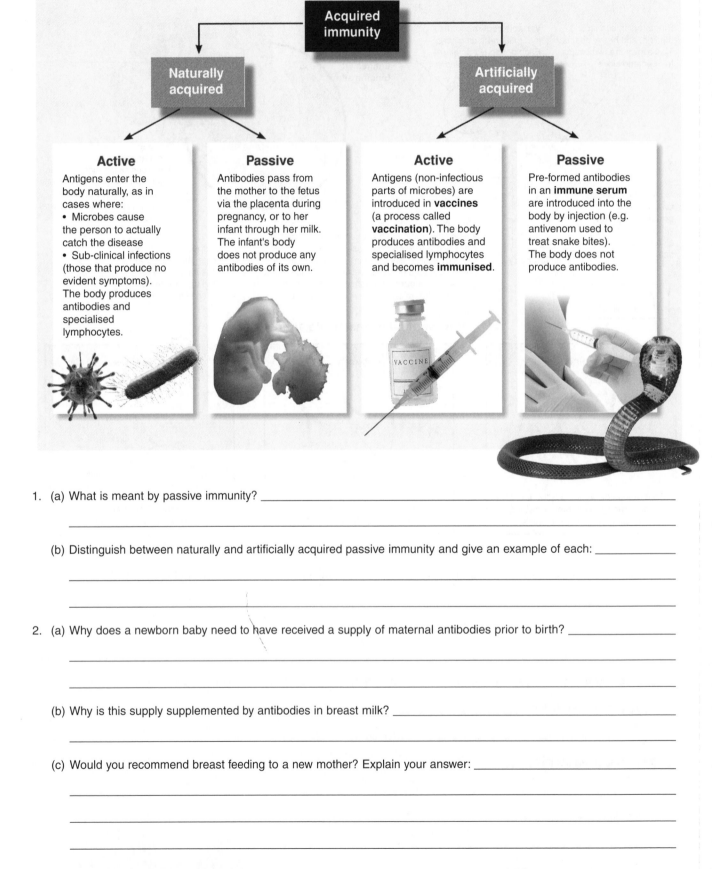

Acquired immunity

Naturally acquired

Artificially acquired

Active

Antigens enter the body naturally, as in cases where:
• Microbes cause the person to actually catch the disease
• Sub-clinical infections (those that produce no evident symptoms). The body produces antibodies and specialised lymphocytes.

Passive

Antibodies pass from the mother to the fetus via the placenta during pregnancy, or to her infant through her milk. The infant's body does not produce any antibodies of its own.

Active

Antigens (non-infectious parts of microbes) are introduced in **vaccines** (a process called **vaccination**). The body produces antibodies and specialised lymphocytes and becomes **immunised**.

Passive

Pre-formed antibodies in an **immune serum** are introduced into the body by injection (e.g. antivenom used to treat snake bites). The body does not produce antibodies.

1. (a) What is meant by passive immunity? _____

_____

(b) Distinguish between naturally and artificially acquired passive immunity and give an example of each: _____

_____

_____

2. (a) Why does a newborn baby need to have received a supply of maternal antibodies prior to birth? _____

_____

_____

(b) Why is this supply supplemented by antibodies in breast milk? _____

_____

(c) Would you recommend breast feeding to a new mother? Explain your answer: _____

_____

_____

© 2017 **BIOZONE** International
ISBN: 978-1-927309-26-1
Photocopying Prohibited

If a person has not been immunised against a disease, exposure to the pathogen causes them to become ill and their body forms antibodies against it.

Antibodies passing from the mother's milk to her newborn baby provide protection until the baby develops its own antibodies.

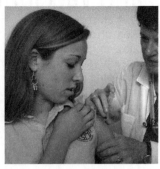

Vaccines provide immunity to specific pathogens and greatly reduce the risk of contracting the disease.

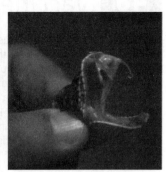

Without treatment with the appropriate preformed antibodies in antivenom, the bites of many snake species can be fatal.

Primary and secondary response to antigens

When the B cells encounter antigens and produce antibodies, the body develops active immunity against that antigen.

The initial response to antigenic stimulation, caused by the sudden increase in B cell clones, is called the primary response. Antibody levels as a result of the primary response peak a few weeks after the response begins and then decline. However, because the immune system develops an immunological memory of that antigen, it responds much more quickly and strongly when presented with the same antigen subsequently (the secondary response).

This forms the basis of immunisation programmes where one or more booster shots are provided following the initial vaccination.

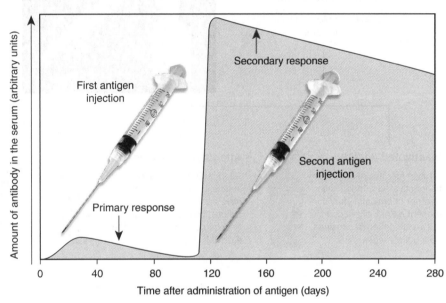

3. (a) What is active immunity? _____

(b) Distinguish between naturally and artificially acquired active immunity and give an example of each: _____

4. (a) Describe two differences between the primary and secondary responses to presentation of an antigen: _____

(b) Why is the secondary response so different from the primary response? _____

© 2017 **BIOZONE** International
ISBN: 978-1-927309-26-1
Photocopying Prohibited

48 Vaccines and Vaccination

Key Idea: A vaccine is a suspension of antigens that is deliberately introduced into the body to protect against disease. If enough of the population are vaccinated, herd immunity provides protection to unvaccinated individuals.

A **vaccine** is a preparation of a harmless foreign antigen that is deliberately introduced into the body to protect against a specific disease. The antigen in the vaccine is usually some part of the pathogen and it triggers the immune system to

produce antibodies against the antigen, but it does not cause the disease. The immune system remembers its response and will produce the same antibodies if it encounters the antigen again. If enough of the population are vaccinated, herd immunity (indirect protection) provides unvaccinated individuals in the population with a measure of protection against the disease. There are two basic types of vaccine, subunit vaccines and whole-agent vaccines (below).

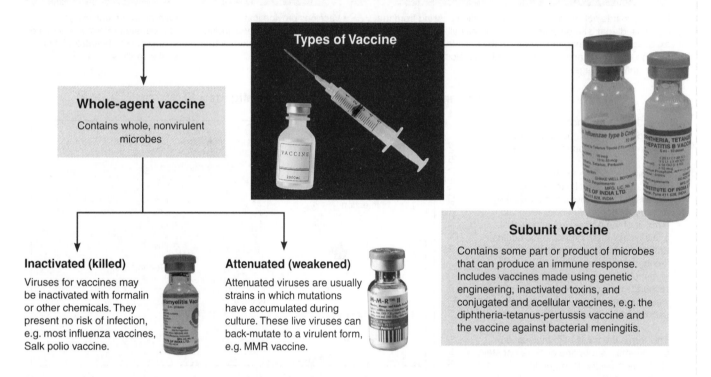

Types of Vaccine

Whole-agent vaccine
Contains whole, nonvirulent microbes

Inactivated (killed)
Viruses for vaccines may be inactivated with formalin or other chemicals. They present no risk of infection, e.g. most influenza vaccines, Salk polio vaccine.

Attenuated (weakened)
Attenuated viruses are usually strains in which mutations have accumulated during culture. These live viruses can back-mutate to a virulent form, e.g. MMR vaccine.

Subunit vaccine
Contains some part or product of microbes that can produce an immune response. Includes vaccines made using genetic engineering, inactivated toxins, and conjugated and acellular vaccines, e.g. the diphtheria-tetanus-pertussis vaccine and the vaccine against bacterial meningitis.

Why are vaccinations given?

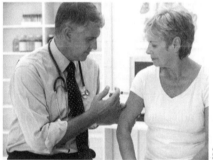

Vaccines against common diseases are given at various stages during childhood according to an immunisation schedule. Vaccination has been behind the decline of some once-common childhood diseases, such as mumps and measles.

Most vaccinations are given in childhood, but adults may be vaccinated against a disease (e.g. TB, tetanus) if they are in a high risk group (e.g. the elderly or farmers) or to provide protection against seasonal diseases such as influenza.

Tourists may need specific vaccines if the country they are visiting has a high incidence of a certain disease. For example, travellers to South America should be immunised against yellow fever, a disease that does not occur in Australia.

1. (a) What is a vaccine? _____

_____

(b) Provide some examples of when vaccinations are needed: _____

_____

_____

_____

© 2017 **BIOZONE** International
ISBN: 978-1-927309-26-1
Photocopying Prohibited

Vaccination can provide herd immunity

Herd immunity occurs when the vaccination of a significant portion of a population provides some protection for individuals who have not developed immunity (e.g. have not been vaccinated and are not immunised). In order to be effective for any particular disease, a high percentage of the population needs to be vaccinated against that disease. High vaccination rates make it difficult for the disease to spread because there are very few susceptible people in the population. Herd immunity is important for people who cannot be vaccinated (e.g. the very young, people with immune system disorders, or people who are very sick, such as cancer patients).

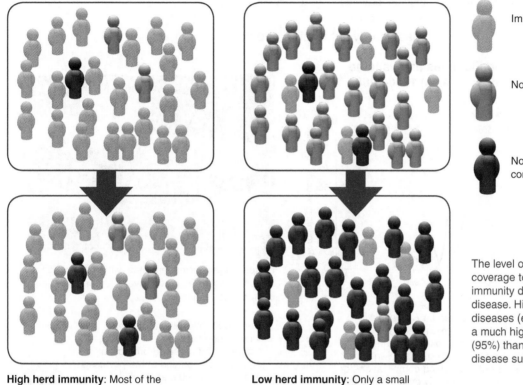

Immunised and healthy

Not immunised and healthy

Not immunised, sick and contagious

DID YOU KNOW?

The level of vaccination coverage to obtain herd immunity differs for each disease. Highly contagious diseases (e.g. measles) need a much higher vaccine uptake (95%) than a less contagious disease such as polio (80-85%).

High herd immunity: Most of the population is immunised. The spread of the disease is limited. Only a few people are susceptible and become infected.

Low herd immunity: Only a small proportion of the population is immunised. The disease spreads more readily through the population infecting many more people.

2. Attenuated viruses provide long term immunity to their recipients and generally do not require booster shots. Why do you think attenuated viruses provide such effective long-term immunity when inactivated viruses do not?

_____

_____

_____

_____

3. (a) What is herd immunity? _____

_____

_____

   (b) Why are health authorities concerned when the vaccination rates for an infectious disease fall? _____

_____

_____

4. Some members of the population are unable to be vaccinated. Give an example and explain why herd immunity is very important to them?

_____

_____

_____

49 Vaccines Can Eliminate Infectious Disease

Key Idea: Vaccination programmes have been successful in the global eradication of smallpox, but other diseases (such as influenza) are more difficult to eradicate.

To date, the only infectious disease globally eradicated has been smallpox. Several factors lead to this success. Smallpox is easily identifiable by its characteristic rash making surveillance and containment of infected patients

easier. It has no other natural carriers, so once immunisation rates reached a critical level, its spread through the population was limited. Other diseases can be more difficult to eradicate. This is especially true for diseases that have a long period between infection and the symptoms showing (e.g. TB) or diseases caused by pathogens with high rates of mutation (e.g. *influenzavirus*).

Case study: whooping cough

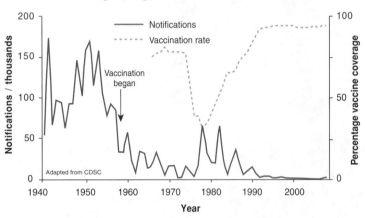

Whooping cough notifications and vaccine coverage (England and Wales) 1940-2008

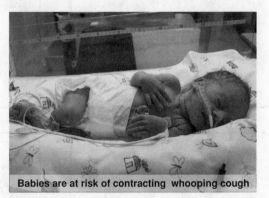

Babies are at risk of contracting whooping cough

Despite high vaccination rates, whooping cough is increasing in England. Several factors may be contributing to this:

▶ Whooping cough is caused by the bacterium *Bordetella pertussis*, and may last for two to three months. It is characterised by a whooping cough and painful coughing spasms, which may be followed by vomiting. Infants under six months of age are most at risk of developing complications or dying because they are too young to be fully protected by the vaccine. Inclusion of the whooping cough vaccine into the UK immunisation schedule greatly reduced the incidence rates of the disease (above).

▶ In 2012 England experienced a whooping cough epidemic. Over 9000 cases were reported (more than ten times the expected). The number of cases has begun to fall again, but the levels are still significantly higher than prior to 2012.

▶ Several young babies died in this recent epidemic, so a new vaccination programme providing the whooping cough vaccine to pregnant women was launched so that babies would have protection against *B. pertussis*.

▶ Until 1997, a whole vaccine was used. It contained hundreds of different antigens and provided protection against many strains of the pertussis pathogen. In 1999, an acellular vaccine (right) was introduced. It only contains five antigens and so provides less protection.

▶ New strains of *B. pertussis* are evolving, and the new vaccine is not effective against them.

▶ More adults who were vaccinated against whooping cough in childhood are contracting the disease. This suggests the effectiveness of the vaccine declines over time.

1. With reference to the graph of whooping cough notifications in England and Wales (above):

   (a) What effect did the introduction of the whooping cough vaccine have on the incidence of whooping cough?

   _____

   _____

   (b) Suggest why the whooping cough rates are increasing despite high vaccination rates: _____

   _____

   _____

   _____

2. How will vaccinating pregnant women help reduce whooping cough in young babies? _____

   _____

   _____

© 2017 **BIOZONE** International
ISBN: 978-1-927309-26-1
Photocopying Prohibited

50 Questions about Vaccines

Key Idea: People choose not to vaccinate for ethical reasons or because they perceive the vaccine to carry an unacceptable level of risk. Perceptions of risk are not supported by scientific data. Vaccines are rigorously tested to ensure their safety.

Despite the proven efficacy of vaccination in protecting against disease, some people choose to opt out of vaccination programmes. Their reasons for doing so include concerns about the testing and research protocols associated with vaccine development, the potential side effects of vaccination, or religious or philosophical objections. For childhood vaccinations, parents decide whether to vaccinate or not. Some people argue that the child cannot give informed consent (permission to vaccinate) and therefore their rights are compromised. A different ethical issue concerns access to vaccines when supply is limited. Who should get the vaccine and who should miss out and be left vulnerable?

Testing vaccine safety

CDC

Vaccines are tested using a rigorous scientific process before they are given routinely. Several regulating authorities ensure that the trials are carried out properly and that the vaccine meets safety guidelines. The steps are outlined below.

▶ Literature review and theoretical planning

▶ Laboratory testing and development

▶ Phase I clinical study. Initial safety trial on a small group of adults to determine dose.

▶ Phase II clinical study. Administration to a large target group to determine if the vaccine produces an immune response.

▶ Phase III clinical study. Administered to an even larger group to gain statistically significant safety and efficacy data.

▶ Licensing. Regulating bodies review all the data to see it is effective and safe.

▶ Phase IV clinical study. Continued surveillance to monitor the vaccine's effects in the population.

Does the MMR vaccine cause autism?

Some people do not vaccinate their children because they believe vaccination causes autism. Autism is a developmental disability affecting the ability to communicate and relate to others.

In 1998, Dr Andrew Wakefield and his colleagues published a paper linking the measles, mumps, and rubella vaccine (MMR) to an increase in autism rates. As a result, the uptake of the MMR vaccine in the UK dropped, and several measles outbreaks occurred.

Dr Wakefield's paper has since been retracted as it was found to be fraudulent and flawed in several aspects, e.g. sample size of only 12, with no control group.

Since the publication of Wakefield's paper, 20 large scale epidemiologic studies into MMR and autism have been carried out in several countries. All have shown that the MMR vaccine does not cause autism. However, the damage has been done, and health authorities must now convince the public the vaccine is still safe.

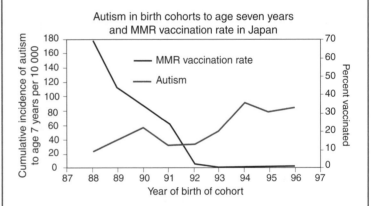

Autism in birth cohorts to age seven years and MMR vaccination rate in Japan

Japan stopped using the MMR vaccine in 1993, opting to administer three single vaccines instead. Autism rates have continued to increase despite the fact that the MMR vaccine is no longer given. The data indicate there is no link between autism and the MMR vaccine. Many experts say the increase in autism is largely due to better diagnosis methods and a broadening of the definition and symptoms of autism.

---

1. (a) Describe the trend in UK MMR vaccination rates shown right:

_____

_____

_____

(b) What happened to the measles cases during this time?

_____

_____

_____

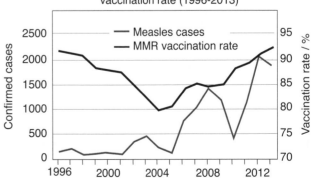

Confirmed measles cases in the UK and vaccination rate (1996-2013)

© 2017 **BIOZONE** International
ISBN: 978-1-927309-26-1
Photocopying Prohibited

LINK 49   LINK 48   **KNOW**

51 Chapter Review

Summarise what you know about this topic under the headings and sub-headings provided. You can draw diagrams or mind maps, or write short notes to organise your thoughts. Use the images and hints to help you and refer back to the introduction to check the points covered:

Pathogens and antimicrobials

HINT: Identify the transmission, mode of action, and pathogenic effect of named pathogens. Describe how antibiotics work and the significance of bacterial resistance to them.

Microbial techniques

HINT: Describe techniques used to grow and identify microorganisms.

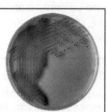

© 2017 **BIOZONE** International
ISBN: 978-1-927309-26-1
Photocopying Prohibited

Response to infection: the immune system

HINT: Summarise the structure and role of phagocytes and the specific immune response.

Response to infection: vaccinations

HINT: Describe the principles and applications of vaccination.

52 KEY TERMS AND IDEAS: Did You Get It?

1. Test your vocabulary by matching each term to its correct definition, as identified by its preceding letter code.

aseptic technique

active immunity

antibodies (*sing*. antibody)

antigen

B cells

clonal selection

exotoxin

immunity

lag phase

passive immunity

phagocytes

stationary phase

specific (=adaptive) immune response

streak plating

T cells

vaccination

A A technique to isolate microbial species through physical dilution of a culture.

B A phase of microbial growth in closed culture when there is no net population growth.

C A phase of microbial growth in closed culture in which there is little or no cell division.

D The delivery of antigenic material (the vaccine) to produce immunity to a disease.

E Long-lasting immunity that is induced in the host itself by the antigen.

F Lymphocytes that are responsible for the cell mediated immune response.

G Immunity gained by the receipt of ready-made antibodies.

H A molecule that is recognised by the immune system as foreign.

I A pathogen and antigen-specific immune response with both cell-mediated and humoral components. Characterised by immunological memory.

J Resistance of an organism to infection or disease.

K Bacterial toxins released from gram negative cells on cell death.

L A model for how B and T cells are selected to target specific antigens.

M Immunoglobulin proteins in the blood or other bodily fluids, which identify and neutralise foreign material, such as bacteria and viruses.

N Lymphocytes that make antibodies against specific antigens.

O White blood cells that destroy foreign material, e.g. bacteria, by ingesting them.

P A handling and safety technique to prevent contamination of a microbial culture.

2. The graph right shows a primary and secondary immune response to an artificially introduced antigen.

(a) What type of immunity is this? _____

(b) What has occurred at point A? _____

_____

(c) What has occurred at point B? _____

_____

(d) Describe and explain the differences in the amount of antibody detected after each of the two events:

_____

_____

_____

Amount of antibody in the serum (arbitrary units)

A   B

Time after administration of antigen

3. An agar plate with a bacterial lawn was used to test the effectiveness of different antibiotics at inhibiting growth. Six paper discs impregnated with six different antibiotics were placed on the law. The result after 48 hours incubation is shown:

Antibiotic disc   Bacterial lawn

B   C

A

D

F   E

(a) Which antibiotic(s) were the most effective? _____

(b) Which antibiotics were the least effective? _____

(c) Antibiotics, A, C, D, and F are from the penicillin family of antibiotics. What does this tell you about the bacteria involved in this test?

_____

4. (a) A bactericidal antibiotic kills/inhibits bacteria (delete one). Example: _____

(b) A bacteriostatic antibiotic kills/inhibits bacteria (delete one). Example: _____

© 2017 **BIOZONE** International
ISBN: 978-1-927309-26-1
Photocopying Prohibited

Topic 7

Modern genetics

Key terms

adult stem cell (ASC)

cellular differentiation

DNA amplification

DNA ligase

DNA methylation

DNA profiling

embyonic stem cell (ESC)

epigenetic modification

exon

exon splicing

forensics

gene expression

gene gun

gene sequencing

genetic modification

genome

GMO

histone modification

intron

iPS

knock-out mice

marker gene

miRNA

multipotent

paternity testing

plasmid

pluripotent

polymerase chain reaction

recombinant DNA

replica plating

restriction endonucleases

siRNA

somatic cell

stem cell

totipotent

transcription factor

transgenic organism

vector

7.1 Using gene sequencing

Learning outcomes

		Activity number
☐	i Explain what is meant by an organism's genome.	53
☐	ii Describe how the polymerase chain reaction (PCR) is used to amplify DNA samples and how these samples can be used:	55
	• to predict the amino acid sequence of proteins and possible links to genetically determined conditions, using gene sequencing.	54 56
	• in forensic science to identify criminals and test paternity, using DNA profiling.	57 58

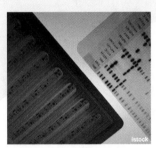 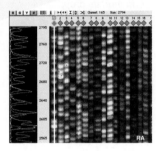 

7.2 Factors affecting gene expression

Learning outcomes

		Activity number
☐	i Explain what is meant by a transcription factor and know that they bind to DNA.	59 60
☐	ii Describe the role of transcription factors in regulating gene expression.	59 60
☐	iii Explain how post-transcriptional modification of mRNA in eukaryotic cells (exon splicing) can produce different gene products.	59 61
☐	iv Explain how gene expression can be changed by epigenetic modification to include non-coding RNAs (e.g. miRNA and siRNA)	62 63 64
☐	v Explain the involvement of epigenetic modification in cellular differentiation.	66

7.3 Stem cells

Learning outcomes

		Activity number
☐	i Explain what is meant by a stem cell, including the differences between totipotent, pluripotent, and multipotent stem cells and their source.	65
☐	ii Explain how pluripotent stem cells from embryos can be used in medicine. Discuss the ethical considerations of these technologies.	65 67
☐	iii Using an example, explain how epigenetic modifications can result in totipotent stem cells in the embryo developing into pluripotent cells in the blastocyst, and then fully differentiated somatic cells.	66
☐	iv Explain how differentiated fibroblasts can be reprogrammed to form induced pluripotent stem cells (iPS) by the artificial introduction of specific genes. Outline potential applications of iPS.	65 67
☐	v Explain why the use of iPS stem cells may alleviate some of the ethical issues associated with stem cell technologies.	65 67

7.4 Gene technology

Learning outcomes

☐ i Explain what is meant by recombinant DNA and explain how it is produced, including the role of restriction endonucleases in producing DNA fragments and DNA ligase in joining fragments together. — 68

☐ ii Explain how recombinant DNA can be inserted into other cells. Include reference to the role of vectors (e.g. viral vectors, plasmids, and liposomes) and modes of vector delivery (e.g. gene guns and electroporation). — 68 69 70

☐ iii Explain how antibiotic resistance marker genes and replica plating are used to identify recombinant cells. Recognise potential problems with the use of antibiotic resistance marker genes and identify alternatives (such as gfp). — 71

☐ iv Describe and explain the use of knock-out mice as an animal model to investigate gene function. — 72

☐ v Explain what is meant by a transgenic organism. Describe the genetic modification of soya beans as an example of a GM food crop. Explain how it has been used to improve production (yield) and storage life by altering the balance of fatty acids to prevent oxidation of soya products. — 73 74 75

☐ vi Explain the social, ethical, and biological issues associated with the production and use of transgenic organisms, including the genetic modification of major commercial crops. — 76

53 Genomes

Key Idea: A genome is the entire haploid amount of genetic material, including all the genes, of a cell or organism. Eukaryotes can have different versions of a gene (alleles) because they have two copies of each gene.

The **genome** refers to all the genetic material in one haploid set of chromosomes. The genome contains all of the information the organism needs to function and reproduce.

Every cell in an individual has a complete copy of the genome. Within the genome are sections of DNA, called genes, which code for proteins. Collectively, genes determine what an organism looks like (its traits). Eukaryotes have two copies of each gene (one inherited from each parent), so it is possible for one individual to have two different versions of a gene. These different versions are called **alleles**.

The location and size of the genome varies between organisms

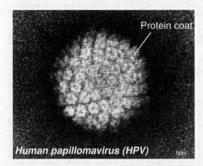

Human papillomavirus (HPV)

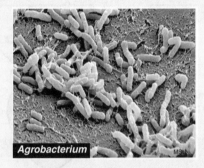

Agrobacterium

Human: a eukaryote

Genome size	Small	Large

Number of genes	Few	Many

The viral genome is contained within the virus's outer protein coat. Viral genomes are typically small and highly variable. They can consist of single stranded or double stranded DNA or RNA and contain only a small number of genes.

In bacteria (prokaryotes) most of the DNA is located within a single circular chromosome, which makes them haploid (i.e. one allele) for most genes. Many bacteria also have small accessory chromosomes called plasmids, which carry genes for special functions such as antibiotic resistance and substrate metabolism.

In eukaryotes, most of the DNA is located inside the cell's nucleus. A small amount resides in the mitochondria and chloroplasts (in plants). The DNA is arranged into linear chromosomes and most eukaryotes are diploid, with two sets of chromosomes, one from each parent.

The HPV genome consists of a double stranded circular DNA molecule ~8000 bp long.

The *Agrobacterium* genome is 5.7 Mb long and consists of a linear chromosome and two plasmids, one of which enables it to infect plants.

The human genome is ~3 000 Mb long in 23 chromosomes. The diploid number is 46 chromosomes.

Measuring genomes

Genome size is often expressed as the number of base pairs. The unit most often used to show the size of a genome is the megabase (Mb). Note: 1 megabase = 1 million base pairs. The image right is of the φX174 bacteriophage, a virus that infects bacterial cells. Its entire genome is only 5375 base pairs long (0.005375 Mb) and it contains only nine genes, coding for nine different proteins. At least 2000 times this amount of DNA would be found in a single bacterial cell. Half a million times the quantity of DNA would be found in the genome of a single human cell.

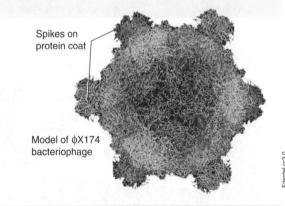

Spikes on protein coat

Model of φX174 bacteriophage

F.dardel cc3.0

1. Define the following terms:

(a) Genome: _____

(b) Gene: _____

(c) Allele: _____

2. Describe the general trend for genome size and gene number for viruses, bacteria, and eukaryotic organisms:

_____

3. Explain why an individual eukaryote can have different versions of a gene (allele) but viruses and bacteria do not:

_____

_____

_____

© 2017 **BIOZONE** International
ISBN: 978-1-927309-26-1
Photocopying Prohibited

LINK 56   LINK 55   WEB 53   **KNOW**

54 PCR and Modern Genetics

Key Idea: PCR uses a polymerase enzyme to copy a DNA sample, producing billions of copies in a few hours.

Many procedures in DNA technology, e.g. DNA sequencing and profiling, require substantial amounts of DNA yet, very often, only small amounts are obtainable (e.g. DNA from a crime scene or from an extinct organism). **PCR (polymerase** chain reaction) is a technique for reproducing large quantities of DNA in the laboratory from an original sample. For this reason, it is often called **DNA amplification**. The technique is outlined below for a single cycle of replication. Subsequent cycles replicate DNA at an exponential rate, so PCR can produce billions of copies of DNA in only a few hours.

A single cycle of PCR

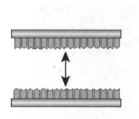

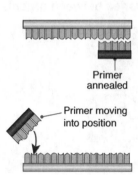
Primer annealed

Primer moving into position

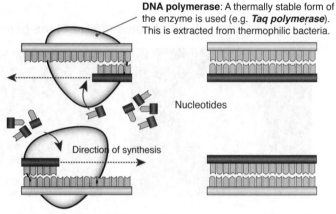
DNA polymerase: A thermally stable form of the enzyme is used (e.g. *Taq polymerase*). This is extracted from thermophilic bacteria.

Nucleotides

Direction of synthesis

A DNA sample (called target DNA) is obtained. It is denatured (DNA strands are separated) by heating at 98°C for 5 minutes.

The sample is cooled to 60°C. Primers are annealed (bonded) to each DNA strand. In PCR, the primers are short strands of DNA; they provide the starting sequence for DNA extension.

Free nucleotides and the enzyme DNA polymerase are added. DNA polymerase binds to the primers andsynthesises complementary strands of DNA, using the free nucleotides.

After one cycle, there are now two copies of the original DNA.

Repeat cycle of heating and cooling until enough copies of the target DNA have been produced

Repeat for about 25 cycles

Loading tray
Prepared samples in PCR tubes are placed in the loading tray and the lid is closed.

Temperature control
Inside the machine are heating and refrigeration mechanisms to rapidly change the temperature.

Dispensing pipette
Pipettes with disposable tips are used to dispense DNA samples into the PCR tubes.

Thermal cycler

Amplification of DNA can be carried out with machines called thermal cyclers. Once a DNA sample has been prepared, the amount of DNA can be increased billions of times in just a few hours.

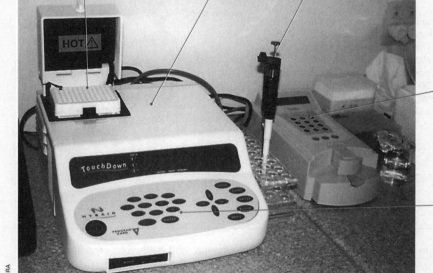

DNA quantitation
The amount of DNA in a sample can be determined by placing a known volume in this quantitation machine. For many genetic engineering processes, a minimum amount of DNA is required.

Controls
The control panel allows a number of different PCR programmes to be stored in the machine's memory. Carrying out a PCR run usually just involves starting one of the stored programmes.

Reducing contamination

The PCR process will amplify all the DNA within the sample including unwanted DNA from contamination. Therefore great care must be taken not to contaminate the sample with unwanted DNA (e.g from microbes in the environment, from dirty equipment, or from the researcher). Contamination is reduced by following strict protocols. The researcher must make sure that they are wearing appropriate clothing (hair net, gloves, coat) to stop their DNA contaminating the sample. In addition clean work surfaces, sterile solutions, and use of disposable equipment (e.g. pipettes and tubes) will help reduce contamination.

© 2017 **BIOZONE** International
ISBN: 978-1-927309-26-1
Photocopying Prohibited

1. What is the purpose of PCR? _____

_____

_____

_____

2. Describe how the polymerase chain reaction works: _____

_____

_____

_____

_____

_____

_____

_____

_____

3. Describe two situations where only very small DNA samples may be available for sampling and PCR could be used:

(a) _____

_____

(b) _____

_____

4. After only two cycles of replication, four copies of the double-stranded DNA exist. Calculate how much a DNA sample will have increased after:

(a) 10 cycles: _____   (b) 25 cycles: _____

5. The risk of contamination in the preparation for PCR is considerable.

(a) Describe the effect of having a single molecule of unwanted DNA in the sample prior to PCR:

_____

_____

_____

_____

(b) Describe two possible sources of DNA contamination in preparing a PCR sample:

Source 1: _____

Source 2: _____

(c) Describe two precautions that could be taken to reduce the risk of DNA contamination:

Precaution 1: _____

_____

_____

Precaution 2: _____

_____

55 Applications of Gene Sequencing

Key Idea: The development of automatic, high throughput DNA sequencing methods and the increase in computing technology have provided the tools to better analyse genes and their protein products and identify genetic disorders.

PCR has provided the means to amplify tiny segments of DNA for analysis. With the advent of rapid, inexpensive DNA sequencing and powerful computing technology, biologists are learning more about the normal functions of genes and gaining greater insight into the causes and treatments for genetic disorders. Powerful analytical tools are identifying meaningful DNA variations and making connections between genes, their protein products, and the causes of complex diseases, such as diabetes or cancer. Each new finding has the potential to lead to new diagnostic tools or treatments.

Using sequence data

DNA sequencing determines the sequence (order) of bases within a DNA molecule and so provides information about the genome or its genes. The DNA sequence can be used to predict the mRNA sequence, and thus the amino acid sequence (and protein product) of any given gene.

Comparing sequence data for individuals affected or not affected by a particular disease enables the mutation and its effect on the protein to be determined. This is illustrated for the simple example of the β chain of the human haemoglobin molecule (pictured right). Each haemoglobin molecule is made up of two α-chains (light) and two β-chains (dark) linked together.

The sickle cell mutation results in the substitution of the hydrophilic glutamic acid for the hydrophobic amino acid valine. This makes the haemoglobin collapse in on itself when deprived of oxygen.

More complex genomic variations (including single nucleotide variations called SNPs, which are carried by all individuals) can be analysed and possible links to disease established using statistical methods.

The HBB gene encoding the β-chain of haemoglobin is on chromosome 11 and consists of 438 bases. The 438 nucleotides produce a protein of 146 amino acids.

The first part of the sequence is shown below. A mutation to the 6th triplet produces the sickle cell allele (Hb^s). The mutated strands are shown in blue.

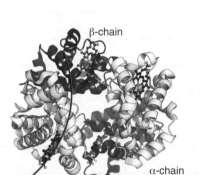

β-chain

α-chain

Normal base: T

DNA
`T A C C A C G T G G A C T G A G G A C T C C T C`

START
mRNA
`A U G G U G C A C C U G A C U C C U G A G G A G`

Code corresponding to the 1st amino acid of the β chain

Amino acids
(Met)–(Val)–(His)–(Leu)–(Thr)–(Pro)–(Glu)–(Glu)

Methionine is cleaved to form the functional beta chain

Substituted base: A

DNA
`T A C C A C G T G G A C T G A G G A C A C C T C`

START
mRNA
`A U G G U G C A C C U G A C U C C U G U G G A G`

Amino acids
(Met)–(Val)–(His)–(Leu)–(Thr)–(Pro)–(Val)–(Glu)

Each red blood cell (RBC) contains about 270 million haemoglobin molecules. Cells with normal Hb have a flattened disc shape.

The mutated haemoglobin has poor solubility and precipitates when deprived of oxygen. This deforms the red blood cells giving them a rigid sickle shape, which blocks capillaries.

1. Explain how DNA sequence data can be used to determine the amino acid sequence of a protein:

    _____

    _____

2. Explain how DNA sequence data can be used to look for genotypes associated with genetic disorders?

    _____

    _____

© 2017 **BIOZONE** International
ISBN: 978-1-927309-26-1
Photocopying Prohibited

56 Gene Sequencing and Medicine

Key Idea: Analysis of gene sequences could lead to new and more efficient ways of treating or preventing disease.

Once a genome or gene has been sequenced, it can be compared to sequence information already stored in databases. The DNA sequence data from pathogens can provide valuable information about antigenic genes and proteins, which can be used to develop or refine new drugs. The development of vaccines and drugs may accelerate if there is already a drug to treat a similar gene product. Bioinformatics (the collection, analysis and storage of biological information using computer science and mathematics) allows large volumes of data to be compared. The high throughput of bioinformatics can potentially increase the ability of medical technologies to identify, prevent, and treat disease.

Using bioinformatics in medicine

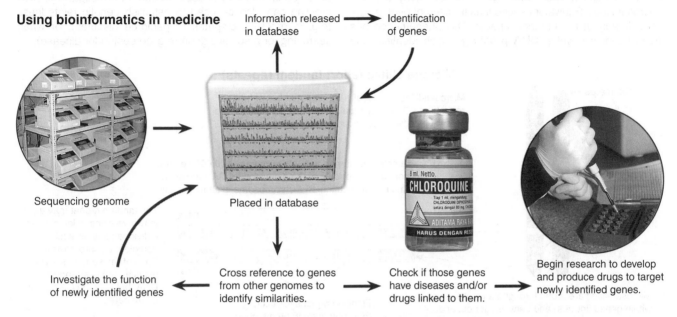

Information released in database → Identification of genes

Sequencing genome

Placed in database

Investigate the function of newly identified genes ← Cross reference to genes from other genomes to identify similarities. → Check if those genes have diseases and/or drugs linked to them. → Begin research to develop and produce drugs to target newly identified genes.

One of the new directions of research in medicine is the development of drugs targeting the gene function or gene products (proteins) of a pathogen. This begins with sequencing a genome (e.g. *Plasmodium*) and adding it to the database of already sequenced genomes. Genes are identified, cross referenced with other known similar genes, and their functions investigated. Any existing drugs targeting similar genes or gene products can then be identified and their effectiveness against the newly identified genes and their products tested. Novel genes can be identified and ways of exploiting them for medical purposes can be investigated.

Malaria and bioinformatics

▶ **Reverse vaccinology** is a bioinformatics technique in which the entire genome of a pathogen is screened for genes that may produce antigenic properties, e.g. genes that code for extracellular products such as surface proteins.

▶ Once the gene is identified, the gene product (protein) is synthesised in the lab and tested in a model organism for an immune response. If successful, the product can then be used as the basis of a vaccine.

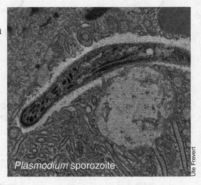

Plasmodium sporozoite

Malaria is a disease caused by the protozoan parasite *Plasmodium* of which *P. falciparum* is the most deadly. *Plasmodium* is becoming increasingly drug-resistant so a vaccine offers the best hope of controlling the disease.

The genome of *P. falciparum* was published in 2002. Fifteen loci have been identified as encoding antigens that may be useful in vaccines, including an antigen-rich region on chromosome 10. However only six of the loci appear to be similar to other *Plasmodium* species, reducing the likelihood of developing a single vaccine effective against all species.

1. Explain how bioinformatics and genome sequencing can help produce new vaccines or drugs for a disease:

_____

_____

_____

2. Explain how the completion of *P. falciparum* genome has helped make the development of a malaria vaccine more likely:

_____

_____

_____

_____

LINK 55 WEB 56

KNOW

57 DNA Profiling

Key Idea: Short units of DNA called STRs, which repeat a different number of times in different people, can be used to produce individual genetic profiles.

In chromosomes, non-coding, repetitive nucleotide sequences are found scattered throughout the genome. Some repeating sequences, called **microsatellites** or **short tandem repeats** (STRs), are very short (2-6 base pairs) and can repeat up to 100 times. The human genome has many different microsatellites. Equivalent sequences in different people vary considerably in the number repeats. This phenomenon has been used to develop **DNA profiling**, which identifies the

natural variations in every person's DNA. Identifying these DNA differences is a useful tool in forensic investigations. In the UK, DNA testing is carried out by the Forensic Science Service (FSS). The FSS targets 10 STR sites; enough to guarantee that the odds of someone else sharing the same result are extremely unlikely (~one in a thousand million). DNA profiling has been used to help solve previously unsolved crimes and to assist in current investigations. DNA profiling can also be used to establish genetic relatedness (e.g. in paternity disputes or pedigree disputes), or when searching for a specific gene (e.g. screening for disease).

Microsatellites (short tandem repeats)

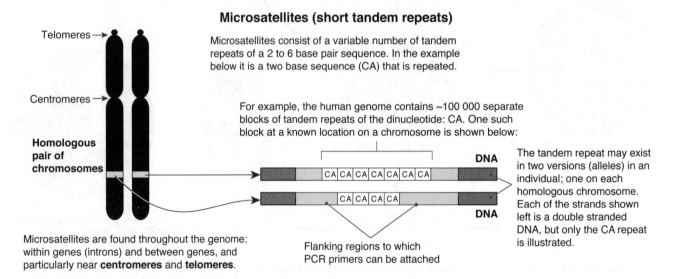

Microsatellites consist of a variable number of tandem repeats of a 2 to 6 base pair sequence. In the example below it is a two base sequence (CA) that is repeated.

For example, the human genome contains ~100 000 separate blocks of tandem repeats of the dinucleotide: CA. One such block at a known location on a chromosome is shown below:

The tandem repeat may exist in two versions (alleles) in an individual; one on each homologous chromosome. Each of the strands shown left is a double stranded DNA, but only the CA repeat is illustrated.

Telomeres →
Centromeres →
Homologous pair of chromosomes

Microsatellites are found throughout the genome: within genes (introns) and between genes, and particularly near **centromeres** and **telomeres**.

Flanking regions to which PCR primers can be attached

How short tandem repeats are used in DNA profiling

This diagram shows how three individuals can have quite different microsatellite arrangements at the same point (locus) in their DNA. Each will produce a different DNA profile using gel electrophoresis:

1 Extract DNA from sample

A sample collected from the tissue of a living or dead organism is treated with chemicals and enzymes to extract the DNA, which is separated and purified.

2 Amplify microsatellite using PCR

Specific primers (arrowed) that attach to the flanking regions (light grey) either side of the microsatellite are used to make large quantities of the microsatellite and flanking regions sequence only (no other part of the DNA is amplified/replicated).

3 Visualise fragments on a gel

The fragments are separated by length, using **gel electrophoresis**. DNA, which is negatively charged, moves toward the positive terminal. The smaller fragments travel faster than larger ones.

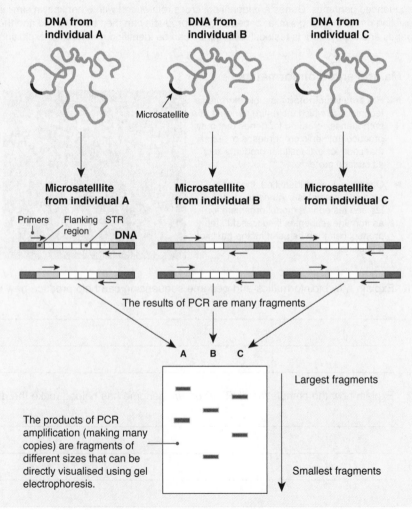

The products of PCR amplification (making many copies) are fragments of different sizes that can be directly visualised using gel electrophoresis.

© 2017 **BIOZONE** International
ISBN: 978-1-927309-26-1
Photocopying Prohibited

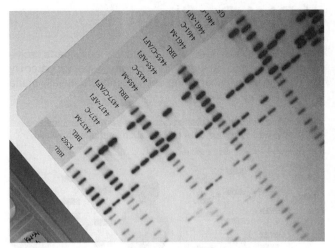

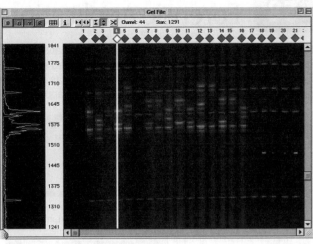

The photo above shows a film output from a DNA profiling procedure. Those lanes with many regular bands are used for calibration; they contain DNA fragment sizes of known length. These calibration lanes can be used to determine the length of fragments in the unknown samples.

DNA profiling can be automated in the same way as DNA sequencing. Powerful computer software is able to display the results of many samples that are run at the same time. In the photo above, the sample in lane 4 has been selected and displays fragments of different length on the left of the screen.

1. Describe the properties of short tandem repeats that are important to the application of DNA profiling technology:

_____

_____

_____

_____

_____

2. Explain the role of each of the following techniques in the process of DNA profiling:

(a) Gel electrophoresis: _____

_____

_____

(b) PCR: _____

_____

_____

3. Describe the three main steps in DNA profiling using PCR:

(a) _____

_____

_____

(b) _____

_____

_____

(c) _____

_____

_____

_____

4. Explain why as many as 10 STR sites are used to gain a DNA profile for forensic evidence: _____

_____

© 2017 **BIOZONE** International
ISBN: 978-1-927309-26-1
Photocopying Prohibited

58 Forensic Applications of DNA Profiling

Key Idea: DNA profiling has many forensic applications, from identifying criminal offenders to saving endangered species. The use of DNA as a tool for solving crimes such as homicide is well known, but it can also has several other applications.

DNA evidence has been used to identify body parts, solve cases of industrial sabotage and contamination, for paternity testing, and even in identifying animal products illegally made from endangered species.

1

Offender was wearing a cap but lost it when disturbed. DNA can be retrieved from flakes of skin and hair.

DNA left behind when offender drunk from a cup in the kitchen.

Bloodstain. DNA can be extracted from white blood cells in the sample

Hair. DNA can be recovered from cells at the base of the strand of hair.

During the initial investigation, samples of material that may contain DNA are taken for analysis. At a crime scene, this may include blood and body fluids as well as samples of clothing or objects that the offender might have touched. Samples from the victim are also taken to eliminate them as a possible source of contamination.

2 DNA is isolated and profiles are made from all samples and compared to known DNA profiles such as that of the victim.

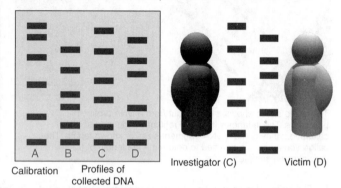

Calibration   Profiles of collected DNA   Investigator (C)   Victim (D)

3 Unknown DNA samples are compared to DNA databases of convicted offenders and to the DNA of the alleged offender.

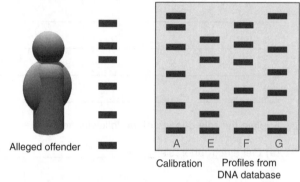

Alleged offender

Calibration   Profiles from DNA database

4 Although it does not make a complete case, DNA profiling, in conjunction with other evidence, is one of the most powerful tools in identifying offenders or unknown tissues.

The role of frequency and probability

Every person has two copies of each chromosome and therefore two copies (alleles) of every testable DNA marker. For example, the short tandem repeat (STR) known as CSF1PO contains between 7 and 15 repeats of GATA and has 9 possible alleles. Some alleles (and therefore genotypes) are more common in the population that others. For the CSF1PO STR, the frequency of the genotype 10,11 (allele 10 and allele 11) is 0.1270, i.e. it appears in 12.7% of the population. When DNA is tested, a number of STRs are sampled (the exact number varies between countries). When the data from all STRs is considered, levels of probability that the DNA came from a certain person can be calculated to 1 in 500 trillion.

Allele frequencies of the CSF1PO STR

Allele (number of repeats)	Frequency	Allele (number of repeats)	Frequency
7	0.0232	12	0.3446
8	0.0212	13	0.0656
9	0.0294	14	0.0092
10	0.2321	15	0.0010
11	0.2736		

1. Why are DNA profiles obtained for both the victim and investigator? _____

_____

_____

2. Use the evidence to decide if the alleged offender is innocent or guilty and explain your decision: _____

_____

_____

3. What is the frequency of the following CSF1PO alleles:

   (a) 9: _____   (b) 12: _____

   (c) The 9, 12 genotype (*hint, use 2pq from the Hardy-Weinberg equation*): _____

Paternity testing

DNA profiling can be used to determine paternity (and maternity) by looking for matches in alleles between parents and children. This can be used in cases such as child support or inheritance. DNA profiling can establish the certainty of paternity (and maternity) to a 99.99% probability of parentage.

Every STR allele is given the number of its repeats as its name, e.g. 8 or 9. In a paternity case, the mother may be 11, 12 and the father may be 8, 13 for a particular STR. The child will have a combination of these. The table below illustrates this:

DNA marker	Mother's alleles	Child's alleles	Father's alleles
CSF1PO	7, 8	8, 9	9, 12
D10S1248	14, 15	11, 14	10, 11
D12S391	16, 17	17, 17	17, 18
D13S317	10, 11	9, 10	8, 9

The frequency of the each allele occurring in the population is important when determining paternity (or maternity). For example, DNA marker CSF1PO allele 9 has a frequency of 0.0294 making the match between father and child very significant (whereas allele 12 has a frequency of 0.3446, making a match less significant). For each allele, a paternity index (PI) is calculated. These indicate the significance of the match. The PIs are combined to produce a probability of parentage. 10-13 different STRs are used to identify paternity. Mismatches of two STRs between the male and child is enough to exclude the male as the biological father.

Whale DNA: tracking illegal slaughter

Under International Whaling Commission regulations, some species of whales can be captured for scientific research and their meat sold legally. Most, including humpback and blue whales, are fully protected and to capture or kill them for any purpose is illegal. Between 1999 and 2003 Scott Baker and associates from Oregon State University's Marine Mammal Institute investigated whale meat sold in markets in Japan and South Korea. Using DNA profiling techniques, they found around 10% of the samples tested were from fully protected whales including western grey whales and humpbacks. They also found that many more whales were being killed than were being officially reported.

4. For the STR D10S1248 in the example above, what possible allele combinations could the child have?

_____

5. A paternity test was carried out and the abbreviated results are shown below:

DNA marker	Mother's alleles	Child's alleles	Man's alleles
CSF1PO	7, 8	8, 9	9, 12
D10S1248	14, 15	11, 14	10, 11
D19S433	9, 10	10,15	14, 16
D13S317	10, 11	9, 10	8, 9
D2S441	7, 15	7, 9	14, 17

(a) Could the man be the biological father? _____

(b) Explain your answer: _____

_____

_____

6. (a) How could DNA profiling be used to refute official claims of the **species** of whales captured and sold in markets?

_____

_____

_____

(b) How could DNA profiling be used to refute official claims of the **number** of whales captured and sold in markets?

_____

_____

_____

© 2017 **BIOZONE** International
ISBN: 978-1-927309-26-1
Photocopying Prohibited

59 Gene Expression Overview

Key Idea: Gene expression is tightly controlled, with regulatory steps throughout. Modifications to DNA, mRNA, and protein products account for the diverse range of proteins produced. Eukaryotic **gene expression** is the process by which the information in a gene is used to synthesise a protein (or other RNA product). It involves **transcription** of the DNA into mRNA in the nucleus and **translation** of the mRNA into protein in the cytoplasm. It is an energy expensive process, so there are many regulatory steps to ensure a protein is only expressed (produced) when needed. Modification of both the mRNA and the protein product allows for a variety of different proteins to be produced from a single gene.

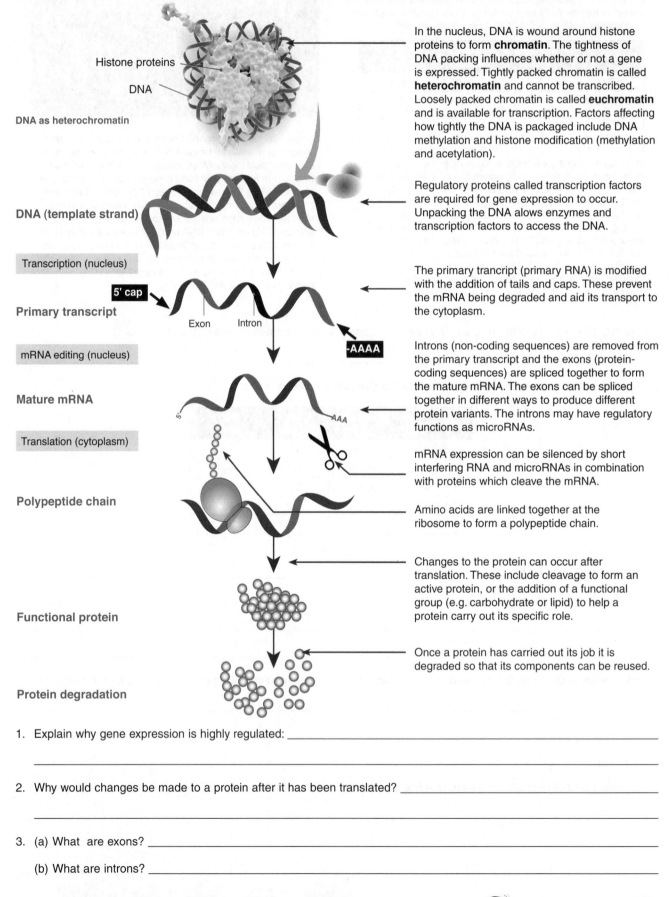

Histone proteins

DNA

DNA as heterochromatin

In the nucleus, DNA is wound around histone proteins to form **chromatin**. The tightness of DNA packing influences whether or not a gene is expressed. Tightly packed chromatin is called **heterochromatin** and cannot be transcribed. Loosely packed chromatin is called **euchromatin** and is available for transcription. Factors affecting how tightly the DNA is packaged include DNA methylation and histone modification (methylation and acetylation).

DNA (template strand)

Regulatory proteins called transcription factors are required for gene expression to occur. Unpacking the DNA alows enzymes and transcription factors to access the DNA.

Transcription (nucleus)

5' cap

Primary transcript

Exon   Intron

-AAAA

The primary trancript (primary RNA) is modified with the addition of tails and caps. These prevent the mRNA being degraded and aid its transport to the cytoplasm.

mRNA editing (nucleus)

Introns (non-coding sequences) are removed from the primary transcript and the exons (protein-coding sequences) are spliced together to form the mature mRNA. The exons can be spliced together in different ways to produce different protein variants. The introns may have regulatory functions as microRNAs.

Mature mRNA

AAA

Translation (cytoplasm)

mRNA expression can be silenced by short interfering RNA and microRNAs in combination with proteins which cleave the mRNA.

Polypeptide chain

Amino acids are linked together at the ribosome to form a polypeptide chain.

Changes to the protein can occur after translation. These include cleavage to form an active protein, or the addition of a functional group (e.g. carbohydrate or lipid) to help a protein carry out its specific role.

Functional protein

Once a protein has carried out its job it is degraded so that its components can be reused.

Protein degradation

1. Explain why gene expression is highly regulated: _____

   _____

2. Why would changes be made to a protein after it has been translated? _____

   _____

3. (a) What are exons? _____

   (b) What are introns? _____

© 2017 **BIOZONE** International
ISBN: 978-1-927309-26-1
Photocopying Prohibited

60 Transcription Factors Control Gene Expression

Key Idea: Eukaryotic genes include both translated and untranslated regions, including control sequences. Regulatory proteins called transcription factors regulate gene expression by ensuring the necessary elements come together.

A eukaryotic gene includes more than just the region of exonic DNA that is translated into protein. It also contains introns, regulatory untranslated regions (UTRs), a promoter to which the RNA polymerase binds, and a terminator region that signals the stop point of transcription. The control

sequences ensure that transcription begins and ends at the correct points and that the necessary sequences are present to create the mature mRNA that can be exported from the nucleus. The promoter region is the binding site for regulatory proteins called transcription factors and it contains several **highly conserved** regions (sequences that have remained unchanged throughout evolution). Transcription's dependence on sequence recognition and transcription factors provides close control over the expression of genes.

The structure of eukaryotic genes

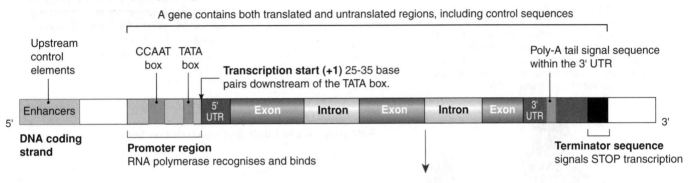

A gene contains both translated and untranslated regions, including control sequences

Upstream control elements

CCAAT box   TATA box

Transcription start (+1) 25-35 base pairs downstream of the TATA box.

Poly-A tail signal sequence within the 3' UTR

Enhancers | 5' UTR | Exon | Intron | Exon | Intron | Exon | 3' UTR

DNA coding strand

Promoter region
RNA polymerase recognises and binds

Terminator sequence
signals STOP transcription

DID YOU KNOW?

Highly conserved sequences within eukaryotic genes include the TATA box within the promoter and parts of the 5' and 3' UTR. These sequences must have very important functions in gene regulation.

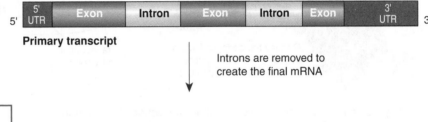

5' UTR | Exon | Intron | Exon | Intron | Exon | 3' UTR

Primary transcript

Introns are removed to create the final mRNA

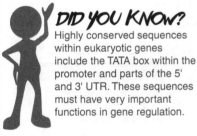

- Transcribed and transported to the cytoplasm but not translated
- Transcribed and removed before transport to the cytoplasm
- Transcribed and translated

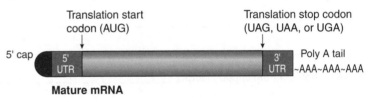

Translation start codon (AUG)

Translation stop codon (UAG, UAA, or UGA)

5' cap | 5' UTR | | 3' UTR | Poly A tail ~AAA~AAA~AAA

Mature mRNA

1. Outline the role of each of the following regions of a eukaryotic gene:

   (a) Promoter region: _____

   _____

   (b) Terminator sequence: _____

   _____

   (c) Transcription start signal: _____

   _____

   (d) AUG codon: _____

   (e) UAA, UAG, and UGA codons: _____

2. What happens to each of the following regions of a eukaryotic gene?

   (a) Exons: _____

   (b) Introns: _____

   (c) 5' and 3' UTR: _____

© 2017 **BIOZONE** International
ISBN: 978-1-927309-26-1
Photocopying Prohibited

RNA polymerase can only transcribe genes in the presence of transcription factors

▶ In eukaryotes, RNA polymerase cannot initiate the transcription of structural genes alone. It requires the presence of **transcription factors**. Transcription factors are encoded by regulatory genes and have a role in creating an initiation complex for transcription.

▶ Transcription factors bind to distinct regions of the DNA, including the promoter and upstream enhancers, and act as a guide to indicate to RNA polymerase where transcription should start.

▶ The TATA binding protein is a subunit of a multiunit general transcription factor. It is the first to bind to DNA, recruiting other transcription factors to form a transcription initiation complex. Once bound to the promoter sequence, the transcription factors capture RNA polymerase, which can then begin transcription.

Assembly of the transcription initiation complex

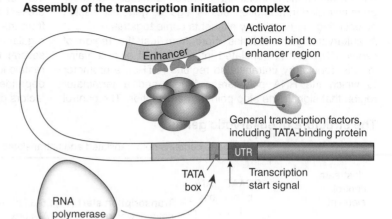

RNA polymerase binds and transcription begins

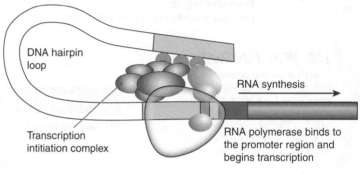

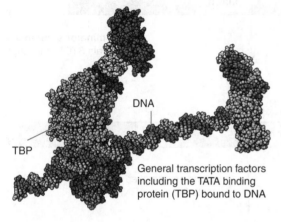

General transcription factors including the TATA binding protein (TBP) bound to DNA

3. Why would a gene contain regions that are transcribed but not translated? _____

_____

_____

4. (a) What is a transcription factor? _____

_____

_____

(b) What sort of genes encode transcription factors? _____

(c) How are transcription factors involved in the regulation of gene expression? _____

_____

_____

_____

_____

5. (a) What does it mean to say a DNA sequence is highly conserved? _____

_____

(b) Some of the most highly conserved regions of genes include untranslated sequences. Why do you think this is?

_____

_____

_____

© 2017 **BIOZONE** International
ISBN: 978-1-927309-26-1
Photocopying Prohibited

61 mRNA Processing

Key Idea: Primary mRNA molecules are modified after transcription so that the mRNA can exit the nucleus. Post transcriptional modification also enables the cell to produce a wide variety of proteins from a smaller number of genes. Once a gene is transcribed, the primary transcript is modified to produce the mRNA strand that will be translated in the cytoplasm. Modifications to the 5' and 3' ends of the transcript enable the mRNA to exit the nucleus and remain stable long enough to be translated. Other post transcriptional modifications remove non-protein coding intronic DNA and splice exons in different combinations to produce different protein end products.

Primary RNA is modified by the addition of caps and tails

▶ After transcription, both ends of the primary RNA are modified by enzymes to create 'caps' and 'tails' (below). These modifications protect the RNA from degradation and help its transport through the nuclear pore.

Primary RNA

5' modification (capping)
A guanine nucleotide cap is added to the 5' end of the primary transcript to protect it from degradation during transport from the nucleus to the cytoplasm.

3' modification (poly-A tails)
Multiple adenosine nucleotides are added to the primary transcript. These poly-A tails aid nuclear export, translation, and stability of the mRNA.

Post transcriptional modification

▶ Human DNA contains 25 000 genes, but produces up to one million different proteins. Each gene must therefore produce more than one protein. This is achieved through both post-transcriptional modification of the mRNA as well as post translational modifications, such as glycosylation and addition of phosphates.

▶ Primary RNA contains both protein coding exons and non-protein coding introns. Introns are usually removed after transcription and may be processed to create regulatory elements such as microRNAs. The exons are then spliced together ready to be translated. However, there are many alternative ways to splice the exons and these alternatives create variations in the translated proteins. The most common method of alternative splicing involves exon skipping, in which not all exons are spliced into the final mRNA (below). Other splicing options create further variants.

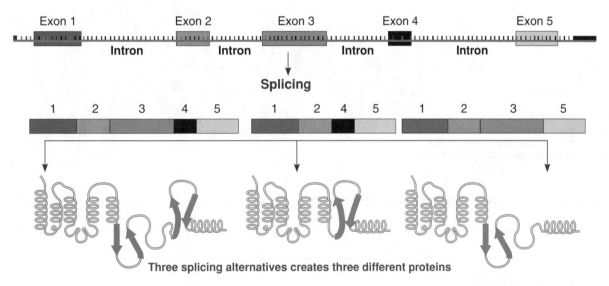

Three splicing alternatives creates three different proteins

1. What is the purpose of the caps and tail on mRNA? _____

_____

2. (a) What happens to the intronic sequences in DNA after transcription? _____

   (b) What is one possible fate for these introns? _____

3. How can so many proteins be produced from so few genes? _____

_____

_____

4. If a human produces 1 million proteins, but human DNA codes for only 25 000 genes, on average how many proteins are produced per gene?

_____

© 2017 **BIOZONE** International
ISBN: 978-1-927309-26-1
Photocopying Prohibited

62 DNA Packaging and Transcription

Key Idea: A chromosome is a single long molecule of DNA coiled around histone proteins. How tightly the DNA is wound will determine whether or not its genes can be expressed. Eukaryotic DNA is complexed with histone proteins to form chromatin. Histones package the DNA in an orderly way, enabling it to fit into the nucleus. The extent of packaging also regulates gene expression by making genes more or less accessible to RNA polymerase and transcription factors. When the DNA is tightly packed (as heterochromatin) transcription is suppressed. When loosely packed (as euchromatin) the genes can be accessed and transcribed. DNA packaging is regulated by **epigenetic factors**, including histone modification and DNA methylation. These are genomic modifications that do not affect the DNA nucleotide sequence itself.

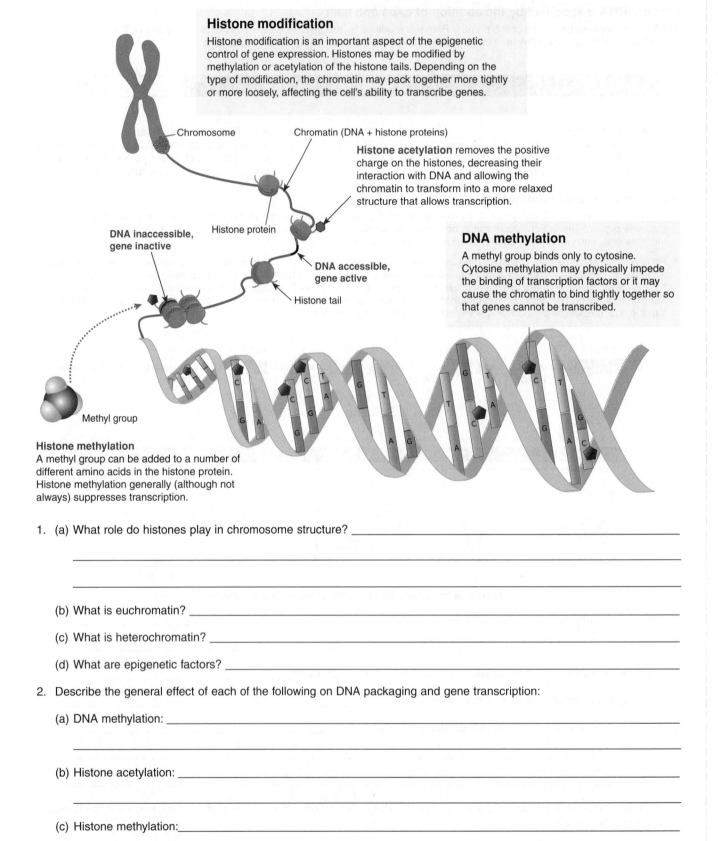

Histone modification

Histone modification is an important aspect of the epigenetic control of gene expression. Histones may be modified by methylation or acetylation of the histone tails. Depending on the type of modification, the chromatin may pack together more tightly or more loosely, affecting the cell's ability to transcribe genes.

Chromosome

Chromatin (DNA + histone proteins)

Histone acetylation removes the positive charge on the histones, decreasing their interaction with DNA and allowing the chromatin to transform into a more relaxed structure that allows transcription.

DNA inaccessible, gene inactive

Histone protein

DNA accessible, gene active

Histone tail

DNA methylation

A methyl group binds only to cytosine. Cytosine methylation may physically impede the binding of transcription factors or it may cause the chromatin to bind tightly together so that genes cannot be transcribed.

Methyl group

Histone methylation

A methyl group can be added to a number of different amino acids in the histone protein. Histone methylation generally (although not always) suppresses transcription.

1. (a) What role do histones play in chromosome structure? _____

_____

_____

   (b) What is euchromatin? _____

   (c) What is heterochromatin? _____

   (d) What are epigenetic factors? _____

2. Describe the general effect of each of the following on DNA packaging and gene transcription:

   (a) DNA methylation: _____

   _____

   (b) Histone acetylation: _____

   _____

   (c) Histone methylation: _____

   _____

© 2017 **BIOZONE** International
ISBN: 978-1-927309-26-1
Photocopying Prohibited

63 The Effect of DNA Methylation

Key Idea: Methylation of the DNA can alter gene expression and therefore phenotype.

Methylation of DNA is an important way of controlling gene expression. Methylated DNA is usually silenced, meaning genes are not transcribed to mRNA. Methylation of cytosine turns off gene expression by changing the state of the chromatin so that transcribing proteins are not able to bind to the DNA. Epigenetic markers such as methylation are usually reset in the early embryo (graph below), although some may be carried over to the next generation. These can account for heritable differences as a result of environment (such as have been documented in the children of famine victims).

DNA methylation

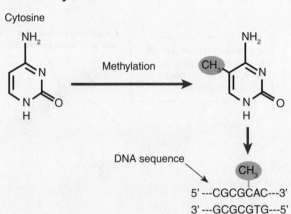

Cytosine

Methylation

DNA sequence

5' ---CGCGCAC---3'
3' ---GCGCGTG---5'

Cytosine methylation is an important process in DNA packaging and gene expression. Cytosine methylation can alter gene expression by enzymes binding to the DNA or it may cause the chromatin to bind tightly together so that genes cannot be copied by the cellular machinery.

Methylation and epigenetics

Methylation and histone modifications can be passed on from a cell's DNA to its daughter cells during DNA replication. In this way, any environmental or other chemical effects encountered by a cell can be passed on to the next generation of cells.

Methylation is very important during embryonic development when a lot of methylation takes place and a lot of cells are being produced. Once a cell has differentiated into a specific cell type, all the daughter cells inherit the modifications and remain the same type of cell.

The study of these modifications and how the environment influences them is called **epigenetics**. *Epi-* means 'on top of' or 'extra to'. Methylation (together with histone modification) are part of epigenetics because they don't directly change the DNA sequence.

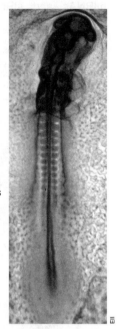

Methylation and gene expression

Gene expression changes as an organism develops. Soon after fertilisation, epigenetic markers are removed (by demethylation) so that the developmental potential of cells is reset and not restricted. Genes are then switched on and off as development proceeds. Methylation is one of the main mechanisms by which the differentiation of cells and tissues is directed.

Enzymes can add or remove methyl groups from cytosine bases to silence or activate genes. Methylation can be affected by changes in the environment and this provides a way for the embryo to respond to changes in the environment.

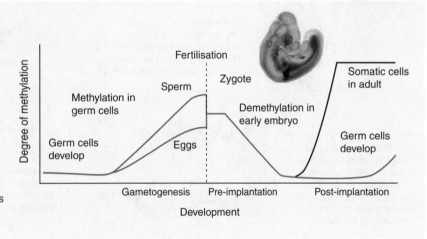

1. (a) Explain why most epigenetic markers are removed by demethylation in the early embryo? _____

_____

_____

(b) What is the result of some markers escaping this resetting process? _____

_____

2. What is the role of methylation during development? _____

_____

_____

3. Why is anything the pregnant mother does particularly likely to affect gene expression in the embryo? _____

_____

_____

64 Non-Coding RNA Can Silence Gene Expression

Key Idea: RNA interference (RNAi) regulates gene expression through miRNAs and siRNAs, which act to silence genes.

RNA plays vital roles in transcribing and translating DNA, forming messenger RNA (mRNA), transfer RNA (tRNA), and ribosomal RNA (rRNA). RNA is also involved in modifying mRNA after transcription and regulating translation. RNA interference (RNAi) regulates gene expression through miRNAs and siRNAs, which bind to specific mRNA sequences, causing them to be cleaved. RNAi is important in regulating gene expression during development and in defense against viruses, which often use double-stranded RNA as an infectious vector. Regulation of translation is achieved by destroying specific mRNA targets using short RNA lengths, which may be exogenous (short interfering RNAs) or endogenous (microRNAs). Mechanisms of **RNA interference** (RNAi) are illustrated below.

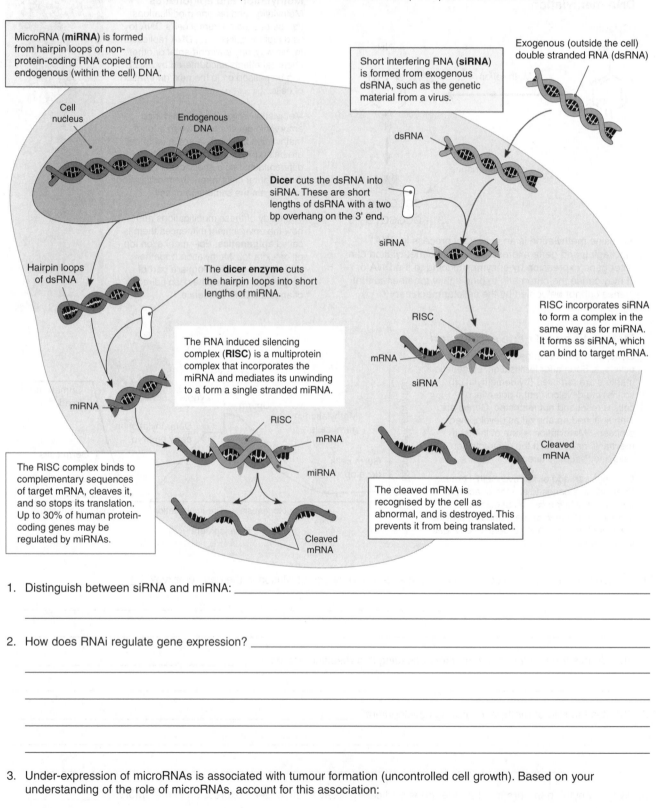

MicroRNA (**miRNA**) is formed from hairpin loops of non-protein-coding RNA copied from endogenous (within the cell) DNA.

Short interfering RNA (**siRNA**) is formed from exogenous dsRNA, such as the genetic material from a virus.

Exogenous (outside the cell) double stranded RNA (dsRNA)

Cell nucleus

Endogenous DNA

dsRNA

Dicer cuts the dsRNA into siRNA. These are short lengths of dsRNA with a two bp overhang on the 3' end.

siRNA

Hairpin loops of dsRNA

The **dicer enzyme** cuts the hairpin loops into short lengths of miRNA.

RISC incorporates siRNA to form a complex in the same way as for miRNA. It forms ss siRNA, which can bind to target mRNA.

The RNA induced silencing complex (**RISC**) is a multiprotein complex that incorporates the miRNA and mediates its unwinding to a form a single stranded miRNA.

RISC

mRNA

siRNA

miRNA

RISC

mRNA

miRNA

The RISC complex binds to complementary sequences of target mRNA, cleaves it, and so stops its translation. Up to 30% of human protein-coding genes may be regulated by miRNAs.

Cleaved mRNA

The cleaved mRNA is recognised by the cell as abnormal, and is destroyed. This prevents it from being translated.

Cleaved mRNA

Cleaved mRNA

1. Distinguish between siRNA and miRNA: _____

_____

2. How does RNAi regulate gene expression? _____

_____

_____

_____

_____

3. Under-expression of microRNAs is associated with tumour formation (uncontrolled cell growth). Based on your understanding of the role of microRNAs, account for this association:

_____

_____

© 2017 **BIOZONE** International
ISBN: 978-1-927309-26-1
Photocopying Prohibited

65 What are Stem Cells?

Key Idea: Stem cells are undifferentiated cells found in multicellular organisms. They are characterised by the properties of self renewal and potency.

A zygote can differentiate into all the cell types of the body because its early divisions produce stem cells. Stem cells are unspecialised cells that can divide repeatedly while remaining unspecialised (**self renewal**). They give rise to the many cell types that make up the tissues of multicellular organisms. For

example, bone marrow stem cells differentiate to produce all the cell types that make up blood. These multipotent (or adult) stem cells are found in most organs, where they replace old or damaged cells and replenish cells throughout life. Different types of stem cell have different abilities to differentiate (called **potency**). Fully differentiated cells cannot normally revert to an undifferentiated state, although in some conditions they can be induced to do so (next page).

Properties of stem cells

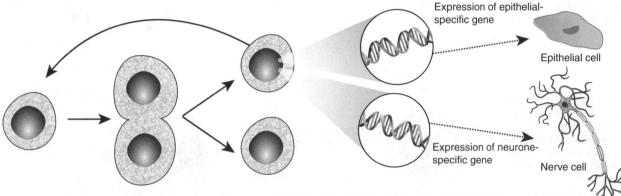

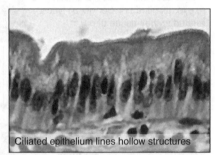

Expression of epithelial-specific gene

Epithelial cell

Expression of neurone-specific gene

Nerve cell

Self renewal: Stem cells have the ability to divide many times while maintaining an unspecialised state.

Potency: The ability to differentiate (transform) into specialised cells. Differentiation is the result of changes in gene regulation. There are different levels of potency that depend on the type of stem cell.

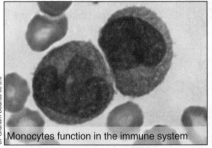

Monocytes function in the immune system

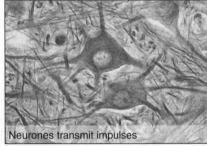

Neurones transmit impulses

Ciliated epithelium lines hollow structures

Each specialised cell type in an organism expresses a subset of all the genes making up the organism's genome. The differentiation of cells into specialised types is the result of specific patterns of gene expression and is controlled by transcription factors. In response to cues during development (e.g. hormones), transcription factors bind to DNA and switch genes on or off, so determining the final structure and function of the cell. As a cell becomes increasingly specialised, its fate becomes fixed and it can no longer return to an undifferentiated state unless it is reprogrammed. This process, called dedifferentiation, happens naturally in some organisms but can be induced in human cells.

1. Describe the two defining features of stem cells:

    (a) _____

    (b) _____

2. How is the differentiation of stem cells controlled? _____

    _____

    _____

    _____

3. Explain the role of stem cells in the development and maintenance of specialised tissues in multicellular organisms:

    _____

    _____

    _____

    _____

    _____

© 2017 **BIOZONE** International
ISBN: 978-1-927309-26-1
Photocopying Prohibited

LINK 67   LINK 66   WEB 65   **KNOW**

Types of stem cells

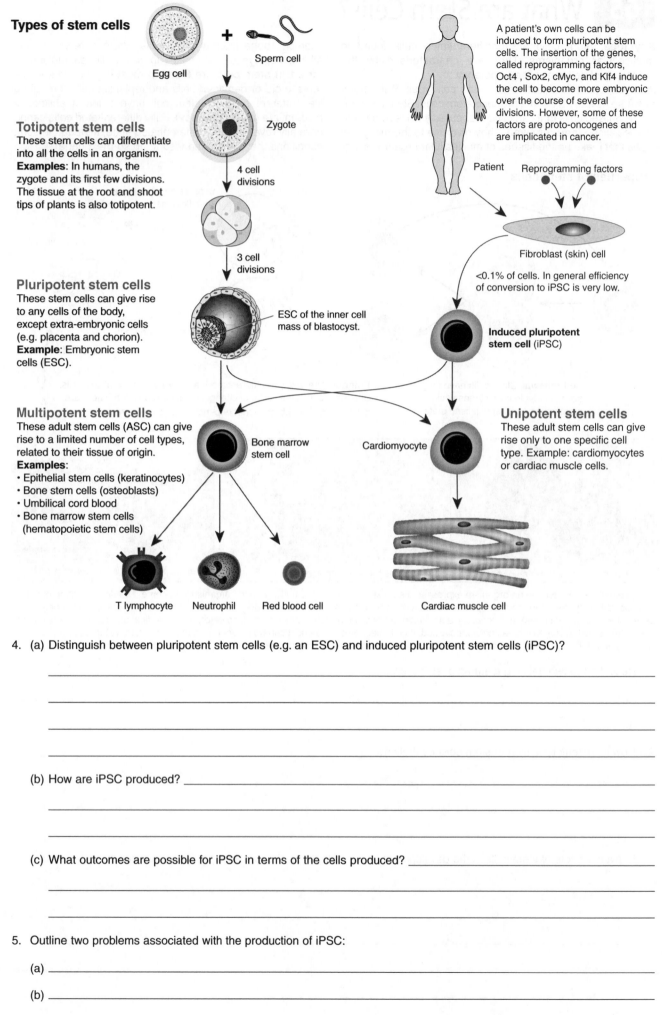

Egg cell

+

Sperm cell

Zygote

Totipotent stem cells
These stem cells can differentiate into all the cells in an organism.
Examples: In humans, the zygote and its first few divisions. The tissue at the root and shoot tips of plants is also totipotent.

4 cell divisions

3 cell divisions

Pluripotent stem cells
These stem cells can give rise to any cells of the body, except extra-embryonic cells (e.g. placenta and chorion).
Example: Embryonic stem cells (ESC).

ESC of the inner cell mass of blastocyst.

A patient's own cells can be induced to form pluripotent stem cells. The insertion of the genes, called reprogramming factors, Oct4 , Sox2, cMyc, and Klf4 induce the cell to become more embryonic over the course of several divisions. However, some of these factors are proto-oncogenes and are implicated in cancer.

Patient   Reprogramming factors

Fibroblast (skin) cell

<0.1% of cells. In general efficiency of conversion to iPSC is very low.

Induced pluripotent stem cell (iPSC)

Multipotent stem cells
These adult stem cells (ASC) can give rise to a limited number of cell types, related to their tissue of origin.
Examples:
• Epithelial stem cells (keratinocytes)
• Bone stem cells (osteoblasts)
• Umbilical cord blood
• Bone marrow stem cells (hematopoietic stem cells)

Bone marrow stem cell

Cardiomyocyte

Unipotent stem cells
These adult stem cells can give rise only to one specific cell type. Example: cardiomyocytes or cardiac muscle cells.

T lymphocyte   Neutrophil   Red blood cell

Cardiac muscle cell

4. (a) Distinguish between pluripotent stem cells (e.g. an ESC) and induced pluripotent stem cells (iPSC)?

_____

_____

_____

_____

(b) How are iPSC produced? _____

_____

_____

(c) What outcomes are possible for iPSC in terms of the cells produced? _____

_____

_____

5. Outline two problems associated with the production of iPSC:

(a) _____

(b) _____

© 2017 **BIOZONE** International
ISBN: 978-1-927309-26-1
Photocopying Prohibited

66 Epigenetic Factors Regulate Cell Differentiation

Key Idea: The differentiation of cell lines from stem cell progenitors is regulated by changes in epigenetic markers. Methylation and demethylation allows cells to progress along a particular pathway after which their fate is determined.

All the information to construct an organism is found in its genome, but because the body is made up of a wide variety of very different cell types, there must be mechanisms to control the way in which the information in the genome is expressed. The process by which different cell types arise is called differentiation and it is regulated through transcription factors, chemical signals, and epigenetic modification. Epigenetic regulation controls a cell's fate and determines its developmental pathway. This is illustrated for hematopoeitic stem cells (HSC), which give rise to cells that will differentiate into different blood cell types, while still retaining their properties of self-renewal and potency. During differentiation, cells progressively lose their ability to self-renew and become specific to their lineage. Key genes, important for lineage commitment and differentiation, are kept in a paused state by methylation and then activated by demethylation/acetylation.

Differentation of hematopoeitic stem cells

Epigenetic modifications regulate cell fate in a dynamic way to maintain multipotent cells and cell types to be renewed. Methylation or demethylation at different stages during the differentiation of a cell line produces different cell fates. Once cell identity is established, only minor changes in DNA methylation occur. DNA methylation therefore acts as a mechanism for a cell to remember its identity and transcriptional programme during development. Not all developmental pathways or cell types are shown.

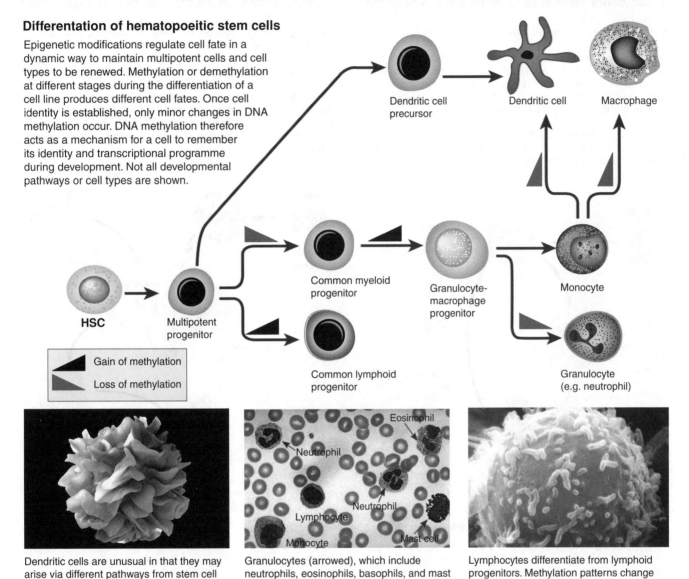

Gain of methylation

Loss of methylation

HSC — Multipotent progenitor — Common myeloid progenitor — Granulocyte-macrophage progenitor — Monocyte — Granulocyte (e.g. neutrophil)

Common lymphoid progenitor

Dendritic cell precursor — Dendritic cell — Macrophage

Dendritic cells are unusual in that they may arise via different pathways from stem cell progenitors (above). Alternative methylation patterns are responsible for these differences.

Granulocytes (arrowed), which include neutrophils, eosinophils, basophils, and mast cells, are key immune system cells. They all differentiate from granulocyte progenitor cells.

Lymphocytes differentiate from lymphoid progenitors. Methylation patterns change during differentiation so that a differentiated cell can be defined by its epigenetic markers.

1. Describe how changes in methylation during cellular differentiation produces cells with different characteristics:

_____

_____

_____

2. Predict how disorders in epigenetic regulation could lead to some cell proliferation disorders such as leukaemia:

_____

_____

_____

67 Stems Cells and the Treatment of Disease

Key Idea: Stem cells have many potentially useful medical applications, but technical difficulties must be overcome first. Stem cell research is at an early stage and there is still much to be learned about the environments that cells require in order to differentiate into specific cell types. The ability of stem cells to differentiate into any cell type means that they have potential applications in cell therapy and in tissue engineering to replace diseased or damaged cells. One of the problems with using stem cells to treat diseased tissues is the response of the recipient's immune system. The immune system has evolved to destroy foreign objects. When stem cells cultured from another person are introduced to a recipient, they are attacked by that person's immune system. There are a few possible ways around this, but none are simple.

How to use stem cells

1. Use donor stem cells to repair tissues or organs

Problem: immune system will attack the donor's cells.

Firstly a donor with a tissue match is selected (the types of cell surface proteins on donor and recipient cells are the same or very similar). This reduces the risk of immune rejection. Secondly the recipient will need to take immunosuppressant drugs to stop their immune system attacking the donated cells.

Another way of getting around the problem is to encase the donated cells in a protective shell, isolating them from the body. This is being investigated with respect to pancreatic cells and diabetes.

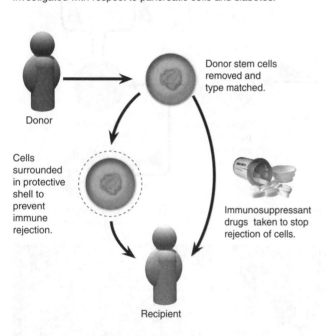

Donor

Donor stem cells removed and type matched.

Cells surrounded in protective shell to prevent immune rejection.

Immunosuppressant drugs taken to stop rejection of cells.

Recipient

2. Reprogramme patient's cells before implantation

Problem: Some diseases are the result of defective genes. Stem cells from the patient will carry these defective genes.

If the disease is due to a genetic fault (e.g. type 1 diabetes), then the stem cells will need to be genetically corrected before use (otherwise the disease may reoccur). Stem cells (e.g. iPSCs) are isolated and cultured in the laboratory in the presence of the corrected gene. The culture is screened for cells that have taken up the gene. These are then transplanted back into the patient, without any immune rejection.

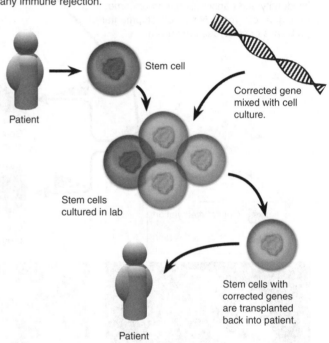

Patient

Stem cell

Corrected gene mixed with cell culture.

Stem cells cultured in lab

Stem cells with corrected genes are transplanted back into patient.

Patient

1. Identify a problem with using stem cells from a donor to treat a recipient patient: _____

_____

_____

2. Explain why stem cells with a defective gene must be corrected before reimplanting them into the patient: _____

_____

_____

_____

3. Umbilical cord blood is promoted as a rich source of multipotent stem cells for autologous (self) transplants. Can you see a problem with the use of a baby's cord blood to treat a disease in that child at a later date?

_____

_____

_____

© 2017 **BIOZONE** International
ISBN: 978-1-927309-26-1
Photocopying Prohibited

Stem cells for type 1 diabetes

Type 1 diabetes results from the body's own immune system attacking and destroying the insulin producing beta cells of the pancreas. Without insulin, the body cannot utilise glucose. In theory, new beta cells could be produced using stem cells. Research is focussed on how to obtain the stem cells and deliver them effectively to the patient. Most techniques currently being investigated use stem cells from non-diabetics, requiring recipients to use immunosuppressant drugs so the cells are not rejected.

A study published in 2014 described a model method for treating type 1 diabetes in mice using fibroblast cells taken from the skin of mice.

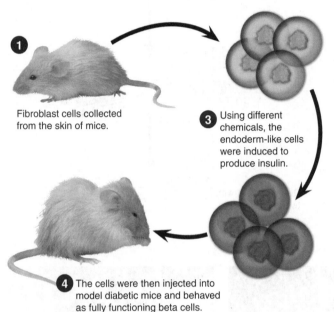

2 Cells treated with chemicals to reprogramme them into endoderm-like cells. These are a type of embryonic cell from which the organs develop.

1 Fibroblast cells collected from the skin of mice.

3 Using different chemicals, the endoderm-like cells were induced to produce insulin.

4 The cells were then injected into model diabetic mice and behaved as fully functioning beta cells.

Use of stem cells: ethical considerations

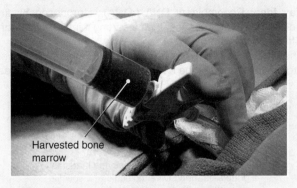

Harvested bone marrow

Stem cell therapy has enormous potential to improve the health of people with certain diseases. However, the ethical issues associated with stem cell therapy mean the technology is still regarded as controversial by many. Embryonic stem cell therapy is more controversial than therapies using adult stem cells. The main objections to embryonic stem cell therapy are:

▸ The technology used to create the embryo could be used for creating a human clone.

▸ The creation of stem cell line requires the destruction of a human embryo and thus human life.

▸ Human embryos have the potential to develop into an individual and thus have the same rights of the individual.

▸ Saving or enhancing the quality of life of an individual does not justify the destruction of the life of another (i.e. the embryo).

▸ ESC research has not produced any viable long term treatment, but adult stem cell therapy has.

▸ There are other stem cell techniques that do not require the creation of an embryo but achieve similar results (e.g. cell lines grown from adult stem cells or umbilical cord blood).

4. (a) What causes type 1 diabetes? _____

_____

_____

(b) How could this be treated with stem cells? _____

_____

_____

_____

5. Discuss some of the ethical issues associated with using stem cell therapies. Include a comment about why therapies using adult stem cells are less controversial than those involving embryonic stem cells:

_____

_____

_____

_____

_____

_____

_____

_____

68 Making Recombinant DNA

Key Idea: Recombinant DNA (rDNA) is produced by first isolating a DNA sequence, then inserting it into the DNA of a different organism.

The production of rDNA is possible because the DNA of every organism is made of the same building blocks (**nucleotides**).

rDNA allows a gene from one organism to be moved into, and expressed in, a different organism. Two important tools used to create rDNA are restriction digestion (chopping up the DNA) using **restriction enzymes** and DNA ligation (joining of sections of DNA) using the enzyme **DNA ligase**.

Information about restriction enzymes

1. A **restriction enzyme** is an enzyme that cuts a double-stranded DNA molecule at a specific **recognition site** (a specific DNA sequence). There are many different types of restriction enzymes, each has a unique recognition site.

2. Some restriction enzymes produce DNA fragments with two **sticky ends** (right). A sticky end has exposed nucleotide bases at each end. DNA cut in such a way is able to be joined to other DNA with matching sticky ends. Such joins are specific to their recognition sites.

3. Some restriction enzymes produce a DNA fragment with two **blunt ends** (ends with no exposed nucleotide bases). The piece it is removed from is also left with blunt ends. DNA cut in such a way can be joined to any other blunt end fragment. Unlike sticky ends, blunt end joins are non-specific because there are no sticky ends to act as specific recognition sites.

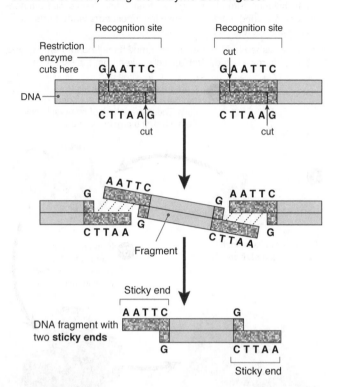

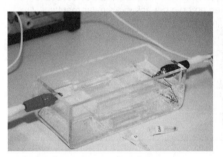

The fragments of DNA produced by the restriction enzymes are mixed with ethidium bromide, a molecule that fluoresces under UV light. The DNA fragments are then placed on an electrophoresis gel to separate the different lengths of DNA.

Once the DNA fragments are separated, the gel is placed on a UV viewing platform. The area of the gel containing the DNA fragments of the correct length is cut out and placed in a solution that dissolves the gel. This releases the DNA into the solution.

The solution containing the DNA is centrifuged at high speed to separate out the DNA. Centrifugation works by separating molecules of different densities. Once isolated, the DNA can be spliced into another DNA molecule.

1. What is the purpose of restriction enzymes in making recombinant DNA? _____

_____

_____

2. Distinguish between sticky end and blunt end fragments: _____

_____

_____

_____

3. Why is it useful to have many different kinds of restriction enzymes? _____

_____

_____

© 2017 **BIOZONE** International
ISBN: 978-1-927309-26-1
Photocopying Prohibited

Creating a recombinant DNA plasmid

1 Two pieces of DNA are cut by the same restriction enzyme (they will produce fragments with matching **sticky ends**).

2 Fragments with matching sticky ends can be joined by base-pairing. This process is called **annealing.** This allows DNA fragments from different sources to be joined.

3 The fragments of DNA are joined together by the enzyme **DNA ligase**, producing a molecule of **recombinant DNA**.

4 The joined fragments will usually form either a linear or a circular molecule, as shown here (right) as recombinant **plasmid** DNA.

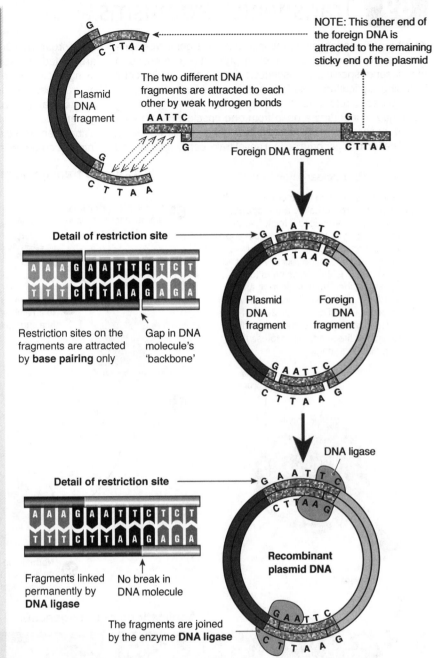

NOTE: This other end of the foreign DNA is attracted to the remaining sticky end of the plasmid

The two different DNA fragments are attracted to each other by weak hydrogen bonds

Plasmid DNA fragment

Foreign DNA fragment

Detail of restriction site

Restriction sites on the fragments are attracted by **base pairing** only

Gap in DNA molecule's 'backbone'

Plasmid DNA fragment   Foreign DNA fragment

Detail of restriction site

Fragments linked permanently by **DNA ligase**

No break in DNA molecule

DNA ligase

Recombinant plasmid DNA

The fragments are joined by the enzyme **DNA ligase**

25kartika

pGLO is a plasmid engineered to contain Green Fluorescent Protein (*gfp*). pGLO has been used to create fluorescent organisms, including the bacteria above (bright patches on agar plates).

4. Explain in your own words the two main steps in the process of joining two DNA fragments together:

    (a) Annealing: _____

    _____

    (b) DNA ligase: _____

    _____

5. Explain why ligation can be considered the reverse of the restriction digestion process: _____

    _____

6. Why can recombinant DNA be expressed in any kind of organism, even if it contains DNA from another species?

    _____

    _____

    _____

    _____

© 2017 **BIOZONE** International
ISBN: 978-1-927309-26-1
Photocopying Prohibited

69 Transgenic Organisms

Key Idea: Transgenesis is the insertion of a gene from one species into another, so its protein product is expressed in the second species. Transgenesis has many applications including agriculture, and food and medical technologies.

Transgenesis refers to the specific genetic engineering technique of inserting a gene from one species into another that does not normally contain the gene. It allows direct modification of a genome so that novel traits can be introduced to an organism. Organisms that have undergone transgenesis are called transgenic organisms. The genes are inserted using vectors or by direct insertion of the DNA. Applications of transgenesis include enhancing desirable features in livestock and crops, producing human proteins, and treating genetic defects with gene therapy. Cloning transgenics, or using them in selective breeding programmes, ensures the introduced gene is inherited in following generations.

Pronuclear injection

A gene that has been transferred into another organism is called a **transgene**. Genes can be introduced directly into an animal cell by microinjection. Multiple copies of the desired transgene are injected via a glass micropipette into a recently fertilised egg cell, which is then transferred to a surrogate mother. Transgenic mice and livestock are produced in this way. However, the process is inefficient: only 2-3% of eggs give rise to transgenic animals and only a proportion of these animals express the transgene adequately.

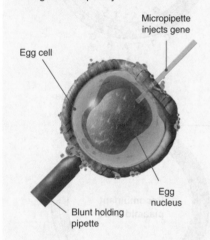

Micropipette injects gene

Egg cell

Egg nucleus

Blunt holding pipette

Creating transgenic mice using pronuclear injection

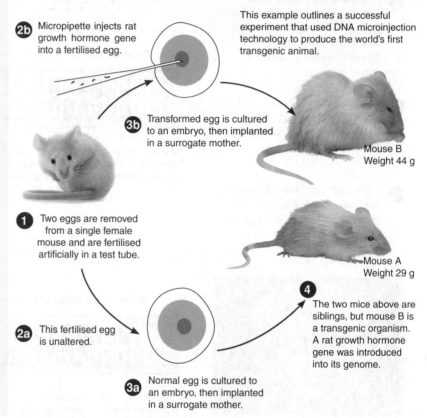

This example outlines a successful experiment that used DNA microinjection technology to produce the world's first transgenic animal.

2b Micropipette injects rat growth hormone gene into a fertilised egg.

3b Transformed egg is cultured to an embryo, then implanted in a surrogate mother.

Mouse B Weight 44 g

1 Two eggs are removed from a single female mouse and are fertilised artificially in a test tube.

Mouse A Weight 29 g

2a This fertilised egg is unaltered.

4 The two mice above are siblings, but mouse B is a transgenic organism. A rat growth hormone gene was introduced into its genome.

3a Normal egg is cultured to an embryo, then implanted in a surrogate mother.

Applications of transgenesis

Modifying crops

Transgenesis has been used to modify the genome of Bt cotton (above) to include genes that produce insecticides. Golden rice contains genes from a bacterium and a daffodil plant to improve its nutritional value.

Medical research

By inserting genes into model animals, the effect of a gene can be studied. Rhesus macaques have been engineered to provide models for the effects and potential treatments of diseases such as Huntington's and Parkinson's.

Livestock improvement

Transgenic sheep have been used to enhance wool production. The keratin protein of wool contains large amounts of the amino acid cysteine. Injecting developing sheep with the genes for the enzymes that generate cysteine produces woollier sheep.

Animals as biofactories

Transgenic animals can be used as biofactories to produce certain proteins. Transgenic sheep with the human α-1-antitrypsin gene produce the protein in their milk from which it can be extracted and used to treat hereditary emphysema.

1. What is transgenesis? _____

_____

2. Describe an application of transgenesis: _____

_____

_____

© 2017 **BIOZONE** International
ISBN: 978-1-927309-26-1
Photocopying Prohibited

70 Vectors for Transgenesis

Key Idea: Several different carriers, called vectors, can be used to introduce a gene into a cell. There are advantages and disadvantages associated with each type of vector.

Gene therapy usually requires a **vector** (carrier) to introduce the DNA to a cell. Viruses are often used as vectors because of their ability to integrate into the host's genome.

Viruses

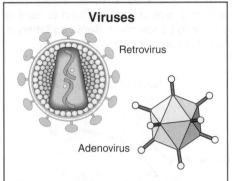

Retrovirus

Adenovirus

Viruses are well known for their ability to insert DNA into a host cell. For this reason they have become a favoured tool in transgenesis. Different types of viruses integrate their DNA into the host in different ways. This allows scientists to control where and for how long the new DNA is expressed in the host. However, the size of the piece of DNA that can be transferred is limited to about 8 kb. Also, integration of the DNA into the host DNA can cause unexpected side effects depending on where in the host's chromosome the DNA inserts itself.

Liposomes

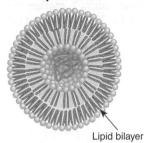

Lipid bilayer

Liposomes are spherical bodies of lipid bilayer. They can be quite large and targeted to specific types of cell by placing specific receptors on their surfaces. Because of their size, liposomes can carry plasmids 20 kb or more. They also do not trigger immune responses when used in gene therapy, but are less efficient than viruses at transferring the plasmid into a target cell.

Plasmids

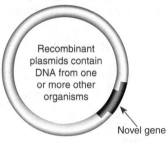

Recombinant plasmids contain DNA from one or more other organisms

Novel gene

Plasmids are circular lengths of DNA that can be up to 1000 kb long (1 kb = 1000 bp). Recombinant plasmids are frequently used to produce transgenic organisms, especially bacteria. The bacteria may be the final target for the recombinant DNA (e.g. transgenic *E. coli* producing insulin) or it can be used as a vector to transfer the DNA to a different host (e.g. *Agrobacterium tumefaciens* is used to transfer the *Ti* plasmid to plants). In gene therapy, plasmids by themselves, as naked DNA, are unstable and not particularly efficient at integrating DNA into a target cell.

Transferring the DNA

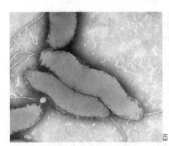

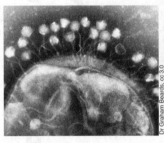

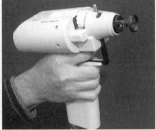

Electroporation cuvettes

Transformation is the direct uptake of foreign DNA and is common in bacteria. Recombinant DNA plasmids are mixed with bacteria and the bacteria that take up the DNA are used.

Transduction is the transfer of DNA into a bacterium by a virus. Bacteriophages (viruses that infect bacteria) are commonly used to integrate recombinant DNA into a target bacterium.

Transfection is the deliberate, often non-viral, introduction of foreign DNA into a cell. There are numerous methods including electroporation and the use of the gene gun (above).

Electroporation is a method in which an electric field is applied to cells, causing the plasma membrane to become more permeable. This allows DNA to cross the plasma membrane.

1. (a) Describe a feature of viruses that make them well suited as **vectors** for DNA transfer: _____

_____

_____

(b) Identify two problems with using viral vectors for DNA transfer: _____

_____

_____

_____

2. Describe two ways in which plasmids are used in genetic engineering: _____

_____

_____

_____

LINK 71   LINK 68   WEB 70

KNOW

71 Plasmids and Gene Cloning

Key Idea: Recombinant plasmids will be taken up by bacterial cells, which will then go on to multiply the gene of interest or produce its protein product.

Recombinant DNA techniques can be used to insert a gene into a vector such as a plasmid. The recombinant vector can then be used to transmit the gene to another organism (such as *E. coli*) where it is replicated with the host DNA. This technique is known as **gene cloning** and it is widely used to produce valuable commodities at low cost. To be useful, all vectors must be able to replicate inside their host organism, they must have one or more sites at which a restriction enzyme can cut, and they must have some kind of genetic marker that allows them to be identified. **Replica plating** is often used to identify organisms of interest.

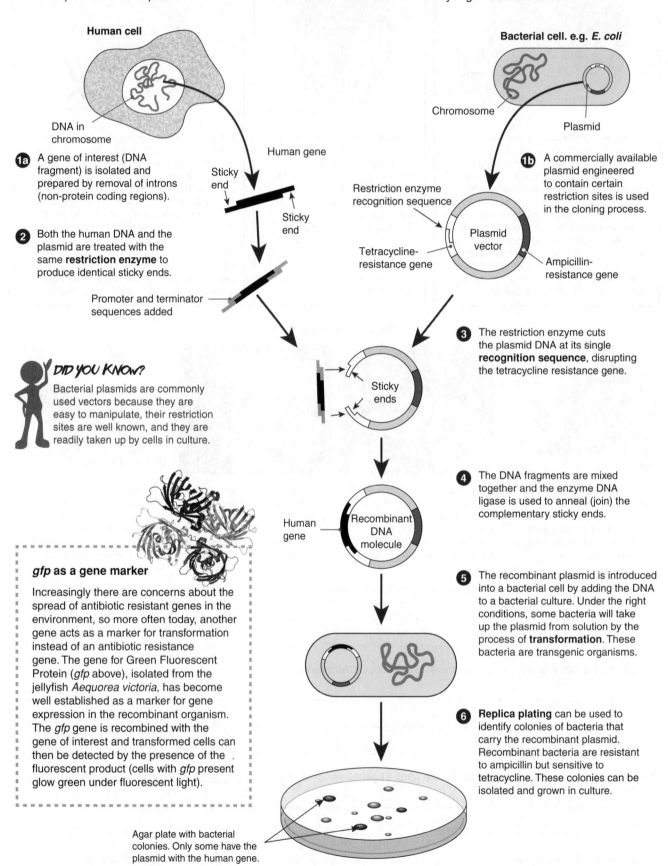

Human cell

DNA in chromosome

1a A gene of interest (DNA fragment) is isolated and prepared by removal of introns (non-protein coding regions).

2 Both the human DNA and the plasmid are treated with the same **restriction enzyme** to produce identical sticky ends.

Human gene

Sticky end

Sticky end

Promoter and terminator sequences added

Bacterial cell. e.g. *E. coli*

Chromosome

Plasmid

1b A commercially available plasmid engineered to contain certain restriction sites is used in the cloning process.

Restriction enzyme recognition sequence

Plasmid vector

Tetracycline-resistance gene

Ampicillin-resistance gene

3 The restriction enzyme cuts the plasmid DNA at its single **recognition sequence**, disrupting the tetracycline resistance gene.

Sticky ends

DID YOU KNOW?

Bacterial plasmids are commonly used vectors because they are easy to manipulate, their restriction sites are well known, and they are readily taken up by cells in culture.

Human gene

Recombinant DNA molecule

4 The DNA fragments are mixed together and the enzyme DNA ligase is used to anneal (join) the complementary sticky ends.

gfp as a gene marker

Increasingly there are concerns about the spread of antibiotic resistant genes in the environment, so more often today, another gene acts as a marker for transformation instead of an antibiotic resistance gene. The gene for Green Fluorescent Protein (*gfp* above), isolated from the jellyfish *Aequorea victoria*, has become well established as a marker for gene expression in the recombinant organism. The *gfp* gene is recombined with the gene of interest and transformed cells can then be detected by the presence of the fluorescent product (cells with *gfp* present glow green under fluorescent light).

5 The recombinant plasmid is introduced into a bacterial cell by adding the DNA to a bacterial culture. Under the right conditions, some bacteria will take up the plasmid from solution by the process of **transformation**. These bacteria are transgenic organisms.

6 **Replica plating** can be used to identify colonies of bacteria that carry the recombinant plasmid. Recombinant bacteria are resistant to ampicillin but sensitive to tetracycline. These colonies can be isolated and grown in culture.

Agar plate with bacterial colonies. Only some have the plasmid with the human gene.

© 2017 **BIOZONE** International
ISBN: 978-1-927309-26-1
Photocopying Prohibited

Replica plating identifies colonies with desirable qualities

After gene cloning, it is important to be able to identify the colonies in which transformation has occurred. This is achieved by **replica plating**.

Replica plating transfers colonies from a master plate to test plates enriched with specific nutrients or antibiotics. The original pattern of colonies (spatial arrangement) is maintained during the transfer. Growth (or lack of) on the test plates can be used to identify colonies of interest (e.g. colonies containing the insulin gene). In the example (right) colonies are tested for their susceptibility to the antibiotic tetracycline. Those with ampicillin resistance but no tetracycline resistance contain the insulin gene (plasmid B). The insulin gene has interrupted the tetracycline gene, so they are sensitive to tetracycline.

Four colonies grow on the ampicillin plate.

Two colonies are T_R, so **do not** contain the insulin gene.

Plates are incubated at 30°C and scored for growth

Master plate

Master plate media

Media containing ampicillin

Media containing tetracycline

The colonies are transferred to different media.

Orientation marker

Sterile velvet is pressed against the colonies on the master plate.

Plasmid A

Plasmid B

Ampicillin resistance (A_R):   YES   YES
Tetracycline resistance (T_R): YES   NO

1. Explain how a human gene is removed from a chromosome and placed into a plasmid: _____

_____

_____

_____

_____

2. (a) What is the purpose of replica plating? _____

_____

_____

(b) Suggest why the colonies are replated onto the master media: _____

_____

_____

(c) In the replica plating example above, explain how the colonies with the recombinant plasmids are identified: _____

_____

_____

_____

_____

(d) What can you say about the colony that did not grow on the ampicillin plate?_____

_____

3. Explain why the *gfp* marker is a more desirable gene marker than genes for antibiotic resistance: _____

_____

_____

_____

72 Determine Gene Function with Knockout Mice

Key Idea: Removing a gene or suppressing its expression are two techniques to determine gene function.

Determining the function of a gene provides an understanding of how organisms develop. This helps develop treatments for genetic diseases, or to improve livestock and crops. One of the best ways to determine the function of a gene is to produce an individual with a non-functional version of the

gene. The gene's function can be determined by comparing the development of the normal and altered individuals. In classical genetics, this is done using mutant organisms with defects in particular genes. However, natural mutations may not occur in the gene being studied, so a modern solution is required. One technique for doing this is called **gene knockout** in which the target gene is altered to become non-functional.

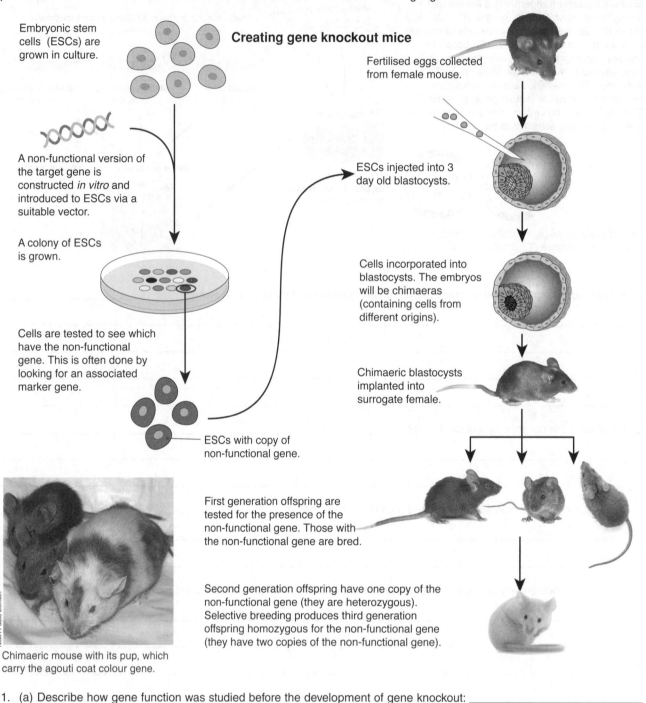

Creating gene knockout mice

Embryonic stem cells (ESCs) are grown in culture.

A non-functional version of the target gene is constructed *in vitro* and introduced to ESCs via a suitable vector.

A colony of ESCs is grown.

Cells are tested to see which have the non-functional gene. This is often done by looking for an associated marker gene.

ESCs with copy of non-functional gene.

Fertilised eggs collected from female mouse.

ESCs injected into 3 day old blastocysts.

Cells incorporated into blastocysts. The embryos will be chimaeras (containing cells from different origins).

Chimaeric blastocysts implanted into surrogate female.

First generation offspring are tested for the presence of the non-functional gene. Those with the non-functional gene are bred.

Second generation offspring have one copy of the non-functional gene (they are heterozygous). Selective breeding produces third generation offspring homozygous for the non-functional gene (they have two copies of the non-functional gene).

Chimaeric mouse with its pup, which carry the agouti coat colour gene.

1. (a) Describe how gene function was studied before the development of gene knockout: _____

_____

_____

(b) Why was this method not as efficient as gene knockout? _____

_____

_____

_____

© 2017 **BIOZONE** International
ISBN: 978-1-927309-26-1
Photocopying Prohibited

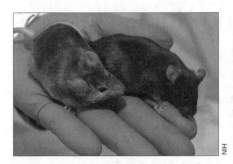

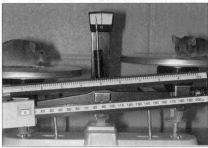

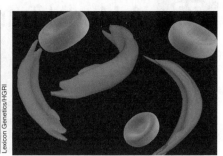

Gene knockout mice are commonly used to determine the effect of genes that humans and mice both have in common. Mice are used because they are the most closely related laboratory animal species to humans to which the gene knockout technique can easily be applied.

Several thousand strains of knockout mice have now been bred, each with different genes removed. These provide models for diseases or behaviour. The knockout mouse above left was created as a model for obesity.

Recently, gene knockout has been used to knockout the BCL11A gene that would usually cause sickle cell disease to develop in mice. The research is helping to develop a drug treatment for human sufferers of sickle cell disease.

Problems with gene knockout mice

About 15% of the gene knockouts are developmentally lethal so mice do not grow into adults, making study of the condition of interest very difficult. Also knockout mice may produce different characteristics to humans with the same gene defect. For example knockout of the gene p53 in mice produces tumours in a completely different set of tissues than is seen in humans with mutant p53 gene.

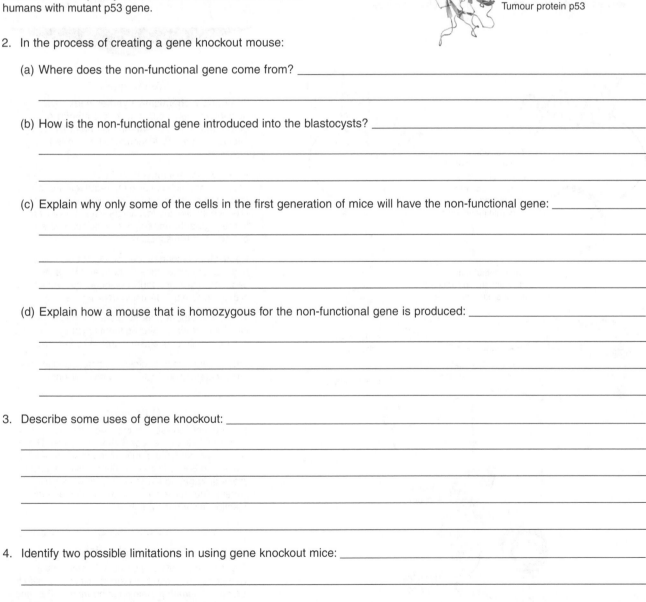

Tumour protein p53

2. In the process of creating a gene knockout mouse:

   (a) Where does the non-functional gene come from? _____

   _____

   (b) How is the non-functional gene introduced into the blastocysts? _____

   _____

   _____

   (c) Explain why only some of the cells in the first generation of mice will have the non-functional gene: _____

   _____

   _____

   _____

   (d) Explain how a mouse that is homozygous for the non-functional gene is produced: _____

   _____

   _____

   _____

3. Describe some uses of gene knockout: _____

   _____

   _____

   _____

   _____

4. Identify two possible limitations in using gene knockout mice: _____

   _____

   _____

   _____

73 A Model Transgenic: Engineering Human Insulin

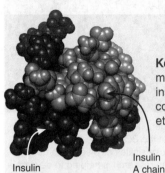

Key Idea: By using microorganisms to make human insulin, problematic issues of cost, allergic reactions, and ethics have been addressed.

Insulin B chain

Insulin A chain

The issue

▶ **Type I diabetes mellitus** is a metabolic disease caused by a lack of **insulin**. Around 25 people in every 100 000 suffer from type I diabetes.

▶ It is treatable only with injections of insulin.

▶ In the past, insulin was taken from the pancreases of cows and pigs and purified for human use. The method was expensive and some patients had severe allergic reactions to the foreign insulin or its contaminants.

Concept 1
DNA can be cut at specific sites using **restriction enzymes** and joined together using **DNA ligase**. Genes can be inserted into self-replicating bacterial **plasmids** at the point where the cuts are made.

Concept 2
Plasmids are small, circular pieces of DNA found in some bacteria. They usually carry genes useful to the bacterium. *E. coli* plasmids can carry promoters required for the transcription of genes.

Concept 3
Under certain conditions, Bacteria are able to lose or pick up plasmids from their environment. Bacteria can be readily grown in vat cultures at little expense.

Concept 4
The DNA sequences coding for the production of the two polypeptide chains (A and B) that form human insulin can be isolated from the human genome.

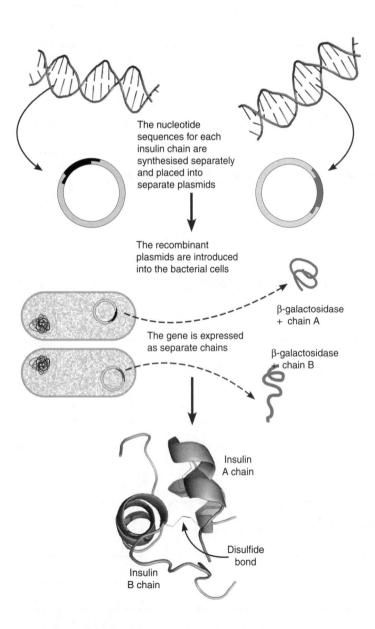

The nucleotide sequences for each insulin chain are synthesised separately and placed into separate plasmids

The recombinant plasmids are introduced into the bacterial cells

The gene is expressed as separate chains

β-galactosidase + chain A

β-galactosidase + chain B

Insulin A chain

Disulfide bond

Insulin B chain

Techniques

The **gene** is **chemically synthesised** as two nucleotide sequences, one for the **insulin A chain** and one for the **insulin B chain**. The two sequences are small enough to be inserted into a plasmid.

Plasmids are extracted from *Escherichia coli*. The gene for the bacterial enzyme β-**galactosidase** is located on the plasmid. To make the bacteria produce insulin, the insulin gene must be linked to the β-**galactosidase** gene, which carries a promoter for transcription.

Restriction enzymes are used to cut plasmids at the appropriate site and the A and B insulin sequences are inserted. The sequences are joined with the plasmid DNA using **DNA ligase**.

The **recombinant plasmids** are inserted back into the bacteria by placing them together in a culture that favours plasmid uptake by bacteria.

The bacteria are then grown and multiplied in vats under carefully controlled growth conditions.

Outcomes

The product consists partly of β-galactosidase, joined with either the A or B chain of insulin. The chains are extracted, purified, and mixed together. The A and B insulin chains connect via **disulfide cross linkages** to form the functional insulin protein. The insulin can then be made ready for injection in various formulations.

Further applications

The techniques used to produce human insulin from genetically modified bacteria can be applied to a range of human proteins and hormones. Proteins currently being produced include human growth hormone, interferon, and factor VIII.

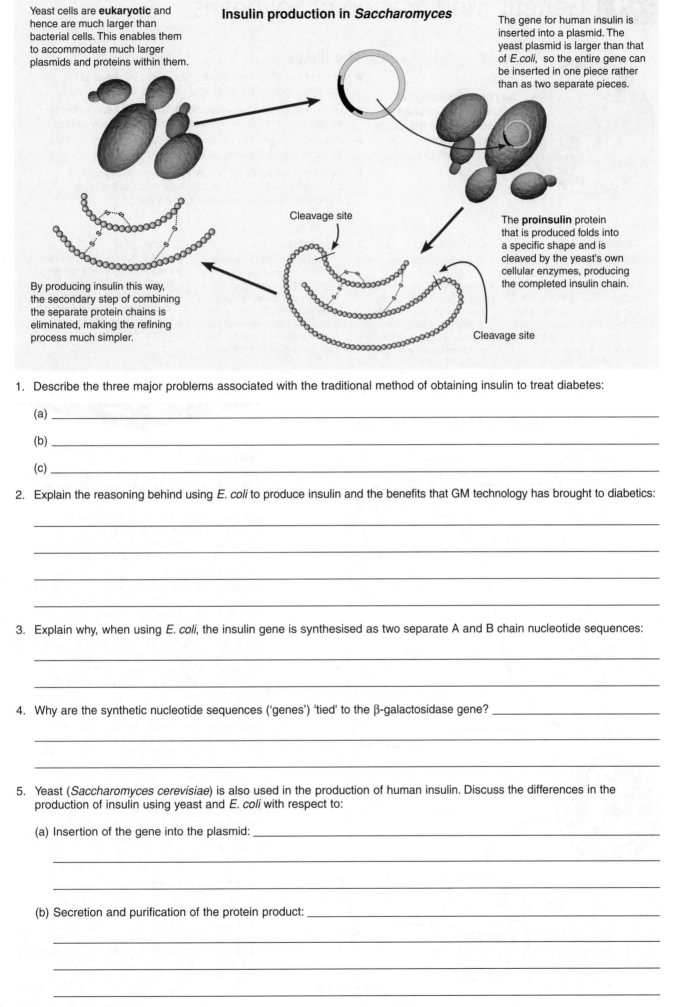

Insulin production in *Saccharomyces*

Yeast cells are **eukaryotic** and hence are much larger than bacterial cells. This enables them to accommodate much larger plasmids and proteins within them.

The gene for human insulin is inserted into a plasmid. The yeast plasmid is larger than that of *E.coli*, so the entire gene can be inserted in one piece rather than as two separate pieces.

Cleavage site

The **proinsulin** protein that is produced folds into a specific shape and is cleaved by the yeast's own cellular enzymes, producing the completed insulin chain.

By producing insulin this way, the secondary step of combining the separate protein chains is eliminated, making the refining process much simpler.

Cleavage site

1. Describe the three major problems associated with the traditional method of obtaining insulin to treat diabetes:

    (a) _____

    (b) _____

    (c) _____

2. Explain the reasoning behind using *E. coli* to produce insulin and the benefits that GM technology has brought to diabetics:

    _____
    _____
    _____
    _____

3. Explain why, when using *E. coli*, the insulin gene is synthesised as two separate A and B chain nucleotide sequences:

    _____
    _____

4. Why are the synthetic nucleotide sequences ('genes') 'tied' to the β-galactosidase gene? _____
    _____

5. Yeast (*Saccharomyces cerevisiae*) is also used in the production of human insulin. Discuss the differences in the production of insulin using yeast and *E. coli* with respect to:

    (a) Insertion of the gene into the plasmid: _____
    _____
    _____

    (b) Secretion and purification of the protein product: _____
    _____
    _____
    _____

74 Genetic Modification of Soybeans

Key Idea: Knocking out genes that are involved in the production of fatty acids can reduce soybean oil's susceptibility to oxidation.

The issue

▶ The fatty acid (oil) profile of soybeans (*Glycine max*) contains about 20% oleic acid and 50% linolenic acid.

▶ Oleic acid is monounsaturated. It is normally converted to linolenic acid which is polyunsaturated and easily oxidised.

▶ Oxidation makes the oil rancid (smell and taste bad). This limits its use to industry as it will not keep for long.

▶ Reducing the linolenic content reduces the amount of oxidation and the need for hydrogenation of the oil to artificially reduce the linoleic acid content.

Concept 1
World production of soybeans (soy) is over 221 million tonnes per year. Soy is a valuable source of protein and oil. The oil can be used for food, feed, and industrial applications such as biodiesel. Soybean oil oxidises easily, which affects its industrial applications.

Concept 2
The fatty acids in soybean oil include oleic acid, palmitic acid, stearic acid, and linolenic acid. Oleic acid is normally converted to linolenic acid by the fatty acid dehydrogenase enzyme encoded by the *FAD2*-1A and *FAD2*-1B genes.

Concept 3
Editing the *FAD2*-1A and *FAD2*-1B genes with engineered restriction enzymes (called TALENs) will deactivate (silence or down regulate) the gene and the production of the fatty acid dehydrogenase enzyme.

Concept 4
DNA can be inserted into an organism's genome using a suitable **vector** such as a plasmid. ***Agrobacterium rhizogene*** is a plant pathogen that can be used to insert novel DNA into plants.

The production of modified soybeans

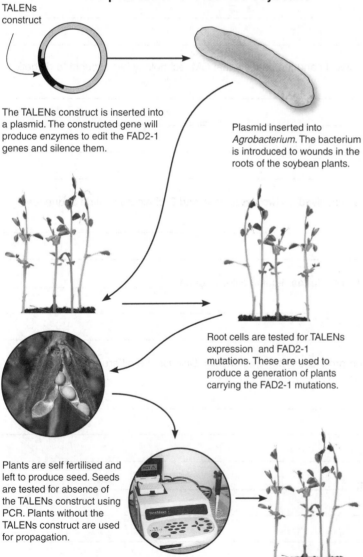

TALENs construct

The TALENs construct is inserted into a plasmid. The constructed gene will produce enzymes to edit the FAD2-1 genes and silence them.

Plasmid inserted into *Agrobacterium*. The bacterium is introduced to wounds in the roots of the soybean plants.

Root cells are tested for TALENs expression and FAD2-1 mutations. These are used to produce a generation of plants carrying the FAD2-1 mutations.

Plants are self fertilised and left to produce seed. Seeds are tested for absence of the TALENs construct using PCR. Plants without the TALENs construct are used for propagation.

Techniques

Using transcription activator-like effector nucleases (TALENs), the *FAD2*-1A and *FAD2*-1B genes can be disrupted and silenced.

The construct for the TALENs is inserted into a plasmid. The plasmid is inserted into the bacterium *Agrobacterium rhizogene*. The bacterium is then introduced to wounds in the soybean roots.

Root cells are assessed for TALENs expression and for mutations in the *FAD2*-1A and *FAD2*-1B genes. Cells expressing mutations in both genes are selected for developing into soybean plants.

This first generation of soya beans are allowed to self fertilise to produce seed. The seed is grown and the resulting plants tested to determine if the mutations to the *FAD2*-1A and *FAD2*-1B genes are transmissible. Plants containing both mutations were left to grow.

PCR is then used to identify plants that lack the TALENs construct. These plants are used to develop non-transgenic soybean plants with high levels of oleic acid and low levels of linolenic acid.

Outcomes

Plants containing both *FAD2*-1A and *FAD2*-1B mutations produced approximately 80% oleic acid (up for 20%) and 4% linolenic acid (down from 50%) in their oil profile.

Further applications

TALENs are relatively easy to construct and can be targeted to any DNA sequence, allowing deletion or insertion of genes in many different plants. The technique could be used to change the oil profile of soybeans to increase or decrease other fatty acids.

© 2017 **BIOZONE** International
ISBN: 978-1-927309-26-1
Photocopying Prohibited

The ability of *Agrobacterium* to transfer genes to plants is exploited for crop improvement. The tumour-inducing *Ti* plasmid is modified to delete the tumour-forming gene and insert a gene encoding a desirable trait. The parts of the *Ti* plasmid required for plant transformation are retained.

Soy has also been genetically modified for insecticide resistance and broad spectrum herbicide resistance (Round-up Ready soy). The first GM soy was planted in the US in 1996. By 2014, nearly 82% of the global soybean crop was genetically modified (the highest of any crop plant).

GM cotton was produced by inserting the gene for the Bt toxin into its genome. The bacterium *Bacillus thuringiensis* naturally produces Bt toxin, which is harmful to a range of insects, including the larvae that eat cotton. The Bt gene causes cotton to produce this insecticide in its tissues.

1. (a) What fatty acids are found in soybean oil? _____

   (b) Which fatty acid is responsible for the oil becoming rancid? _____

   (c) What is the enzyme responsible for the change? _____

   _____

   (d) Why would increasing oleic acid reduce the need for hydrogenation of the oil later? _____

   _____

   _____

   _____

2. (a) Explain how the *FAD2-1A* and *FAD2-1B* genes were silenced: _____

   _____

   _____

   (b) How were non-transgenic soybean plants containing the *FAD2-1* mutations created? _____

   _____

   _____

   _____

3. What property of *Agrobacterium* makes it an ideal vector for introducing new genes into plants?

   _____

   _____

   _____

4. What other useful traits have soybean plants been engineered to have? _____

   _____

5. Various other traits in other crop plants are also desirable. For each of the following traits, suggest why the features could be beneficial for increasing yield:

   (a) Grain size or number: _____

   (b) Maturation rate: _____

   (c) Pest resistance: _____

75 Engineering a Solution: Food for the Masses

Key Idea: Genetic engineering has the potential to solve many of the world's food shortage problems by producing crops with greater yields than those currently grown.

Currently 1/6 of the world's population are undernourished. If trends continue, 1.5 billion people will be at risk of starvation by 2050 and, by 2100 (if global warming is taken into account), nearly half the world's population could be threatened with food shortages. The solution to the problem of food production is complicated. Most of the Earth's arable land has already been developed and currently uses 37% of the Earth's land area, leaving little room to grow more crops or farm more animals. Development of new fast growing and high yield crops appears to be part of the solution, but many crops can only be grown under a narrow range of conditions or are susceptible to disease. Moreover, the farming and irrigation of some areas is difficult, costly, and can be environmentally damaging. Genetic modification of plants may help to solve some of these looming problems by producing plants that will require less intensive culture or that will grow in areas previously considered not arable.

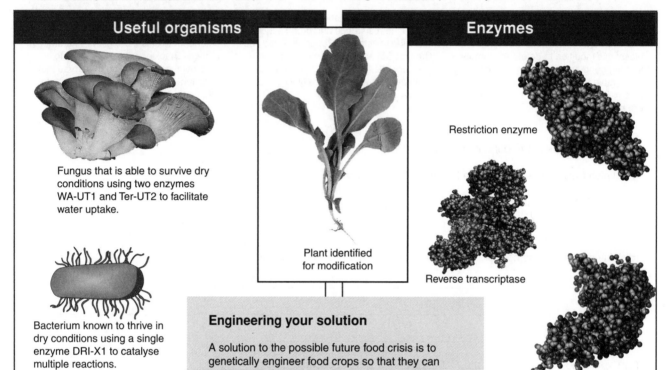

Useful organisms

Fungus that is able to survive dry conditions using two enzymes WA-UT1 and Ter-UT2 to facilitate water uptake.

Bacterium known to thrive in dry conditions using a single enzyme DRI-X1 to catalyse multiple reactions.

Plant identified for modification

Enzymes

Restriction enzyme

Reverse transcriptase

DNA ligase

Engineering your solution

A solution to the possible future food crisis is to genetically engineer food crops so that they can maximize their growth under adverse conditions. Standard selective breeding techniques could be used to do this, but in some plants this may not be possible or feasible and it may require more time than is available. A selection of genetic tools and organisms with useful characteristics are described. **Your task** is to use the items shown to devise a technique to successfully create a plant that could be successfully farmed in semi-desert environments such as sub-Saharan Africa. The following page will take you through the procedure. Not all the items will need to be used.

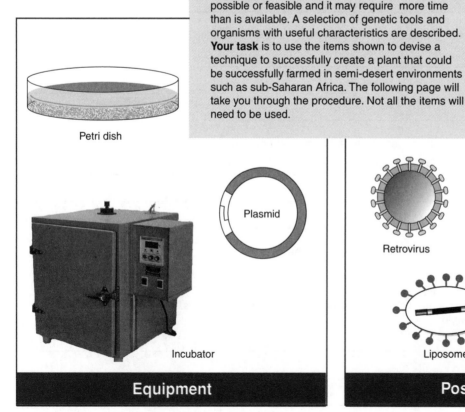

Petri dish

Plasmid

Incubator

Equipment

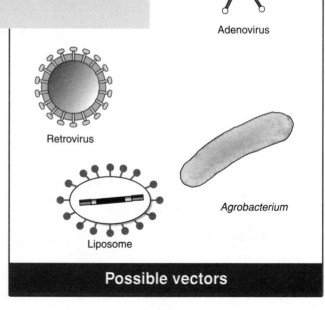

Adenovirus

Retrovirus

Liposome

Agrobacterium

Possible vectors

© 2017 **BIOZONE** International
ISBN: 978-1-927309-26-1
Photocopying Prohibited

1. Identify the organism you would chose as a 'donor' of drought survival genes and explain your choice: _____

_____

_____

2. Describe a process to identify and isolate the required gene(s) and identify the tools to be used: _____

_____

_____

_____

_____

_____

_____

_____

3. Identify a vector for the transfer of the isolated gene(s) into the crop plant and explain your decision: _____

_____

_____

4. Explain how the isolated gene(s) would be integrated into the vector's genome: _____

_____

_____

_____

_____

_____

5. (a) Explain how the vector will transform the identified plant: _____

_____

_____

    (b) Identify the stage of development at which the plant would most easily be transformed. Explain your choice: _____

_____

_____

_____

_____

6. Explain how the transformed plants could be identified: _____

_____

_____

_____

_____

_____

7. Explain how a large number of plants can be grown from the few samples that have taken up the new DNA: _____

_____

_____

_____

76 The Ethics of GMO Technology

Key Idea: There are many potential benefits, risks, and ethical questions in using genetically modified organisms.

Genetically modified organisms (GMOs) have many potential benefits, but their use raises a number of biological and ethical concerns. Some of these include risk to human health, animal welfare issues, and environmental safety. Currently a matter of concern to consumers is the adequacy of government regulations for the labelling of food products with GMO content. In some countries GM products must be clearly labelled, while other countries have no requirements for GM labelling. This can take away consumer choice about the types of products they buy. The use of GM may also have trade implications for countries exporting and importing GMO produce.

Potential benefits of GMOs

1. Increase in crop yields, including crops with more nutritional value and that store for longer.

2. Decrease in use of pesticides, herbicides and animal remedies.

3. Production of crops that are drought tolerant or salt tolerant.

4. Improvement in the health of the human population and the medicines used to achieve it.

5. Development of animal factories for the production of proteins used in manufacturing, the food industry, and health.

Potential risks of GMOs

1. Possible (uncontrollable) spread of transgenes into other species of plants, or animals.

2. Concerns that the release of GMOs into the environment may be irreversible.

3. Animal welfare and ethical issues: GM animals may suffer poor health and reduced life span.

4. GMOs may cause the emergence of pest, insect, or microbial resistance to traditional control methods.

5. May create a monopoly and dependence of developing countries on companies who are seeking to control the world's commercial seed supply.

Issue: Genetically modified crops

Background: Soybeans are the world's largest agricultural crop. The United States produces 33% of the world's soybean crop, worth US$38.5 billion. Pests do a lot of damage to the crop so reducing pest damage would increase crop yields and value. Pesticide use is common and there has been a 130 fold increase in insecticide use in the US since 2001.

Genetic modification of crops to resist pests reduces the dependence on pesticides. This has already been successfully performed in corn (Bt corn) and soybeans (resistance against soybean cyst nematodes).

Problem: Plants that produce toxins may be toxic to humans.

Pests may become resistant to the pest-resistant properties of the engineered plant rendering it ineffective. The ultimate outcome of this is unknown.

Possible solution: Careful testing of the toxic properties of the plant under a variety of circumstances is required to ensure it is safe for human consumption.

Plans must be in place in the event that pests become resistant to the engineered plant.

Issue: Adding genes to organisms to produce pharmaceuticals for human use or study.

Background: Traditionally, producing protein-based drugs, e.g. insulin, has been costly and unreliable. Proteins are continuously made in living organisms and these living systems can be exploited to produce the products need by humans. Genetic modification of plants and animals to produce pharmaceutical proteins means the protein can be produced in large quantities relatively cheaply (once a stable GM organism is produced). This is already done with rennin (an enzyme used in cheese making) and human insulin (used to treat diabetes). Mammals can be genetically modified and induced to secrete useful proteins in their milk (e.g. transgenic goats produce antithrombin to prevent blood clots).

Problem: There are concerns with animal health. Many genetically modified mammals have congenital defects and reproductive difficulties (low conception to term rates).

There is also the question of animal rights and values. Is the genetic modification of an animal to produce proteins then valuing the protein over the animal?

Possible solution: Testing and monitoring animal health is important. Continued development of non-animal based methods for developing proteins.

Issue: Who owns the technology?

Background: Crop seed and animal breeders spend large amounts of money on development. The genetic modification of plants and animals requires Government approval to develop the technology, carry out testing, and bring the product to market. This is a lengthy process that can cost millions of dollars. Companies therefore wish to make a profit or at least recoup costs on their product. This leads to patents to protect the technology and increased costs to farmers.

Problem: Biotech companies may have some leverage over farmers. For example, a seed producing company produces GE seeds, which cost a lot to develop. To ensure sales and a profit, they sell only these seeds (at great cost) to the farmer, who has little choice.

GE crops may be sold to overseas markets with little regulation and little choice. These markets will carry the load of potential problems, increasing the divide between developed nations and developing ones.

Possible solution: Legislation must be in place to ensure intellectual property is protected while also ensuring farmers have access to all available seed and stock. There must be careful consideration of the effect of GE crops on the agriculture of developing countries.

WEB **76**   LINK **69**   LINK **73**   LINK **74**

© 2017 **BIOZONE** International
ISBN: 978-1-927309-26-1
Photocopying Prohibited

1. Describe an advantage and a problem with the use of plants genetically engineered to be resistant to crop pests:

   (a) Advantage: _____

   _____

   (b) Problem: _____

   _____

2. Describe an advantage and a problem with using plants and animals to produce pharmaceuticals:

   (a) Advantage: _____

   _____

   (b) Problem: _____

   _____

3. Describe two uses of transgenic animals within the livestock industry:

   (a) _____

   (b) _____

   (c) Describe the possible problems that may occur over the ownership of genetically modified organisms.

   _____

   _____

   _____

4. Some years ago, Britain banned the import of a GM, pest resistant corn variety containing marker genes for ampicillin antibiotic resistance. Suggest why the use of antibiotic-resistance genes as markers is no longer common practice:

   _____

   _____

5. Many agricultural applications of DNA technology make use of transgenic bacteria which infect plants and express a foreign gene. Explain one advantage of each of the following applications of genetic engineering to crop biology:

   (a) Development of nitrogen-fixing *Rhizobium* bacteria that can colonise non-legumes such as corn and wheat:

   _____

   _____

   (b) Addition of transgenic *Pseudomonas fluorescens* bacteria into seeds (bacterium produces a pathogen-killing toxin):

   _____

   _____

6. Some of the public's fears and concerns about genetically modified food stem from moral or religious convictions, while others have a biological basis and are related to the potential biological threat posed by GMOs.

   (a) Conduct a class discussion or debate to identify these fears and concerns, and list them below:

   _____

   _____

   _____

   (b) Identify which of those you have listed above pose a real biological threat: _____

   _____

   _____

   _____

© 2017 **BIOZONE** International
ISBN: 978-1-927309-26-1
Photocopying Prohibited

77 Chapter Review

Summarise what you know about this topic under the headings and sub-headings provided. You can draw diagrams or mind maps, or write short notes to organise your thoughts. Use the images and hints to help you and refer back to the introduction to check the points covered:

Using gene sequencing

HINT: What is PCR and how is it used in genomic analysis and DNA profiling?

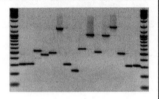

Factors affecting gene expression

HINT: How is DNA packaged? How do transcription factors and epigenetic modification regulate gene expression?

© 2017 **BIOZONE** International
ISBN: 978-1-927309-26-1
Photocopying Prohibited

Stem cells

HINT: Describe the types of stem cells and their applications, including any ethical considerations.

Gene technology: recombinant DNA

HINT: How is recombinant DNA produced and what are its uses?

Gene technology: transgenic organisms

HINT: What is a transgenic organism. Describe the applications of transgenic organisms, including any ethical considerations.

78 KEY TERMS AND IDEAS: Did You Get It?

1. Test your vocabulary by matching each term to its definition, as identified by its preceding letter code.

DNA amplification _____

DNA methylation _____

epigenetic modifications _____

gene expression _____

genome _____

multipotent _____

PCR _____

plasmid _____

pluripotent _____

recombinant DNA _____

restriction enzyme _____

stem cell _____

totipotent _____

transgenesis _____

vector _____

A An organism or artificial vehicle that is capable of transferring a DNA sequence to another organism.

B The process of producing more copies of a length of DNA, normally using PCR.

C Capable of giving producing all of the differentiated cells in an organism.

D DNA that has had a new sequence added so that the original sequence has been changed.

E An enzyme that is able to cut a length of DNA at a specific sequence or site.

F The entire haploid amount of genetic material, including all the genes, of a cell.

G The process of inserting of a gene from one species into another that would not normally contain the gene. The gene is then expressed in the next generation.

H Unspecialised cells characterised by the properties of self renewal and potency.

I A technique to amplify DNA fragments using cycles of heating and cooling (abbrev).

J A small circular piece of DNA commonly found in bacteria and often used as a vector in genetic modification.

K Changes to the genomic information that do not involve a change in the DNA nucleotide sequence.

L An epigenetic modification that acts to silence genes by preventing their transcription.

M Capable of giving rise to a limited number of cell types related to the tissue of origin.

N Capable of giving rise to any cell type in the body (except extra-embryonic cells).

O The process by which the information in a gene is used to synthesise a protein.

2. The electrophoresis gel (below, right) shows four profiles containing five STR sites: the mother (A) her daughter (B) and two possible fathers (C and D). Which of the possible fathers is the biological father?

(a) The biological father is: _____

(b) Why do profiles B and D only have 9 bands?

_____

_____

_____

_____

_____

A   B   C   D

3. Give an example of each of the following stem cell types:

(a) Unipotent: _____

(b) Multipotent: _____

(c) Pluripotent: _____

(d) Totipotent: _____

4. (a) In what state must the DNA be in order to be transcribed? _____

_____

(b) This is achieved by (select the correct answer):

(i) DNA methylation   (ii) Histone acetylation   (iii) Histone methylation

© 2017 **BIOZONE** International
ISBN: 978-1-927309-26-1
Photocopying Prohibited

Topic 8

Origins of Genetic Variation

8.1 Origins of genetic variation

Learning outcomes

Activity number

☐ i Understand that mutations are the source of all new alleles (genetic variation). Recall how the processes of independent assortment and crossing over during meiosis produce combinations of alleles in the gametes.

79 81

☐ ii Explain how random fertilisation of gametes during sexual reproduction produces genetic variation in the offspring.

79

8.2 Transfer of genetic information

Learning outcomes

Activity number

☐ i Define the following terms: genotype, phenotype, homozygote, heterozygote. Explain what is meant by dominant allele, recessive allele, codominant alleles, and multiple alleles.

79 80

☐ ii Demonstrate understanding of genetic crosses by constructing and using Punnett squares and pedigree diagrams to solve genetic problems. Include:
• monohybrid crosses with a simple dominant-recessive pattern.
• crosses involving codominance and multiple alleles.
• use of a test cross to determine an unknown genotype.

82-85
86 87
83

☐ iii Use a Punnett square to explain and solve problems involving dihybrid inheritance of unlinked, autosomal genes for two independent characteristics.

88 90 94

☐ iv Describe autosomal linkage. Explain the results of dihybrid crosses involving linkage, including black (ebony)/grey body and long/vestigial wing in *Drosophila*.

89 91

☐ v Describe and explain sex linkage involving the X chromosome (X-linkage), including reference to haemophilia in humans.

95 96 97

☐ vi Use the chi-squared test (for goodness of fit) to test the significance of differences between the observed and expected results of genetic crosses.

92 93

MATH ▶ **A.1.9**: Select and use a statistical test.

92 93

8.3 Gene pools

Learning outcomes

Activity number

☐ i Understand how selection can alter the allele frequencies in a population leading to speciation or maintain the current phenotype:
• stabilising selection to maintain the phenotypic norm (status quo).
• directional selection leading to a directional shift in the common phenotype.
• disruptive (diversifying) selection leading to two common phenotypes.

98 99 102
103 104
105
106 107
108

☐ ii Explain how random changes in allele frequencies can occur as a result of chance events (genetic drift). Describe the consequences of genetic drift and the conditions under which it is important.

109

☐ iii Explain how allele frequencies can be influenced by population (genetic) bottlenecks and the founder effect

110 111

☐ iv Demonstrate understanding of how the Hardy-Weinberg equation can be used to monitor changes in allele frequencies in a population.

100 101

79 Sources of Genetic Variation

Key Idea: Sexually reproducing organisms show variation in their phenotype (appearance) as a result of mutation and the processes involved in meiosis and fertilisation. Both genes and environment contribute to the final phenotype.

Variation refers to the diversity of **genotypes** (allele combinations) and phenotypes (**appearances**) in a population. Phenotypic variation is a feature of sexually reproducing populations and is the product of both genotype and environmental effects on the expression of that genotype.

In sexually reproducing organisms, variation in genotype accounts for most of the phenotypic variation we see. Sexual reproduction (meiosis and random fertilisation) creates new allele combinations in the offspring and these many variants are tested in the prevailing environment for their ability to survive and leave their own offspring (their fitness). Thus, the variation generated by sexual reproduction provides raw material for selecting the best suited phenotypes. This process is called natural selection.

Mutations

Mutations are changes to the DNA
Mutations change the DNA sequence and are the source of all new alleles. Not all mutations change the amino acid sequence because of degeneracy of the genetic code.

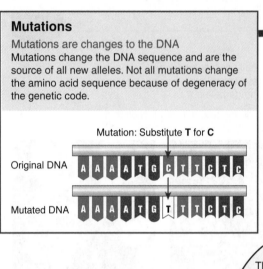

Mutation: Substitute **T** for **C**

Original DNA A A A A T G C T T C T C

Mutated DNA A A A A T G **T** T T C T C

Sexual reproduction

Sexual reproduction involves meiosis and fertilisation
Sexual reproduction rearranges and reshuffles the genetic material into new combinations. Fertilisation unites dissimilar gametes to produce more variation.

Don Horne

Genotype

The genetic make up of the individual is its genotype. The genotype determines the genetic potential of an individual.

Gene interactions and epigenetics

Dominant, recessive, codominant, and multiple alleles, epigenetic modifications (such as methylation), and interactions between genes, combine in their effects.

Environmental factors

The environment can influence the expression of the genotype. Both the external environment (e.g. physical and biotic factors) and internal environment (e.g. hormones) can be important.

Phenotype

The phenotype is the physical appearance of an individual. An individual's phenotype is the result of the interaction of genetic and environmental factors during its lifetime. Gene expression can be influenced by both the internal and external environment during and after development.

1. (a) What is the basis of the genetic variation of sexually reproducing organisms? _____

_____

_____

_____

_____

(b) How does the environment contribute to the phenotype we see: _____

_____

_____

© 2017 **BIOZONE** International
ISBN: 978-1-927309-26-1
Photocopying Prohibited

Why is variation important?

▶ **Variation** refers to the diversity of phenotypes or genotypes within a population or species. Variation provides the raw material for natural selection. Different phenotypic variants will have different relative survival and reproductive success (fitness) in the prevailing environment. Only the most successful variants will proliferate.

▶ Variation enables populations to adapt to changes in their environment. Very gradual environmental changes, e.g. mountain building, allow sufficient time for populations (even those that reproduce asexually) to acquire the variability to adapt. However rapid environmental changes, e.g. the emergence of a new strain of disease, demand a more rapid response.

▶ Variation is important in providing adaptable defences against disease. Species with adaptations to survive a disease flourish. Those without, die out. It is thought that sexual reproduction is an adaptation to increase the chances that any one of the offspring produced will have the allele combinations that enable them to survive a disease.

▶ Variation in species that reproduce asexually is generated by mutation and sometimes (as in bacteria) by gene transfers.

Aphids can reproduce both sexually and asexually. Females hatch in spring and give birth to clones. Many generations are produced asexually. Just before autumn, the aphids reproduce sexually. The males and females mate and the females produce eggs which hatch in spring. This increases variability in the next generation.

These diagrams show how three beneficial mutations could be combined through sexual or asexual reproduction.

Variation by sexual reproduction

Variation from recombining alleles

Mutation A

Mutation B

AB AB AB

AB AB AB

Mutation C

ABC ABC ABC

During meiosis, alleles are recombined in new combinations. Some combinations of alleles may be better suited to a particular environment than others. This variability is produced without the need for mutation. Beneficial mutations in separate lineages can be quickly combined through sexual reproduction.

Variation by asexual reproduction

Clones

Mutation D

D D D

Mutation E

DE D D

Mutation F

DEF DEF DEF DEF

Some asexually reproducing organisms (e.g. bacteria) are able to exchange genes occasionally. Bacteria exchange genes with other bacteria during a process called conjugation (shown by the thicker blue line). This allows mutations arising in one lineage to be passed to another.

2. (a) Why is phenotypic variation important in the process of natural selection? _____

_____

(b) Why is variation important in a changing environment? _____

_____

What does variation look like?

▶ Phenotypic variation can be either continuous, with a large number of phenotypic variants approximating a bell shaped (normal) curve or discontinuous, with only a limited number of phenotypic variants in the population.

▶ Phenotypic characteristics showing discontinuous variation are determined by only one or two genes, e.g. flower colour.

▶ Phenotypic characteristics showing continuous variation are determined by a large number of genes and are often heavily influenced by environment, e.g. milk production influenced by diet.

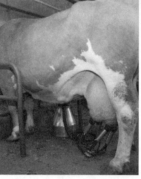

Albinism (above) is the result of the inheritance of recessive alleles for melanin production. Those with the albino phenotype lack melanin pigment in the eyes, skin, and hair.

Comb shape in poultry is a **qualitative trait** and birds have one of four phenotypes depending on which combination of four alleles they inherit. The dash (missing allele) indicates that the allele may be recessive or dominant.

Quantitative traits are characterised by **continuous variation**, with individuals falling somewhere on a normal distribution curve of the phenotypic range. Typical examples include skin colour and height in humans (left), grain yield in corn (above), growth in pigs (above, left), and milk production in cattle (far left). Quantitative traits are determined by genes at many loci (polygenic) but most are also influenced by environmental factors.

Marc King

Single comb	Walnut comb	Pea comb	Rose comb
rrpp	**R_P_**	**rrP_**	**R_pp**

Flower colour in snapdragons (right) is also a **qualitative trait** determined by two alleles (red and white) The alleles show incomplete dominance and the heterozygote (C^RC^W) exhibits an intermediate phenotype between the two homozygotes.

C^RC^R

C^WC^W

3. How could a favourable mutation spread through different bacterial lineages? _____

_____

_____

4. Describe the differences between continuous and discontinuous variation, giving examples to illustrate your answer:

_____

_____

_____

_____

_____

_____

_____

_____

5. Identify each of the following phenotypic characteristics as continuous (quantitative) or discontinuous (qualitative):

(a) Wool production in sheep: _____

(b) Hand span in humans: _____

(c) Blood groups in humans: _____

(d) Albinism in mammals: _____

(e) Body weight in mice: _____

(f) Flower colour in snapdragons: _____

© 2017 **BIOZONE** International
ISBN: 978-1-927309-26-1
Photocopying Prohibited

80 Alleles

Key Idea: Eukaryotes generally have paired chromosomes. Each chromosome contains many genes and each gene may have a number of versions called alleles.

Sexually reproducing organisms usually have paired sets of chromosomes, one set from each parent. The equivalent chromosomes that form a pair are termed **homologues**. They carry equivalent sets of genes, but there is the potential for different versions of a gene (**alleles**) to exist in a population.

Homologous chromosomes

In sexually reproducing organisms, most cells have a homologous pair of chromosomes (one coming from each parent). This diagram shows the position of three different genes on the same chromosome that control three different traits (A, B and C).

Chromosomes are formed from DNA and proteins. DNA tightly winds around special proteins to form the chromosome.

Having two different versions (**alleles**) of gene A is a **heterozygous** condition. Only the dominant allele (A) will be expressed. Alleles differ by only a few bases.

When both chromosomes have identical copies of the dominant allele for gene B the organism is **homozygous dominant** for that gene.

When both chromosomes have identical copies of the recessive allele for gene C the organism is said to be **homozygous recessive** for that gene.

Maternal chromosome originating from the egg of this individual's mother.

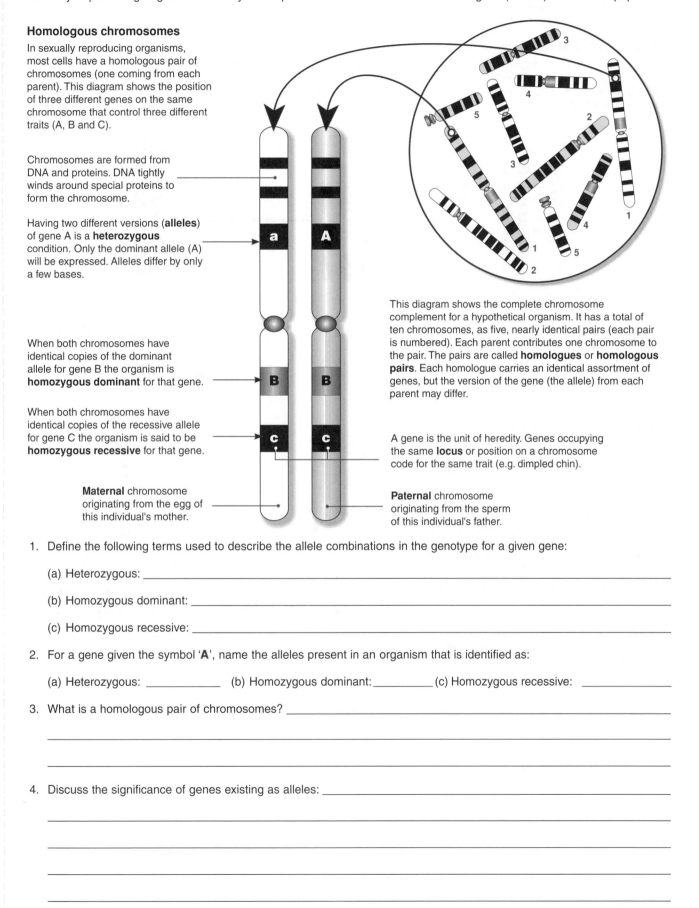

This diagram shows the complete chromosome complement for a hypothetical organism. It has a total of ten chromosomes, as five, nearly identical pairs (each pair is numbered). Each parent contributes one chromosome to the pair. The pairs are called **homologues** or **homologous pairs**. Each homologue carries an identical assortment of genes, but the version of the gene (the allele) from each parent may differ.

A gene is the unit of heredity. Genes occupying the same **locus** or position on a chromosome code for the same trait (e.g. dimpled chin).

Paternal chromosome originating from the sperm of this individual's father.

1. Define the following terms used to describe the allele combinations in the genotype for a given gene:

   (a) Heterozygous: _____

   (b) Homozygous dominant: _____

   (c) Homozygous recessive: _____

2. For a gene given the symbol '**A**', name the alleles present in an organism that is identified as:

   (a) Heterozygous: _____   (b) Homozygous dominant: _____ (c) Homozygous recessive: _____

3. What is a homologous pair of chromosomes? _____

   _____

   _____

4. Discuss the significance of genes existing as alleles: _____

   _____

   _____

   _____

   _____

81 Meiosis and Variation

Key Idea: Meiosis produces variation. Independent assortment and crossing over are two important ways of introducing variation into the gametes formed during meiosis. Variation in offspring can arise because of events during meiosis (crossing over and recombination), but it can also occur because of how the gametes produced from meiosis pair up. The way in which gametes pair up is random. Therefore the offspring will carry a random combination of alleles from the mother and from the father.

Crossing over and recombination

Chromosomes replicate during interphase, before meiosis, to produce replicated chromosomes with sister chromatids held together at the centromere (see below). When the replicated chromosomes are paired during the first stage of meiosis, non-sister chromatids may become entangled and segments may be exchanged in a process called **crossing over**. Crossing over results in the **recombination** of alleles (variations of the same gene) producing greater variation in the offspring than would otherwise occur.

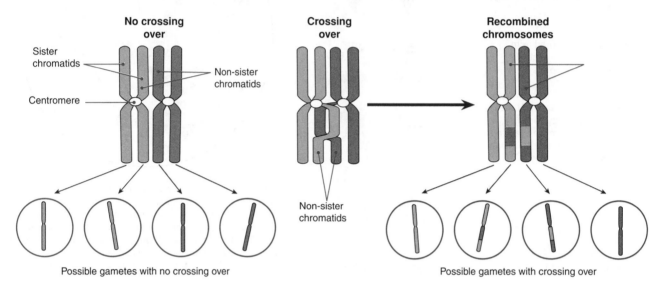

Possible gametes with no crossing over

Possible gametes with crossing over

Independent assortment

▶ Independent assortment is the random alignment and distribution of chromosomes during meiosis. It is an important mechanism for producing variation in gametes.

▶ The law of independent assortment states that the alleles for separate traits are passed independently of one another from parents to offspring. In other words, the allele a gamete receives for one gene does not influence the allele received for another gene.

▶ This results in the production of 2^x different possible combinations (where x is the number of chromosome pairs).

▶ For the example right, there are two chromosome pairs. The number of possible allele combinations in the gametes is $2^2 = 4$.

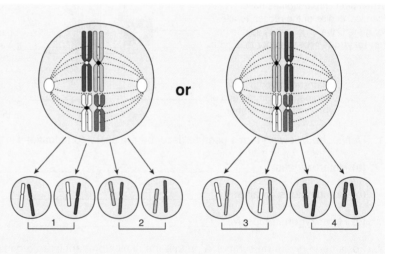

1. How does crossing over increase the variation in the gametes (and hence the offspring)? _____

_____

_____

_____

2. How does independent assortment increase genetic variation in gametes?_____

_____

_____

_____

© 2017 **BIOZONE** International
ISBN: 978-1-927309-26-1
Photocopying Prohibited

82 The Monohybrid Cross

Key Idea: The outcome of a cross depends on the parental genotypes and can be determined using Punnett squares. Examine the diagrams below on monohybrid (one gene) and dihybrid (two gene) inheritance. The F$_1$ generation describes the offspring of a cross between **true-breeding** (homozygous) parents. A **back cross** is a cross between an offspring and one of its parents. If the back cross is to a homozygous recessive, it can be used as a **test cross**.

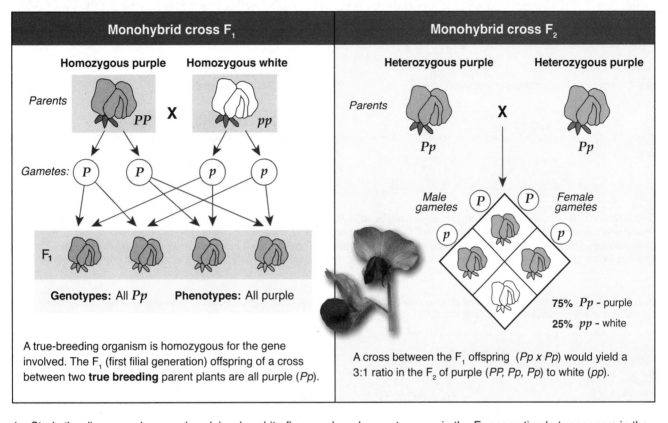

Monohybrid cross F$_1$	Monohybrid cross F$_2$

Monohybrid cross F$_1$

Homozygous purple Homozygous white

Parents PP X pp

Gametes: P P p p

F$_1$

Genotypes: All *Pp*   **Phenotypes:** All purple

A true-breeding organism is homozygous for the gene involved. The F$_1$ (first filial generation) offspring of a cross between two **true breeding** parent plants are all purple (*Pp*).

Monohybrid cross F$_2$

Heterozygous purple Heterozygous purple

Parents Pp X Pp

Male gametes P P Female gametes
p p

75% *Pp* - purple
25% *pp* - white

A cross between the F$_1$ offspring (*Pp* x *Pp*) would yield a 3:1 ratio in the F$_2$ of purple (*PP, Pp, Pp*) to white (*pp*).

1. Study the diagrams above and explain why white flower colour does not appear in the F$_2$ generation but reappears in the F$_2$ generation:

_____

_____

_____

_____

2. Complete the crosses below:

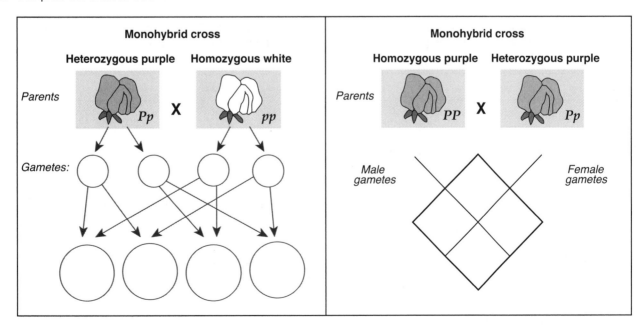

Monohybrid cross

Heterozygous purple Homozygous white

Parents Pp X pp

Gametes:

Monohybrid cross

Homozygous purple Heterozygous purple

Parents PP X Pp

Male gametes Female gametes

83 The Test Cross

Key Idea: If an individual's genotype is unknown it can be determined using a test cross.

It is not always possible to determine an organism's genotype by its appearance because gene expression is complicated by patterns of dominance and by gene interactions. The **test cross** was developed by Mendel as a way to establish the genotype of an organism with the dominant phenotype for a particular trait. The principle is simple. The individual with the unknown genotype is bred with a homozygous recessive individual for the trait(s) of interest. The homozygous recessive can produce only one type of allele (recessive), so the phenotypes of the offspring will reveal the genotype of the unknown parent (below). The test cross can be used to determine the genotype of single genes or multiple genes.

Parent 1
Unknown genotype
(but with dominant traits)

X

Parent 2
Homozygous recessive genotype
(no dominant traits)

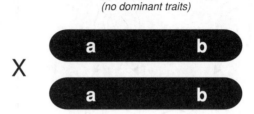

The common fruit fly (*Drosophila melanogaster*) is often used to illustrate basic principles of inheritance because it has several genetic markers whose phenotypes are easily identified. Once such phenotype is body colour. Wild type (normal) *Drosophila* have yellow-brown bodies. The allele for yellow-brown body colour (E) is dominant. The allele for an ebony coloured body (e) is recessive. The test crosses below show the possible outcomes for an individual with homozygous and heterozygous alleles for ebony body colour.

A. A homozygous recessive female (ee) with an ebony body is crossed with a homozyogous dominant male (EE).

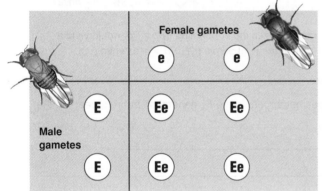

Cross A:
(a) Genotype frequency: 100% Ee
(b) Phenotype frequency: 100% yellow-brown

B. A homozygous recessive female (ee) with an ebony body is crossed with a heterozygous male (Ee).

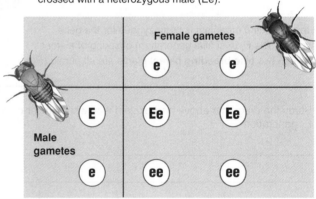

Cross B:
(a) Genotype frequency: 50% Ee, 50% ee
(b) Phenotype frequency: 50% yellow-brown, 50% ebony

1. In *Drosophila*, the allele for brown eyes (b) is recessive, while the red eye allele (B) is dominant. How would you set up a two gene test cross to determine the genotype of a male who has a normal body colour and red eyes?

   _____

   _____

   _____

2. List all of the possible genotypes for the male *Drosophila*: _____

   _____

3. 50% of the resulting progeny are yellow-brown bodies with red eyes, and 50% have ebony bodies with red eyes.

   (a) What is the genotype of the male *Drosophila*? _____

   (b) Explain your answer: _____

   _____

   _____

© 2017 **BIOZONE** International
ISBN: 978-1-927309-26-1
Photocopying Prohibited

84 Practising Monohybrid Crosses

Key Idea: A monohybrid cross studies the inheritance pattern of one gene. The offspring of these crosses occur in predictable ratios.

In this activity, you will examine six types of matings possible for a pair of alleles governing coat colour in guinea pigs. A dominant allele (**B**) produces **black** hair and its recessive allele (**b**), produces white. Each parent can produce two types of gamete by meiosis. Determine the **genotype** and **phenotype frequencies** for the crosses below. For questions 3 and 4, also determine the gametes produced by each parent (write these in the circles) and offspring genotypes and phenotypes (write these inside the offspring shapes).

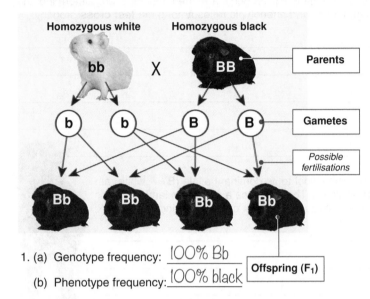

Homozygous white — bb X Homozygous black — BB — **Parents**

b, b, B, B — **Gametes**

Possible fertilisations

Bb, Bb, Bb, Bb

1. (a) Genotype frequency: _100% Bb_

   (b) Phenotype frequency: _100% black_   **Offspring (F₁)**

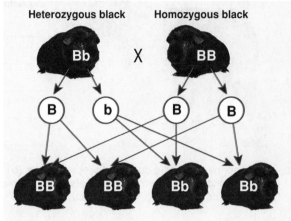

Heterozygous black — Bb X Homozygous black — BB

B, b, B, B

BB, BB, Bb, Bb

2. (a) Genotype frequency: _____

   (b) Phenotype frequency: _____

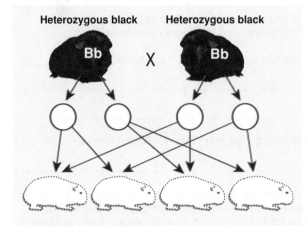

Heterozygous black — Bb X Heterozygous black — Bb

3. (a) Genotype frequency: _____

   (b) Phenotype frequency: _____

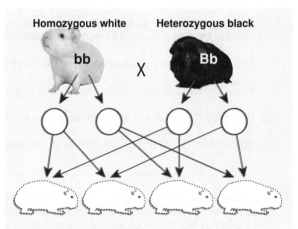

Homozygous white — bb X Heterozygous black — Bb

4. (a) Genotype frequency: _____

   (b) Phenotype frequency: _____

5. Two parent guinea pigs with genotypes bb and Bb are crossed:

   (a) What is the probability that any one offspring is Bb? _____

   (b) What is the probability that any one offspring is black? _____

6. A white guinea pig and a black guinea pig are crossed. All of the guinea pigs that are born are white.

   (a) What is the genotype of the black guinea pig? _____

   (b) Explain the result: _____

   _____

   (c) What is this type of cross called? _____

   (d) Explain why it is diagnostic: _____

   _____

LINK 82   WEB 84   **KNOW**

85 Problems Involving Monohybrid Inheritance

Key Idea: For monohybrid crosses involving autosomal unlinked genes, the offspring appear in predictable ratios. The following problems involve Mendelian crosses. The alleles involved are associated with various phenotypic traits controlled by a single gene. The problems are to give you practise in problem solving using Mendelian genetics.

1. A dominant gene (**W**) produces wire-haired texture in dogs; its recessive allele (**w**) produces smooth hair. A group of heterozygous wire-haired individuals are crossed and their F_1 progeny are then test-crossed. Determine the expected genotypic and phenotypic ratios among the **test cross** progeny:

_____

_____

_____

_____

2. In sheep, black wool is due to a recessive allele (**b**) and white wool to its dominant allele (**B**). A white ram is crossed to a white ewe. Both animals carry the black allele (b). They produce a white ram lamb, which is then back crossed to the female parent. Determine the probability of the **back cross** offspring being black:

_____

_____

_____

3. A homozygous recessive allele, **aa**, is responsible for albinism. Humans can exhibit this phenotype. In each of the following cases, determine the possible genotypes of the mother and father, and their children:

(a) Both parents have normal phenotypes; some of their children are albino and others are unaffected: _____

_____

(b) Both parents are albino and have only albino children: _____

(c) The woman is unaffected, the man is albino, and they have one albino child and three unaffected children:

_____

4. Two mothers give birth to sons at a busy hospital. The son of the first couple has haemophilia, a recessive, X-linked disease. Neither parent from couple #1 has the disease. The second couple has an unaffected son, despite the fact that the father has haemophilia. The two couples challenge the hospital in court, claiming their babies must have been swapped at birth. You must advise as to whether or not the sons could have been swapped. What would you say?

_____

_____

_____

5. In a dispute over parentage, the mother of a child with blood group O identifies a male with blood group A as the father. The mother is blood group B. Draw Punnett squares to show possible genotype/phenotype outcomes to determine if the male is the father and the reasons (if any) for further dispute:

_____

_____

_____

_____

_____

LINK

TEST

82

© 2017 **BIOZONE** International
ISBN: 978-1-927309-26-1
Photocopying Prohibited

86 Codominance of Alleles

Key Idea: In inheritance involving codominant alleles, neither allele is recessive and both alleles are equally and independently expressed in the heterozygote.

Codominance is an inheritance pattern in which both alleles in a heterozygote contribute to the phenotype and both alleles are **independently** and **equally expressed**. Examples include the human blood group AB and certain coat colours in horses and cattle. Reddish coat colour is equally dominant with white. Animals that have both alleles have coats that are roan (both red and white hairs are present).

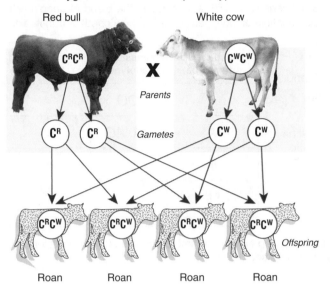

Red bull   White cow

C^R C^R   X   C^W C^W

Parents

C^R   C^R   Gametes   C^W   C^W

C^R C^W   C^R C^W   C^R C^W   C^R C^W

Offspring

Roan   Roan   Roan   Roan

A roan shorthorn heifer

In the shorthorn cattle breed, coat colour is inherited. White shorthorn parents always produce calves with white coats. Red parents always produce red calves. However, when a red parent mates with a white one, the calves have a coat colour that is different from either parent; a mixture of red and white hairs, called roan. Use the example (left) to help you to solve the problems below.

1. Explain how codominance of alleles can result in offspring with a phenotype that is different from either parent:

_____

2. A white bull is mated with a roan cow (right):

(a) Fill in the spaces to show the genotypes and phenotypes for parents and calves:

(b) What is the phenotype ratio for this cross?

_____

(c) How could a cattle farmer control the breeding so that the herd ultimately consisted of only red cattle:

_____

_____

_____

_____

_____

White bull   Roan cow

X

3. A farmer has only roan cattle on his farm. He suspects that one of the neighbours' bulls may have jumped the fence to mate with his cows earlier in the year because half the calves born were red and half were roan. One neighbour has a red bull, the other has a roan.

(a) Fill in the spaces (right) to show the genotype and phenotype for parents and calves.

(b) Which bull serviced the cows? **red** or **roan** (*delete one*)

4. Describe the classical phenotypic ratio for a codominant gene resulting from the cross of two heterozygous parents (e.g. a cross between two roan cattle):

_____

_____

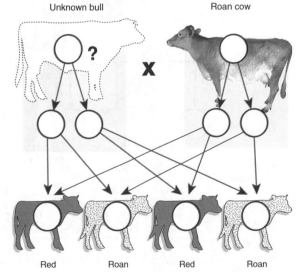

Unknown bull   Roan cow

?   X

Red   Roan   Red   Roan

© 2017 **BIOZONE** International
ISBN: 978-1-927309-26-1
Photocopying Prohibited

LINK   WEB

82   **84**   **KNOW**

87 Codominance in Multiple Allele Systems

Key Idea: The human ABO blood group system is a multiple allele system involving the codominant alleles *A* and *B* and the recessive allele *O*.

On the surface of red blood cells there are sugars called the ABO antigens. These antigens are made by enzymes that link particular combinations of sugars (antigens) together. The codominant alleles **A** and **B** each encode a different enzyme that adds a different, specific sugar to the basic sugar molecule. Because alleles A and B are codominant they are expressed equally. The recessive allele **O** produces a non-functioning enzyme and is unable to make any changes to the basic sugar molecule. Blood group A and B antigens react with antibodies in the blood of people with incompatible blood types so must be matched for transfusion.

Recessive allele: **O** produces a non-functioning protein
Dominant allele: **A** produces an enzyme which forms **A antigen**
Dominant allele: **B** produces an enzyme which forms **B antigen**

If a person has the **AO** allele combination then their blood group will be group A. The presence of the recessive allele (*O*) has no effect on the blood group in the presence of a dominant allele. AA also produces blood group A.

Blood group (phenotype)	Possible genotypes	Frequency in the UK
O	*OO*	47%
A	*AA, AO*	42%
B		8%
AB		3%

Source: http://www.transfusionguidelines.org.uk/ Allele terminology follows latest recommended (use of *I* allele terminology has been discontinued as inaccurate)

1. Use the information above to complete the table for the possible genotypes for blood group B and group AB.

2. Below are four crosses possible between couples of various blood group types. The first example has been completed for you. Complete the genotype and phenotype for the other three crosses below:

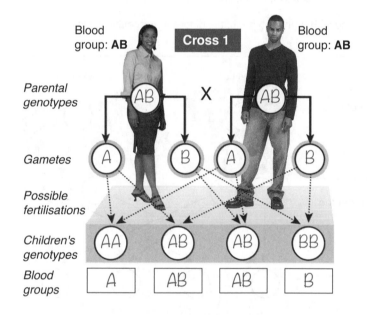

Cross 1 — Blood group: **AB** × Blood group: **AB**
Parental genotypes: AB × AB
Gametes: A, B, A, B
Children's genotypes: AA, AB, AB, BB
Blood groups: A, AB, AB, B

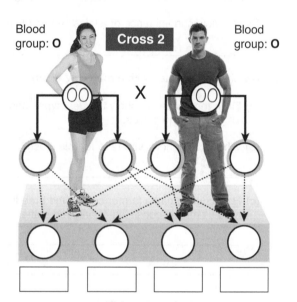

Cross 2 — Blood group: **O** × Blood group: **O**
Parental genotypes: OO × OO

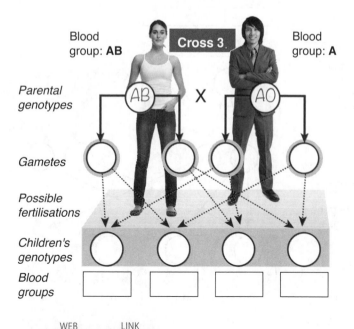

Cross 3 — Blood group: **AB** × Blood group: **A**
Parental genotypes: AB × AO

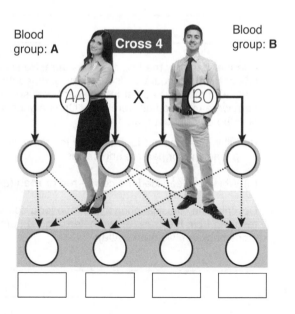

Cross 4 — Blood group: **A** × Blood group: **B**
Parental genotypes: AA × BO

3. A woman is heterozygous for blood group **A** and the man has blood group **O**.

   (a) Give the genotypes of each parent (fill in spaces on the diagram on the right).

   Determine the probability of:

   (b) One child having blood group **O**:

   _____

   (c) One child having blood group **A**:

   _____

   (d) One child having blood group **AB**:

   _____

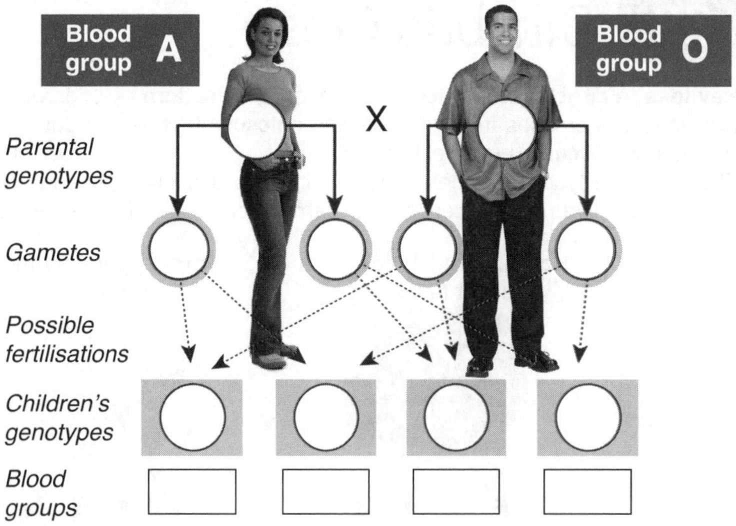

Blood group A X **Blood group O**

Parental genotypes

Gametes

Possible fertilisations

Children's genotypes

Blood groups

4. In a court case involving a paternity dispute (i.e. who is the father of a child) a man claims that a male child (blood group **B**) born to a woman is his son and wants custody. The woman claims that he is not the father.

   (a) If the man has a blood group **O** and the woman has a blood group **A**, could the child be his son? Use the diagram on the right to illustrate the genotypes of the three people involved.

   (b) State with reasons whether the man can be correct in his claim:

   _____

   _____

   _____

   _____

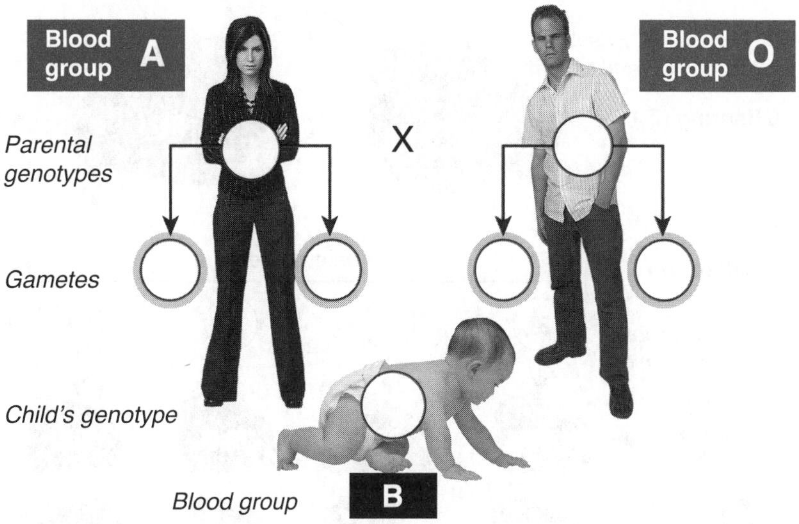

Blood group A X **Blood group O**

Parental genotypes

Gametes

Child's genotype

Blood group **B**

5. The pedigree chart on the right shows the phenotypes of two children. Their father is blood group B and their mother is blood group AB.

   (a) State the sex of the children: _____

   _____

   (b) Explain why child 1 has two possible genotypes and child 2 has only one possible genotype:

   _____

   _____

   _____

   _____

   _____

   _____

   _____

   _____

   _____

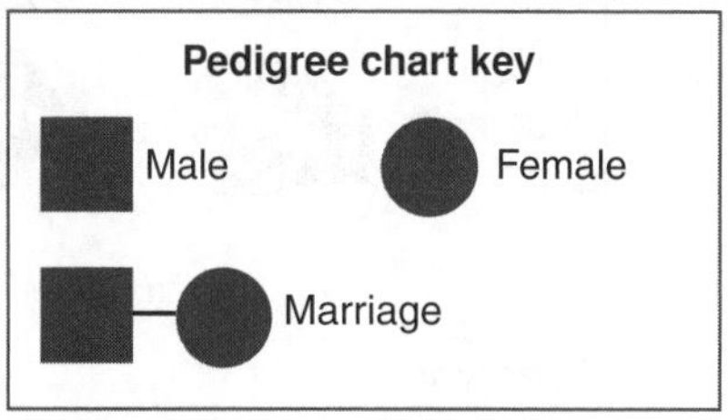

Pedigree chart key

■ Male ● Female

■—● Marriage

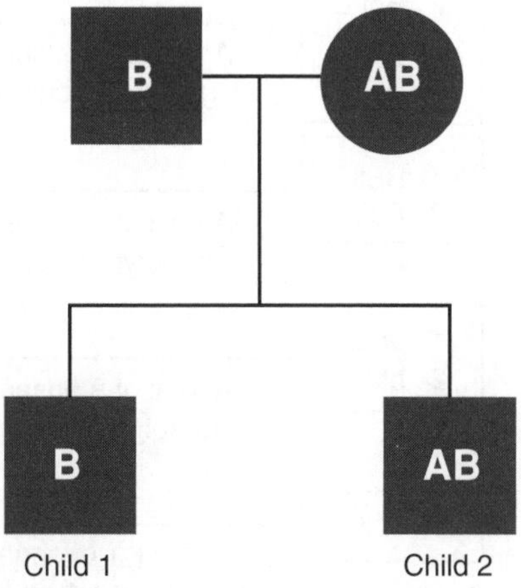

B ——— AB

B (Child 1)   AB (Child 2)

88 Dihybrid Cross

Key Idea: A dihybrid cross studies the inheritance pattern of two genes. In crosses involving unlinked autosomal genes, the offspring occur in predictable ratios.

There are four types of gamete produced in a cross involving two genes, where the genes are carried on separate chromosomes and are sorted independently of each other during meiosis. The two genes in the example below are on separate chromosomes and control two unrelated characteristics, **hair colour** and **coat length**. Black (B) and short (L) are dominant to white and long.

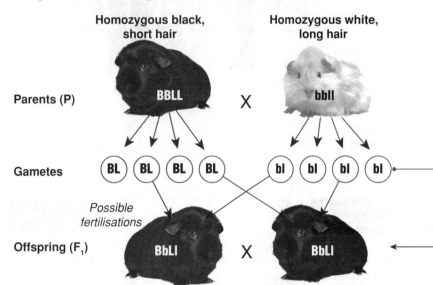

Homozygous black, short hair

Homozygous white, long hair

Parents (P)   BBLL   X   bbll

Gametes   BL BL BL BL   bl bl bl bl

Possible fertilisations

Offspring (F₁)   BbLl   X   BbLl

Parents: The notation P, is only used for a cross between true breeding (homozygous) parents. In this case black hair (B) and short hair (L) are dominant. The genes are on separate chromosomes (the alleles assort independently).

Gametes: Each parent is homozygous for both traits so only one type of gamete is produced from each parent.

F₁ offspring: The first generation offspring are all the same genotype. The notation F₁ is used for the hybrid offspring of genetically distinct parents.

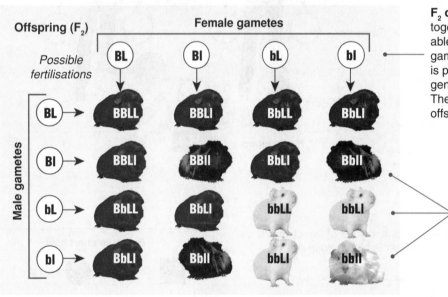

Offspring (F₂)

Female gametes

Possible fertilisations   BL   Bl   bL   bl

Male gametes:

BL → BBLL BBLl BbLL BbLl
Bl → BBLl BBll BbLl Bbll
bL → BbLL BbLl bbLL bbLl
bl → BbLl Bbll bbLl bbll

F₂ offspring: The F₁ were mated together. Each individual from the F₁ is able to produce four different kinds of gamete. Using a **Punnett square** (left), it is possible to determine the expected genotype and phenotype ratios in the F₂. The notation F₂ is generally used for the offspring of F₁ heterozygotes.

Each of the 16 animals represents the possible zygotes formed by different combinations of gametes coming together at fertilisation.

The offspring can be arranged in groups with similar phenotypes

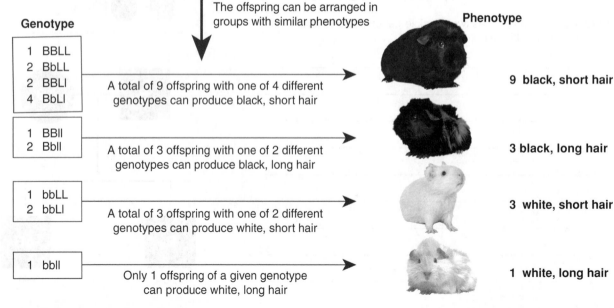

Genotype

1 BBLL
2 BbLL
2 BBLl
4 BbLl

A total of 9 offspring with one of 4 different genotypes can produce black, short hair

1 BBll
2 Bbll

A total of 3 offspring with one of 2 different genotypes can produce black, long hair

1 bbLL
2 bbLl

A total of 3 offspring with one of 2 different genotypes can produce white, short hair

1 bbll

Only 1 offspring of a given genotype can produce white, long hair

Phenotype

9 black, short hair

3 black, long hair

3 white, short hair

1 white, long hair

© 2017 **BIOZONE** International
ISBN: 978-1-927309-26-1
Photocopying Prohibited

Cross Nº· 1

The dihybrid cross on the right has been partly worked out for you. You must determine:

1. The genotype and phenotype for each animal (write your answers in its dotted outline).

2. Genotype ratio of the offspring:

_____

_____

_____

_____

_____

3. Phenotype ratio of the offspring:

_____

_____

_____

_____

_____

_____

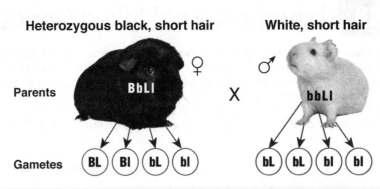

Heterozygous black, short hair ♀   **White, short hair** ♂

Parents   BbLl   X   bbLl

Gametes   (BL) (Bl) (bL) (bl)   (bL) (bL) (bl) (bl)

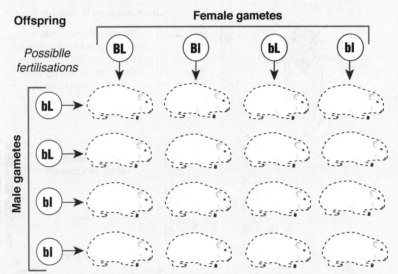

Offspring   **Female gametes**

Possible fertilisations   (BL)   (Bl)   (bL)   (bl)

Male gametes: (bL) (bL) (bl) (bl)

Cross Nº· 2

For the dihybrid cross on the right, determine:

4. Gametes produced by each parent (write these in the circles).

5. The genotype and phenotype for each animal (write your answers in its dotted outline).

6. Genotype ratio of the offspring:

_____

_____

_____

_____

_____

7. Phenotype ratio of the offspring:

_____

_____

_____

_____

_____

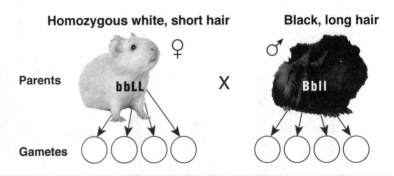

Homozygous white, short hair ♀   **Black, long hair** ♂

Parents   bbLL   X   Bbll

Gametes   ( ) ( ) ( ) ( )   ( ) ( ) ( ) ( )

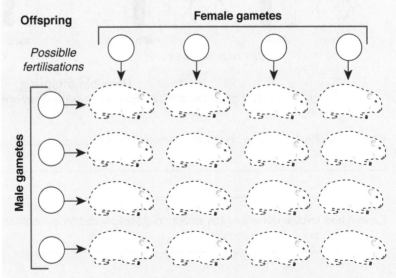

Offspring   **Female gametes**

Possible fertilisations   ( ) ( ) ( ) ( )

Male gametes: ( ) ( ) ( ) ( )

89 Inheritance of Linked Genes

Key Idea: Linked genes are genes found on the same chromosome and tend to be inherited together. Linkage reduces the genetic variation in the offspring.

Genes are **linked** when they are on the same chromosome. Linked genes tend to be inherited together and the extent of crossing over depends on how close together they are on the

chromosome. In genetic crosses, linkage is indicated when a greater proportion of the offspring from a cross are of the parental type (than would be expected if the alleles were on separate chromosomes and assorting independently). Linkage reduces the genetic variation that can be produced in the offspring.

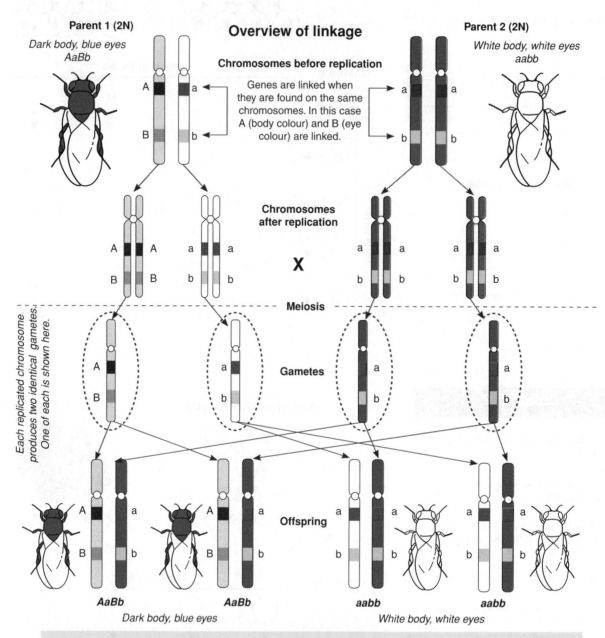

Parent 1 (2N)
Dark body, blue eyes
AaBb

Overview of linkage

Parent 2 (2N)
White body, white eyes
aabb

Chromosomes before replication

Genes are linked when they are found on the same chromosomes. In this case A (body colour) and B (eye colour) are linked.

Chromosomes after replication

X

Each replicated chromosome produces two identical gametes. One of each is shown here.

Meiosis

Gametes

Offspring

AaBb
AaBb
Dark body, blue eyes

aabb
aabb
White body, white eyes

Possible offspring

Only two kinds of genotype combinations are possible. They are they same as the parent genotype.

1. What is the effect of linkage on the inheritance of genes? _____

_____

_____

2. Explain how linkage decreases the amount of genetic variation in the offspring: _____

_____

_____

_____

 © 2017 **BIOZONE** International
ISBN: 978-1-927309-26-1
Photocopying Prohibited

An example of linked genes in *Drosophila*

The genes for wing shape and body colour are linked (they are on the same chromosome).

	Wild type female	Mutant male
Parent		
Phenotype	Straight wing Grey body	Curled wing Ebony body
Genotype	Cucu Ebeb	cucu ebeb
Linkage	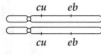	

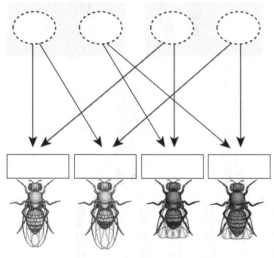

Gametes from female fly (N)   *Gametes from male fly (N)*

Sex of offspring is irrelevant in this case

Contact **Newbyte Educational Software** for details of their superb *Drosophila Genetics* software package which includes coverage of linkage and recombination. *Drosophila* images © Newbyte Educational Software.

Drosophila and linked genes

In the example shown left, wild type alleles are dominant and are given an upper case symbol of the mutant phenotype (Cu or Eb). This notation used for *Drosophila* departs from the convention of using the dominant gene to provide the symbol. This is necessary because there are many mutant alternative phenotypes to the wild type (e.g. curled and vestigial wings). A lower case symbol of the wild type (e.g. ss for straight wing) would not indicate the mutant phenotype involved.

Drosophila melanogaster is known as a model organism. Model organisms are used to study particular biological phenomena, such as mutation. *Drosophila melanogaster* is particularly useful because it produces such a wide range of heritable mutations. Its short reproduction cycle, high offspring production, and low maintenance make it ideal for studying in the lab.

Drosophila melanogaster examples showing variations in eye and body colour. The wild type is marked with a w in the photo above.

3. Complete the linkage diagram above by adding the gametes in the ovals and offspring genotypes in the rectangles.

4. (a) List the possible genotypes in the offspring (above, left) if genes Cu and Eb had been on separate chromosomes:

_____

(b) If the female *Drosophila* had been homozygous for the dominant wild type alleles (CuCu EbEb), state:

The genotype(s) of the F_1: _____   The phenotype(s) of the F_1: _____

5. A second pair of *Drosophila* are mated. The female genotype is Vgvg EbEb (straight wings, grey body), while the male genotype is vgvg ebeb (vestigial wings, ebony body). Assuming the genes are linked, carry out the cross and list the genotypes and phenotypes of the offspring. Note vg = vestigial (no) wings:

_____

_____

_____

The genotype(s) of the F_1: _____   The phenotype(s) of the F_1: _____

6. Explain why *Drosophila* are often used as model organisms in the study of genetics: _____

_____

_____

90 Recombination and Dihybrid Inheritance

Key Idea: Recombination is the exchange of alleles between homologous chromosomes as a result of crossing over. Recombination increases the genetic variation in the offspring. The alleles of parental linkage groups separate and new associations of alleles are formed in the gametes. Offspring formed from these gametes are called **recombinants** and show combinations of characteristics not seen in the parents.

In contrast to linkage, recombination increases genetic variation in the offspring. Recombination between the alleles of parental linkage groups is indicated by the appearance of non-parental types in the offspring, although not in the numbers that would be expected had the alleles been on separate chromosomes (independent assortment).

Overview of recombination

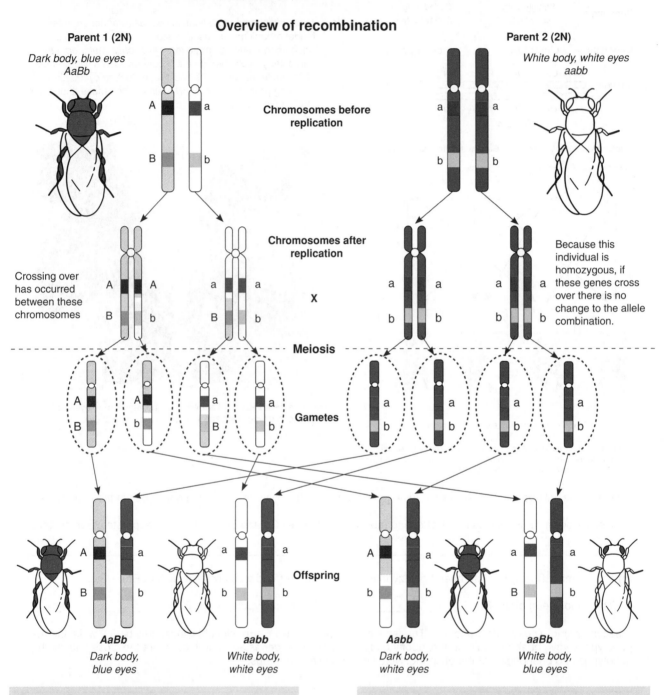

Non-recombinant offspring

These two offspring show allele combinations that are expected as a result of independent assortment during meiosis. Also called parental types.

Recombinant offspring

These two offspring show unexpected allele combinations. They can only arise if one of the parent's chromosomes has undergone crossing over.

1. Describe the effect of recombination on the inheritance of genes: _____

_____

_____

© 2017 **BIOZONE** International
ISBN: 978-1-927309-26-1
Photocopying Prohibited

An example of recombination

In the female parent, crossing over occurs between the linked genes for wing shape and body colour

Parent	Wild type female	Mutant male
Phenotype	Straight wing Grey body	Curled wing Ebony body
Genotype	Cucu Ebeb	cucu ebeb
Linkage	Cu Eb / cu eb	cu eb / cu eb

-------------------------------- *Meiosis* --------------------------------

Gametes from female fly (N)

Crossing over has occurred, giving four types of gametes

Gametes from male fly (N)

Only one type of gamete is produced in this case

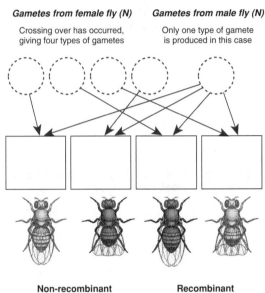

Non-recombinant offspring

Recombinant offspring

The sex of the offspring is irrelevant in this case

The cross (left) uses the same genotypes as the previous activity but, in this case, crossing over occurs between the alleles in a linkage group in one parent. The symbology used is the same.

Recombination produces variation

If crossing over does not occur, the possible combinations in the gametes is limited. **Crossing over and recombination increase the variation in the offspring.** In humans, even without crossing over, there are approximately $(2^{23})^2$ or 70 trillion genetically different zygotes that could form for every couple. Taking crossing over and recombination into account produces at least $(4^{23})^2$ or 5000 trillion trillion genetically different zygotes for every couple.

Family members may resemble each other, but they'll never be identical (except for identical twins).

Using recombination

Analysing recombination gave geneticists a way to map the genes on a chromosome. Crossing over is less likely to occur between genes that are close together on a chromosome than between genes that are far apart. By counting the number of offspring of each phenotype, the **frequency of recombination** can be calculated. The higher the frequency of recombination between two genes, the further apart they must be on the chromosome.

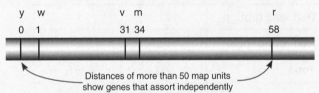

y	w		v	m		r
0	1		31	34		58

Distances of more than 50 map units show genes that assort independently

Map of the X chromosome of *Drosophila*, showing the relative distances between five different genes (in map units).

2. Complete the recombination diagram above, adding the gametes in the ovals and offspring genotypes and phenotypes in the rectangles:

3. Explain how recombination increases the amount of genetic variation in offspring: _____

_____

_____

4. Explain why it is not possible to have a recombination frequency of greater than 50% (half recombinant progeny):

_____

_____

5. A second pair of *Drosophila* are mated. The female is Cucu YY (straight wing, grey body), while the male is Cucu yy (straight wing, yellow body). Assuming recombination, perform the cross and list the offspring genotypes and phenotypes:

_____

_____

_____

91 Detecting Linkage in Dihybrid Crosses

Key Idea: Linkage between genes can be detected by observing the phenotypic ratios in the offspring.

Shortly after the rediscovery of Mendel's work early in the 20th century, it became apparent that his ratios of 9:3:3:1 for heterozygous dihybrid crosses did not always hold true.

Experiments on sweet peas by William Bateson and Reginald Punnett, and on *Drosophila* by Thomas Hunt Morgan, showed that there appeared to be some kind of coupling between genes. This coupling, which we now know to be linkage, did not follow any genetic relationship known at the time.

Sweet pea cross

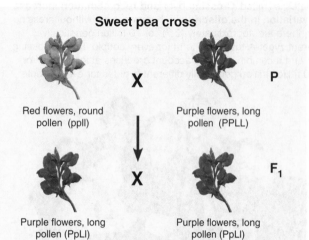

Red flowers, round pollen (ppll)   X   Purple flowers, long pollen (PPLL)   **P**

X   **F₁**

Purple flowers, long pollen (PpLl)   Purple flowers, long pollen (PpLl)

Bateson and Punnett studied sweet peas in which purple flowers (P) are dominant to red (p), and long pollen grains (L) are dominant to round (l). If these genes were unlinked, the outcome of an cross between two heterozygous sweet peas should have been a 9:3:3:1 ratio.

Table 1: Sweet pea cross results

	Observed	Expected
Purple long (P_L_)	284	
Purple round (P_ll)	21	
Red long (ppL_)	21	
Red round (ppll)	55	
Total	381	381

Morgan performed experiments to investigate linked genes in *Drosophila*. He crossed a heterozygous red-eyed normal-winged (Prpr Vgvg) fly with a homozygous purple-eyed vestigial-winged (prpr vgvg) fly. The table (below) shows the outcome of the cross.

X

Red eyed normal winged (Prpr Vgvg)   Purple eyed vestigial winged (prpr vgvg)

Table 2: *Drosophila* cross results

Genotype	Observed	Expected	Gamete type
Prpr Vgvg	1339	710	Parental
prpr Vgvg	152		
Prpr vgvg	154		
prpr vgvg	1195		
Total	2840	2840	

1. Fill in the missing numbers in the **expected** column of **Table 1**, remembering that a 9:3:3:1 ratio is expected:

2. (a) Fill in the missing numbers in the **expected** column of **Table 2**, remembering that a 1:1:1:1 ratio is expected:

   (b) Add the gamete type (parental/recombinant) to the gamete type column in Table 2:

   (c) What type of cross did Morgan perform here?

   _____

3. (a) Use the pedigree chart below to determine if nail-patella syndrome is dominant or recessive, giving reasons for your choice:

   _____

   _____

   _____

   _____

   (b) What evidence is there that nail-patella syndrome is linked to the ABO blood group locus?

   _____

   _____

   _____

   (c) Suggest a likely reason why individual III-3 is not affected despite carrying the B allele:

   _____

   _____

   _____

Pedigree for nail-patella syndrome

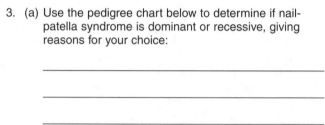

Individual with nail-patella syndome ●♀ ■♂
Blood types   OO, BO, AO, AB

Linked genes can be detected by pedigree analysis. The diagram above shows the pedigree for the inheritance of nail-patella syndrome, which results in small, poorly developed nails and kneecaps in affected people. Other body parts such as elbows, chest, and hips can also be affected. The nail-patella syndrome gene is linked to the ABO blood group locus.

© 2017 **BIOZONE** International
ISBN: 978-1-927309-26-1
Photocopying Prohibited

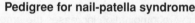
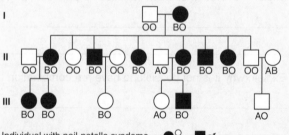

92 Chi-Squared in Genetics

Key Idea: The chi-squared test (χ^2) can be used for testing the outcome of dihybrid crosses against an expected (predicted) Mendelian ratio.

When using the chi-squared test, the null hypothesis predicts the ratio of offspring of different phenotypes according to the expected Mendelian ratio for the cross, assuming independent assortment of alleles (no linkage). Significant departures from the predicted Mendelian ratio indicate linkage of the alleles in question. Raw counts should be used and a large sample size is required for the test to be valid.

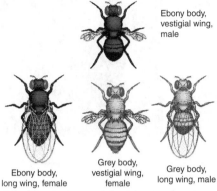

Ebony body, vestigial wing, male

Ebony body, long wing, female

Grey body, vestigial wing, female

Grey body, long wing, male

All images of *Drosophila* courtesy of **Newbyte Educational Software**: *Drosophila* Genetics Lab (www.newbyte.com)

Using χ^2 in Mendelian genetics

In a *Drosophila* genetics experiment, two individuals were crossed (the details of the cross are not relevant here). The predicted Mendelian ratios for the offspring of this cross were 1:1:1:1 for each of the four following phenotypes: grey body-long wing, grey body-vestigial wing, ebony body-long wing, ebony body-vestigial wing. The observed results of the cross were not exactly as predicted. The following numbers for each phenotype were observed in the offspring of the cross:

Observed results of the example *Drosophila* cross			
Grey body, long wing	98	Ebony body, long wing	102
Grey body, vestigial wing	88	Ebony body, vestigial wing	112

Using χ^2, the probability of this result being consistent with a 1:1:1:1 ratio could be tested. Worked example as follows:

Step 1: Calculate the expected value (E)

In this case, this is the sum of the observed values divided by the number of categories (see note below)

$$\frac{400}{4} = 100$$

Step 2: Calculate O – E

The difference between the observed and expected values is calculated as a measure of the deviation from a predicted result. Since some deviations are negative, they are all squared to give positive values. This step is usually performed as part of a tabulation (right, darker blue column).

Category	O	E	O – E	$(O – E)^2$	$\dfrac{(O – E)^2}{E}$
Grey, long wing	98	100	–2	4	0.04
Grey, vestigial wing	88	100	–12	144	1.44
Ebony, long wing	102	100	2	4	0.04
Ebony, vestigial wing	112	100	12	144	1.44

Total = 400 $\qquad$ χ^2 $\qquad$ $\Sigma = 2.96$

Step 3: Calculate the value of χ^2

$$\chi^2 = \sum \frac{(O – E)^2}{E}$$

Where:
O = the observed result
E = the expected result
Σ = sum of

The calculated χ^2 value is given at the bottom right of the last column in the tabulation.

Step 5a: Using the χ^2 table

On the χ^2 table (part reproduced in Table 1 below) with 3 degrees of freedom, the calculated value for χ^2 of 2.96 corresponds to a probability of between 0.2 and 0.5 (see arrow). *This means that by chance alone a χ^2 value of 2.96 could be expected between 20% and 50% of the time.*

Step 4: Calculating degrees of freedom

The probability that any particular χ^2 value could be exceeded by chance depends on the number of degrees of freedom. This is simply **one less than the total number of categories** (this is the number that could vary independently without affecting the last value). **In this case: 4–1 = 3.**

Step 5b: Using the χ^2 table

The probability of between 0.2 and 0.5 is higher than the 0.05 value which is generally regarded as significant. The null hypothesis cannot be rejected and we have no reason to believe that the observed results differ significantly from the expected (at $P = 0.05$).

Footnote: Many Mendelian crosses involve ratios other than 1:1. For these, calculation of the expected values is not simply a division of the total by the number of categories. Instead, the total must be apportioned according to the ratio. For example, for a total of 400 as above, in a predicted 9:3:3:1 ratio, the total count must be divided by 16 (9+3+3+1) and the expected values will be 225: 75: 75: 25 in each category.

Table 1: Critical values of χ^2 at different levels of probability. By convention, the critical probability for rejecting the null hypothesis (H_0) is 5%. If the test statistic is less than the tabulated critical value for $P = 0.05$ we cannot reject H_0 and the result is not significant. If the test statistic is greater than the tabulated value for $P = 0.05$ we reject H_0 in favour of the alternative hypothesis.

Degrees of freedom	Level of probability (P)									
	0.98	0.95	0.80	0.50	0.20	0.10	0.05	0.02	0.01	0.001
1	0.001	0.004	0.064	0.455	1.64	2.71	3.84	5.41	6.64	10.83
2	0.040	0.103	0.466	1.386	3.22	4.61	5.99	7.82	9.21	13.82
3	0.185	0.352	1.005	2.366	4.64	6.25	7.82	9.84	11.35	16.27
4	0.429	0.711	1.649	3.357	5.99	7.78	9.49	11.67	13.28	18.47
5	0.752	0.145	2.343	4.351	7.29	9.24	11.07	13.39	15.09	20.52

$\leftarrow$ Do not reject H_0 $\qquad$ Reject H_0 $\longrightarrow$

(In the 0.50 column next to row 1 is labelled χ^2; arrow pointing down at row 3 value 2.366 to 4.64)

© 2017 **BIOZONE** International
ISBN: 978-1-927309-26-1
Photocopying Prohibited

93 Using Chi-Squared in Genetics

Key Idea: The following problems examine the use of the chi-squared (χ^2) test in genetics.

A worked example illustrating the use of the chi-squared test for a genetic cross is provided on the previous page.

1. In a tomato plant experiment, two heterozygous individuals were crossed (the details of the cross are not relevant here). The predicted Mendelian ratios for the offspring of this cross were **9:3:3:1** for each of the **four following phenotypes**: purple stem-jagged leaf edge, purple stem-smooth leaf edge, green stem-jagged leaf edge, green stem-smooth leaf edge.

The observed results of the cross were not exactly as predicted.
The numbers of offspring with each phenotype are provided below:

Observed results of the tomato plant cross			
Purple stem-jagged leaf edge	12	Green stem-jagged leaf edge	8
Purple stem-smooth leaf edge	9	Green stem-smooth leaf edge	0

(a) State your null hypothesis for this investigation (H_0): _____

_____

(b) State the alternative hypothesis (H_A): _____

_____

2. Use the chi-squared (χ^2) test to determine if the differences observed between the phenotypes are significant. The table of critical values of χ^2 at different P values is provided on the previous page.

(a) Enter the observed values (number of individuals) and complete the table to calculate the χ^2 value:

Category	O	E	O — E	(O — E)^2	$\frac{(O-E)^2}{E}$
Purple stem, jagged leaf					
Purple stem, smooth leaf					
Green stem, jagged leaf					
Green stem, smooth leaf					
	Σ				Σ

(b) Calculate χ^2 value using the equation:

$$\chi^2 = \Sigma \frac{(O-E)^2}{E} \qquad \chi^2 = \text{_____}$$

(c) Calculate the degrees of freedom: _____

(d) Using the χ^2 table, state the P value corresponding to your calculated χ^2 value:

_____

(e) State your decision: *(circle one)*

reject H_0 / do not reject H_0

3. Students carried out a pea plant experiment, where two heterozygous individuals were crossed. The predicted Mendelian ratios for the offspring were **9:3:3:1** for each of the **four following phenotypes**: round-yellow seed, round-green seed, wrinkled-yellow seed, wrinkled-green seed.

The observed results were as follows:

Round-yellow seed	441	Wrinkled-yellow seed	143
Round-green seed	159	Wrinkled-green seed	57

Use a separate piece of paper to complete the following:

(a) State the null and alternative hypotheses (H_0 and H_A).

(b) Calculate the χ^2 value.

(c) Calculate the degrees of freedom and state the P value corresponding to your calculated χ^2 value.

(d) State whether or not you reject your null hypothesis: reject H_0 / do not reject H_0 (circle one)

4. Comment on the whether the χ^2 values obtained above are similar. Suggest a reason for any difference:

_____

_____

_____

© 2017 **BIOZONE** International
ISBN: 978-1-927309-26-1
Photocopying Prohibited

94 Problems Involving Dihybrid Inheritance

Key Idea: For dihybrid crosses involving autosomal unlinked genes, the offspring appear in predictable ratios.

Test your understanding of dihybrid inheritance by solving problems involving the inheritance of two genes.

1. In cats, the following alleles are present for coat characteristics: black (**B**), brown (**b**), short (**L**), long (**l**), tabby (**T**), blotched tabby (**tb**). Use the information to complete the dihybrid crosses below:

(a) A black short haired (**BBLl**) male is crossed with a black long haired (**Bbll**) female. Determine the genotypic and phenotypic ratios of the offspring:

Genotype ratio: _____

_____

Phenotype ratio: _____

_____

_____

(b) A tabby, short haired male (**TtbLl**) is crossed with a blotched tabby, short haired (**tbtbLl**) female. Determine ratios of the offspring:

Genotype ratio: _____

_____

Phenotype ratio: _____

_____

_____

2. A plant with orange-striped flowers was cultivated from seeds. The plant was self-pollinated and the F_1 progeny appeared in the following ratios: 89 orange with stripes, 29 yellow with stripes, 32 orange without stripes, 9 yellow without stripes.

(a) Describe the dominance relationships of the alleles responsible for the phenotypes observed: _____

_____

_____

(b) Determine the genotype of the original plant with orange striped flowers: _____

_____

_____

3. In rabbits, spotted coat **S** is dominant to solid colour **s**, while for coat colour, black **B** is dominant to brown **b**. A brown spotted rabbit is mated with a solid black one and all the offspring are black spotted (the genes are not linked).

(a) State the genotypes:

Parent 1: _____

Parent 2: _____

Offspring: _____

(b) Use the Punnett square to show the outcome of a cross between the F_1 (the F_2):

(c) Using ratios, state the phenotypes of the F_2 generation: _____

_____

_____

LINK
88

WEB
94

TEST

4. In guinea pigs, rough coat **R** is dominant over smooth coat **r** and black coat **B** is dominant over white **b**. The genes are not linked.
A homozygous rough black animal was crossed with a homozygous smooth white:

(a) State the genotype of the F$_1$: _____

(b) State the phenotype of the F$_1$: _____

(c) Use the Punnett square (top right) to show the outcome of a cross between the F$_1$ (the F$_2$):

(d) Using ratios, state the phenotypes of the F$_2$ generation:

_____

_____

(e) Use the Punnett square (right) to show the outcome of a **back cross** of the F$_1$ to the rough, black parent:

(f) Using ratios, state the phenotype of the F$_2$ generation: _____

_____

(g) A rough black guinea pig was crossed with a rough white one produced the following offspring: 28 rough black, 31 rough white, 11 smooth black, and 10 smooth white. Determine the genotypes of the parents:

_____

5. The Himalayan colour-pointed, long-haired cat is a breed developed by crossing a pedigree (true-breeding), uniform-coloured, long-haired Persian with a pedigree colour-pointed (darker face, ears, paws, and tail) short-haired Siamese.

The genes controlling hair colouring and length are on separate chromosomes: uniform colour **U**, colour pointed **u**, short hair **S**, long hair **s**.

Persian   Siamese   Himalayan

(a) Using the symbols above, indicate the genotype _____ _____ _____ of each breed below its photograph (above, right).

(b) State the genotype of the F$_1$ (Siamese X Persian): _____

(c) State the phenotype of the F$_1$: _____

(d) Use the Punnett square to show the outcome of a cross between the F$_1$ (the F$_2$):

(e) State the ratio of the F$_2$ that would be Himalayan: _____

(f) State whether the Himalayan would be true breeding: _____

(g) State the ratio of the F$_2$ that would be colour-point, short-haired cats: _____

6. A *Drosophila* male with genotype **Cucu Ebeb** (straight wing, grey body) is crossed with a female with genotype **cucu ebeb** (curled wing, ebony body). The phenotypes of the F$_1$ were recorded and the percentage of each type calculated. The percentages were: Straight wings, grey body 45%, curled wings, ebony body 43%, straight wings, ebony body 6%, and curled wings grey body 6%.

(a) Is there evidence of crossing over in the offspring? _____

(b) Explain your answer: _____

_____

Straight wing Cucu   Curled wing cucu
Grey body, Ebeb   Ebony body, ebeb

(c) Determine the genotypes of the offspring: _____

© 2017 **BIOZONE** International
ISBN: 978-1-927309-26-1
Photocopying Prohibited

95 Sex Linked Genes

Key Idea: Many genes on the X chromosome do not have a match on the Y chromosome. In males, a recessive allele on the X chromosome cannot therefore be masked by a dominant allele.

Sex linkage occurs when a gene is located on a sex chromosome (usually the X). The result of this is that the character encoded by the gene is usually seen only in one sex (the heterogametic sex). In humans, recessive sex linked genes cause a number of heritable disorders in males, e.g. haemophilia. Women who have a recessive allele are said to be carriers. One of the gene loci controlling coat colour in cats is sex-linked. The two alleles, red and non-red (or black), are found only on the X-chromosome.

Allele types

X_o = Non-red (=black)
X_O = Red

Genotypes **Phenotypes**

X_oX_o, X_oY = Black coated female, male
X_OX_O, X_OY = Orange coated female, male
X_OX_o = Tortoiseshell (intermingled black and orange in fur) in female cats only

1. An owner of a cat is thinking of mating her black female cat with an orange male cat. Before she does this, she would like to know what possible coat colours could result from such a cross. Use the symbols above to fill in the diagram on the right. Summarise the possible genotypes and phenotypes of the kittens in the tables below.

	Genotypes	Phenotypes
Male kittens		

Female kittens		

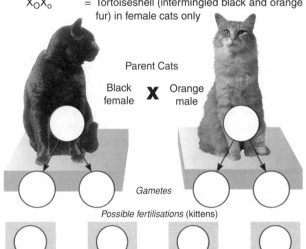

Parent Cats

Black female **X** Orange male

Gametes

Possible fertilisations (kittens)

2. A female tortoiseshell cat mated with an unknown male cat in the neighbourhood and has given birth to a litter of six kittens. The owner of this female cat wants to know what the appearance and the genotype of the father was of these kittens. Use the symbols above to fill in the diagram on the right. Also show the possible fertilisations by placing appropriate arrows.

Describe the father cat's:

(a) Genotype: _____

(b) Phenotype: _____

_____

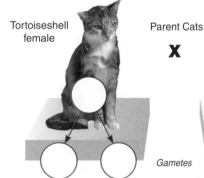
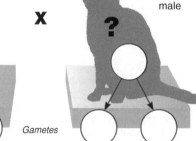

Tortoiseshell female Parent Cats Unknown male **X** ?

Gametes

Possible fertilisations (kittens)

2 orange females | 1 tortoiseshell female | 1 black male | 2 orange males

3. The owner of another cat, a black female, also wants to know which cat fathered her two tortoiseshell female and two black male kittens. Use the symbols above to fill in the diagram on the right. Show the possible fertilisations by placing appropriate arrows.

Describe the father cat's:

(a) Genotype: _____

(b) Phenotype: _____

(c) Was it the same male cat that fathered both this litter and the one above?

YES / NO (*delete one*)

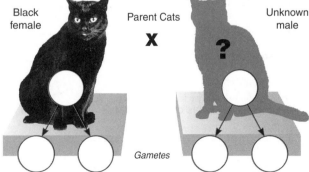

Black female Parent Cats Unknown male **X** ?

Gametes

Possible fertilisations (kittens)

1 tortoiseshell female | 1 tortoiseshell female | 1 black male | 1 black male

LINK WEB
96 **95** **DATA**

Dominant allele in humans

A rare form of rickets in humans is determined by a **dominant** allele of a gene on the **X chromosome** (it is not found on the Y chromosome). This condition is not successfully treated with vitamin D therapy. The allele types, genotypes, and phenotypes are as follows:

Allele types	Genotypes		Phenotypes
X_R = affected by rickets	$X_R X_R$, $X_R X$	=	Affected female
X = normal	$X_R Y$	=	Affected male
	XX, XY	=	Normal female, male

As a genetic counsellor you are presented with a couple where one of them has a family history of this disease. The male is affected by this disease and the woman is normal. The couple, who are thinking of starting a family, would like to know what their chances are of having a child born with this condition. They would also like to know what the probabilities are of having an affected boy or affected girl. Use the symbols above to complete the diagram right and determine the probabilities stated below (expressed as a proportion or percentage).

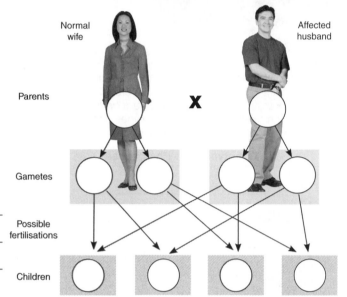

4. Determine the probability of having:

   (a) Affected children: _____

   (b) An affected girl: _____

   (c) An affected boy: _____

Another couple with a family history of the same disease also come in to see you to obtain genetic counselling. In this case, the male is normal and the woman is affected. The woman's father was not affected by this disease. Determine what their chances are of having a child born with this condition. They would also like to know what the probabilities are of having an affected boy or affected girl. Use the symbols above to complete the diagram right and determine the probabilities stated below (expressed as a proportion or percentage).

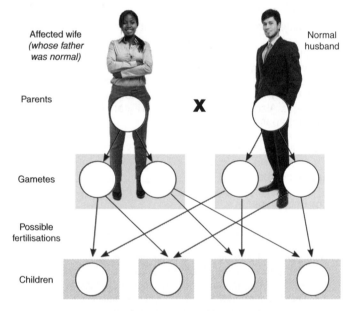

5. Determine the probability of having:

   (a) Affected children: _____

   (b) An affected girl: _____

   (c) An affected boy: _____

6. Describing examples other than those above, discuss the role of sex linkage in the inheritance of genetic disorders:

_____

_____

_____

_____

_____

© 2017 **BIOZONE** International
ISBN: 978-1-927309-26-1
Photocopying Prohibited

96 Inheritance Patterns

Key Idea: Sex-linked traits and autosomal traits have different inheritance patterns.

Complete the following monohybrid crosses for different types of inheritance patterns in humans: autosomal recessive, autosomal dominant, sex linked recessive, and sex linked dominant inheritance.

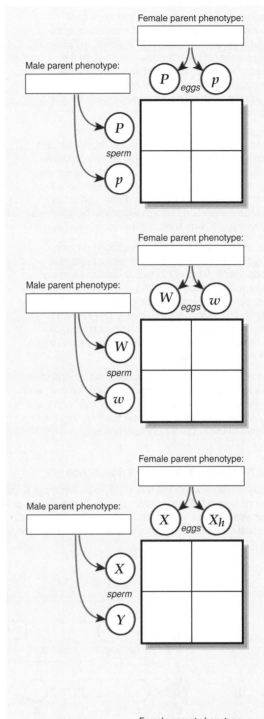

1. **Inheritance of autosomal recessive traits**
   Example: *Albinism*

   Albinism (lack of pigment in hair, eyes and skin) is inherited as an autosomal recessive allele (not sex-linked).

   Using the codes: **PP** (normal) **Pp** (carrier)
   pp (albino)

   (a) Enter the parent phenotypes and complete the Punnett square for a cross between two carrier genotypes.

   (b) Give the ratios for the phenotypes from this cross.

   Phenotype ratios: _____

   _____

2. **Inheritance of autosomal dominant traits**
   Example: *Woolly hair*

   Woolly hair is inherited as an autosomal dominant allele. Each affected individual will have at least one affected parent.

   Using the codes: **WW** (woolly hair)
   Ww (woolly hair, heterozygous)
   ww (normal hair)

   (a) Enter the parent phenotypes and complete the Punnett square for a cross between two heterozygous individuals.

   (b) Give the ratios for the phenotypes from this cross.

   Phenotype ratios: _____

   _____

3. **Inheritance of sex linked recessive traits**
   Example: *Haemophilia*

   Inheritance of haemophilia is sex linked. Males with the recessive (haemophilia) allele, are affected. Females can be carriers.

   Using the codes: **XX** (normal female)
   XX$_h$ (carrier female)
   X$_h$X$_h$ (haemophiliac female)
   XY (normal male)
   X$_h$Y (haemophiliac male)

   (a) Enter the parent phenotypes and complete the Punnett square for a cross between a normal male and a carrier female.

   (b) Give the ratios for the phenotypes from this cross.

   Phenotype ratios: _____

   _____

4. **Inheritance of sex linked dominant traits**
   Example: *Sex linked form of rickets*

   A rare form of rickets is inherited on the X chromosome.

   Using the codes: **XX** (normal female); **XY** (normal male)
   X$_R$X (affected heterozygote female)
   X$_R$X$_R$ (affected female)
   X$_R$Y (affected male)

   (a) Enter the parent phenotypes and complete the Punnett square for a cross between an affected male and heterozygous female.

   (b) Give the ratios for the phenotypes from this cross.

   Phenotype ratios: _____

   _____

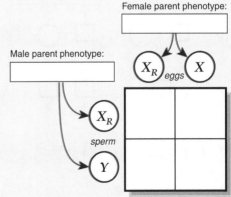

LINK
95

TEST

97 Pedigree Analysis

Key Idea: Pedigree charts are a way to graphically illustrate inheritance patterns over a number of generations. They are used to study the inheritance of genetic disorders and make it possible to follow the genetic history of an individual.

Pedigree charts

A pedigree chart is a diagram that shows the occurrence and appearance of a particular gene or trait from one generation to the next. In humans, pedigree charts are often used to analyse the inheritance of heritable conditions. In domestic animals, pedigree charts are often used to trace the inheritance of characteristics in selective breeding programmes for horses and dogs.

Pedigree charts use symbols to indicate an individual's particular traits. The key (right) explains the meaning of the symbols. Particular individuals are identified by their generation number and their order number in that generation. For example, II-6 is the sixth person in the second row. The arrow indicates the person through whom the pedigree was discovered (i.e. who reported the condition).

If the chart on the right were illustrating a human family tree, it would represent three generations: grandparents (I-1 and I-2) with three sons and one daughter. Two of the sons (II-3 and II-4) are identical twins, but did not marry or have any children. The other son (II-1) married and had a daughter and another child (sex unknown). The daughter (II-5) married and had two sons and two daughters (plus a child that died in infancy).

For the particular trait being studied, the grandfather was expressing the phenotype (showing the trait) and the grandmother was a carrier. One of their sons and one of their daughters also show the trait, together with one of their granddaughters (arrow).

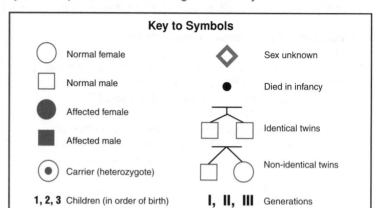

Key to Symbols

- Normal female
- Normal male
- Affected female
- Affected male
- Carrier (heterozygote)
- Sex unknown
- Died in infancy
- Identical twins
- Non-identical twins
- **1, 2, 3** Children (in order of birth)
- **I, II, III** Generations

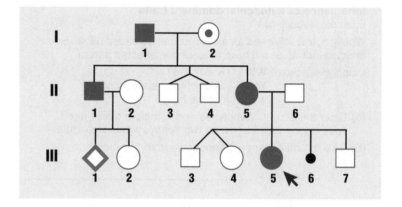

The pedigree of lactose intolerance

Lactose intolerance is the inability to digest the milk sugar lactose. It occurs because some people do not produce lactase, the enzyme needed to break down lactose. The pedigree chart below was one of the original studies to determine the inheritance pattern of lactose intolerance. Researchers concluded that because two lactose tolerant parents can produce a lactose intolerant child, lactose intolerance must be a recessively inherited condition (it needs two copies of the gene for lactose intolerance to show up).

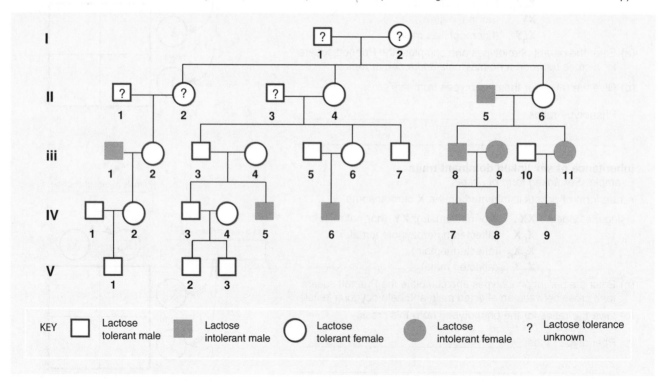

KEY

- Lactose tolerant male
- Lactose intolerant male
- Lactose tolerant female
- Lactose intolerant female
- **?** Lactose tolerance unknown

WEB
LINK
LINK
97 87 95

© 2017 **BIOZONE** International
ISBN: 978-1-927309-26-1
Photocopying Prohibited

1. **Autosomal recessive traits**
   Albinos lack pigment in the hair, skin and eyes. This is an autosomal recessive trait.

   (a) Write the genotype for each of the individuals on the chart using the following letter codes: **PP** normal skin colour; **P-** normal, but unknown if homozygous; **Pp** carrier; **pp** albino.

   (b) Why must the parents (II-3) and (II-4) be **carriers** of a **recessive** allele:

   _____

   _____

Albinism in humans

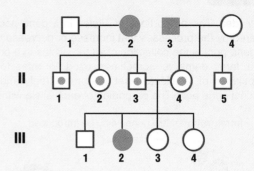

2. **Sex linked recessive traits**
   Haemophilia is a disease where blood clotting is affected. A person can die from a simple bruise (which is internal bleeding). The clotting factor gene is carried on the X chromosome.

   (a) Write the genotype for each of the individuals on the chart using the codes: **XY** normal male; X_hY affected male; **XX** normal female; X_hX female carrier; X_hX_h affected female:

   (b) Why can males never be carriers? _____

   _____

   _____

   _____

   _____

Haemophilia in humans

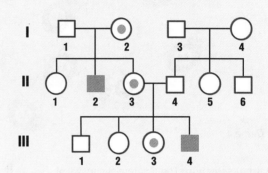

3. **Autosomal dominant traits**
   An unusual trait found in some humans is woolly hair (not to be confused with curly hair). Each affected individual will have at least one affected parent.

   (a) Write the genotype for each of the individuals on the chart using the following letter codes:
   WW woolly hair; **Ww** woolly hair (heterozygous); **W-** woolly hair, but unknown if homozygous; **ww** normal hair

   (b) Describe a feature of this inheritance pattern that suggests the trait is the result of a **dominant** allele:

   _____

   _____

Woolly hair in humans

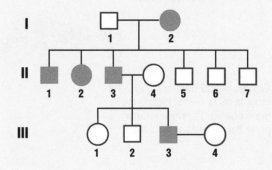

4. **Sex linked dominant traits**
   A rare form of rickets is inherited on the X chromosome. All daughters of affected males will be affected. More females than males will show the trait.

   (a) Write the genotype for each of the individuals on the chart using the following letter codes:
   XY normal male; X_RY affected male; **XX** normal female; X_{R-} female (unknown if homozygous); X_RX_R affected female.

   (b) Why will more females than males be affected?

   _____

   _____

   _____

A rare form of rickets in humans

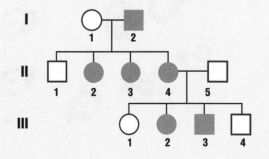

5. Using the examples on this these two pages, make up your own set of guidelines for interpreting pedigree charts. How do you distinguish an autosomal inheritance pattern from an X-linked one? What are the features of autosomal recessive inheritance? Of autosomal dominant? Of X-linked dominant traits and X-linked recessive traits. Attach your summary to this page.

98 Gene Pools and Evolution

Key Idea: The proportions of alleles in a gene pool can be altered by the processes that increase or decrease variation. A gene pool is the collection of all the alleles in a population. The term deme is sometimes used to refer to a local population of individuals that interbreed freely and share a distinct gene pool. The proportion of each allele within a gene pool is called the **allele frequency**. Allele frequencies in populations can vary as a result of the events occurring in the gene pool. These changes over time are called evolution. Four microevolutionary processes contribute to genetic change in populations: mutation, gene flow, natural selection, and genetic drift. These are described below (definitions in blue).

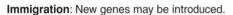

Immigration: New genes may be introduced.

Mutations: Changes to the DNA sequence can create new alleles.

Emigration: Genes may be lost.

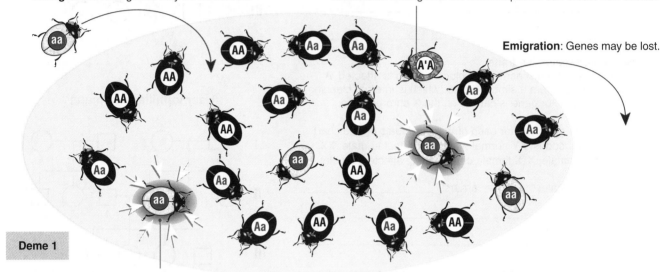

Deme 1

Natural selection: The differential survival of favourable phenotypes (unfavourable allele combinations have lower survival or reproductive success). Natural selection accumulates and maintains favourable allele combinations. It reduces genetic diversity within the gene pool and increases differences between populations.

Gene flow: The exchange of alleles between gene pools as a result of migration. Gene flow is a source of new genetic variation and tends to reduce differences between populations that have accumulated because of natural selection or genetic drift.

Geographical barriers (e.g. mountains or rivers) isolate the gene pool and prevent regular gene flow between populations.

This activity portrays two populations of a beetle species. Each beetle is a "carrier" of genetic information, represented by the alleles (A and a) for a gene that controls colour and has a dominant/recessive inheritance pattern. There are normally two phenotypes: black and pale.

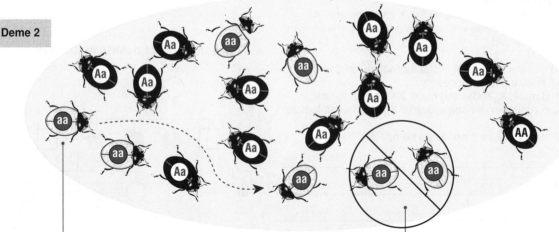

Deme 2

Mate choice (non-random mating): Individuals do not select their mate randomly but may seek out particular phenotypes, increasing the frequency of the associated alleles in the population.

Genetic drift: Random changes to the allele frequencies of populations due to chance events. Genetic drift has a relatively greater effect on small populations and can be an important process in their evolution.

WEB
LINK
LINK
LINK
KNOW
98 99 103 109

1. One of the important theoretical concepts in population genetics is that of **genetic equilibrium**, which state that "*for a large, randomly mating population, allele frequencies do not change from generation to generation*". If allele frequencies in a population are to remain unchanged, all of the following criteria must be met: the population must be large, there must be no mutation or gene flow, mating must be random, and there must be no natural selection. Evolution is a consequence of few if any of these conditions ever being met in natural populations. For each of the five factors (a-e) below, describe how and why each would affect the allele frequency in a gene pool. Use the diagrams to help you.

(a) Population size: _____

_____

_____

_____

_____

(b) Mate selection: _____

_____

_____

_____

_____

(c) Gene flow: _____

_____

_____

_____

_____

_____

_____

(d) Mutation: _____

_____

_____

_____

_____

_____

(e) Natural selection: _____

_____

_____

_____

_____

_____

3. Identify a factor that tends to:

(a) Increase genetic variation in populations:

_____

_____

(b) Decrease genetic variation in populations:

_____

_____

Factors favouring gene pool stability (no evolution)	Factors favouring gene pool change (evolution)

Large population

Small population

Random mating

Assortative mating

Barrier to gene flow

No gene flow

Immigration

Emigration

Gene flow

No mutation

New recessive allele

Mutations

No natural selection

Natural selection

© 2017 **BIOZONE** International
ISBN: 978-1-927309-26-1
Photocopying Prohibited

99 Changes in a Gene Pool

Key Idea: Natural selection and gene flow as a result of migration can alter the allele frequencies in gene pools.

The diagram below shows an hypothetical population of beetles undergoing changes as it is subjected to two 'events'. The three phases represent a progression in time (i.e. the same gene pool, undergoing change). The beetles have two phenotypes (black and pale) determined by the amount of pigment deposited in the cuticle. The gene controlling this character is represented by two alleles **A** and **a**. Your task is to analyse the gene pool as it undergoes changes.

1. For each phase in the gene pool below fill in the tables provided as follows; (some have been done for you):

    (a) Count the number of A and a alleles separately. Enter the count into the top row of the table (left hand columns).
    (b) Count the number of each type of allele combination (AA, Aa and aa) in the gene pool. Enter the count into the top row of the table (right hand columns).
    (c) For each of the above, work out the frequencies as percentages (bottom row of table):

$$\text{Allele frequency} = \text{No. counted alleles} \div \text{Total no. of alleles} \times 100$$

Phase 1: Initial gene pool

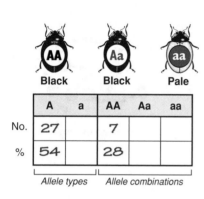

Black (AA)   Black (Aa)   Pale (aa)

	A	a	AA	Aa	aa
No.	27		7		
%	54		28		

Allele types   Allele combinations

Two pale individuals died. Their alleles are removed from the gene pool.

Phase 2: Natural selection

In the same gene pool at a later time there was a change in the allele frequencies. This was due to the loss of certain allele combinations due to natural selection. Some of those with a genotype of aa were eliminated (poor fitness).

These individuals (marked by white arrows) are not counted for allele frequencies; they are dead!

	A	a	AA	Aa	aa
No.					
%					

This individual is entering the population and will add its alleles to the gene pool.

This individual is leaving the population, removing its alleles from the gene pool.

Phase 3: Immigration and emigration

This particular kind of beetle exhibits wandering behaviour. The allele frequencies change again due to the introduction and departure of individual beetles, each carrying certain allele combinations. Individuals coming into the gene pool (AA) are counted for allele frequencies, but those leaving (aa) are not.

	A	a	AA	Aa	aa
No.					
%					

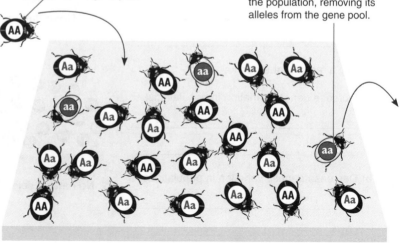

© 2017 **BIOZONE** International
ISBN: 978-1-927309-26-1
Photocopying Prohibited

100 Hardy-Weinberg Calculations

Key Idea: The Hardy-Weinberg equation is a mathematical model used to calculate allele and genotype frequencies in populations.

The Hardy-Weinberg equation provides a simple

mathematical model of genetic equilibrium in a gene pool, but its main application in population genetics is in calculating allele and genotype frequencies in populations, particularly as a means of studying changes and measuring their rate.

Punnett square

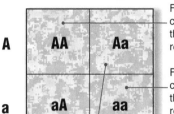

Frequency of allele combination **AA** in the population is represented as p^2

Frequency of allele combination **aa** in the population is represented as q^2

Frequency of allele combination **Aa** in the population (add these together to **2pq**)

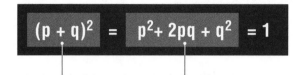

$$(p + q)^2 = p^2 + 2pq + q^2 = 1$$

Frequency of allele types

p = Frequency of allele A

q = Frequency of allele a

Frequency of allele combinations

p^2 = Frequency of AA (homozygous dominant)

2pq = Frequency of Aa (heterozygous)

q^2 = Frequency of aa (homozygous recessive)

The Hardy-Weinberg equation is applied to populations with a simple genetic situation: dominant and recessive alleles controlling a single trait. The frequency of all of the dominant (A) and recessive alleles (a) equals the total genetic complement, and adds up to 1 or 100% of the alleles present (i.e. p + q = 1).

How to solve Hardy-Weinberg problems

In most populations, the frequency of two alleles of interest is calculated from the proportion of homozygous recessives (q^2), as this is the only genotype identifiable directly from its phenotype. If only the dominant phenotype is known, q^2 may be calculated (1 – the frequency of the dominant phenotype). The following steps outline the procedure for solving a Hardy-Weinberg problem:

Remember that all calculations must be carried out using proportions, NOT PERCENTAGES!

1. Examine the question to determine what piece of information you have been given about the population. In most cases, this is the percentage or frequency of the homozygous recessive phenotype q^2, or the dominant phenotype $p^2 + 2pq$ (see note above).

2. The first objective is to find out the value of p or q, If this is achieved, then every other value in the equation can be determined by simple calculation.

3. Take the square root of q^2 to find q.

4. Determine p by subtracting q from 1 (i.e. p = 1 – q).

5. Determine p^2 by multiplying p by itself (i.e. p^2 = p x p).

6. Determine 2pq by multiplying p times q times 2.

7. Check that your calculations are correct by adding up the values for $p^2 + q^2 + 2pq$ (the sum should equal 1 or 100%).

Worked example

Among white-skinned people in the USA, approximately 70% of people can taste the chemical phenylthiocarbamide (PTC) (the dominant phenotype), while 30% are non-tasters (the recessive phenotype).

Determine the frequency of:	*Answers*
(a) Homozygous recessive phenotype(q^2).	30% - provided
(b) The dominant allele (**p**).	45.2%
(c) Homozygous tasters (**p^2**).	20.5%
(d) Heterozygous tasters (**2pq**).	49.5%

Data: The frequency of the dominant phenotype (70% tasters) and recessive phenotype (30% non-tasters) are provided.

Working:

Recessive phenotype: **q^2** = 30%
use 0.30 for calculation

therefore: **q** = 0.5477
square root of 0.30

therefore: **p** = 0.4523
1 – q = p
1 – 0.5477 = 0.4523

Use p and q in the equation (top) to solve any unknown:

Homozygous dominant **p^2** = 0.2046
(p x p = 0.4523 x 0.4523)

Heterozygous: **2pq** = 0.4953

---

1. A population of hamsters has a gene consisting of 90% M alleles (black) and 10% m alleles (grey). Mating is random.

   Data: Frequency of recessive allele (10% m) and dominant allele (90% M).

   Determine the proportion of offspring that will be black and the proportion that will be grey (show your working):

   _____

   _____

Recessive allele:	q =	
Dominant allele:	p =	
Recessive phenotype:	q^2 =	
Homozygous dominant:	p^2 =	
Heterozygous:	2pq =	

LINK 101   LINK 98   WEB 100

DATA

2. You are working with pea plants and found 36 plants out of 400 were dwarf.
   Data: Frequency of recessive phenotype (36 out of 400 = 9%)

   (a) Calculate the frequency of the tall gene: _____

   (b) Determine the number of heterozygous pea plants:

   _____

   _____

Recessive allele:	q =	
Dominant allele:	p =	
Recessive phenotype:	q^2 =	
Homozygous dominant:	p^2 =	
Heterozygous:	2pq =	

3. In humans, the ability to taste the chemical phenylthiocarbamide (PTC) is inherited as a simple dominant characteristic. Suppose you found out that 360 out of 1000 college students could not taste the chemical.
   Data: Frequency of recessive phenotype (360 out of 1000).

   (a) State the frequency of the gene for tasting PTC: _____

   _____

   (b) Determine the number of heterozygous students in this population:

   _____

Recessive allele:	q =	
Dominant allele:	p =	
Recessive phenotype:	q^2 =	
Homozygous dominant:	p^2 =	
Heterozygous:	2pq =	

4. A type of deformity appears in 4% of a large herd of cattle. Assume the deformity was caused by a recessive gene.
   Data: Frequency of recessive phenotype (4% deformity).

   (a) Calculate the percentage of the herd that are carriers of the gene:

   _____

   (b) Determine the frequency of the dominant gene in this case:

   _____

Recessive allele:	q =	
Dominant allele:	p =	
Recessive phenotype:	q^2 =	
Homozygous dominant:	p^2 =	
Heterozygous:	2pq =	

5. Assume you placed 50 pure bred black guinea pigs (dominant allele) with 50 albino guinea pigs (recessive allele) and allowed the population to attain genetic equilibrium (several generations have passed).
   Data: Frequency of recessive allele (50%) and dominant allele (50%).

   Determine the proportion (%) of the population that becomes white:

   _____

   _____

Recessive allele:	q =	
Dominant allele:	p =	
Recessive phenotype:	q^2 =	
Homozygous dominant:	p^2 =	
Heterozygous:	2pq =	

6. It is known that 64% of a large population exhibit the recessive trait of a characteristic controlled by two alleles (one is dominant over the other).
   Data: Frequency of recessive phenotype (64%). Determine the following:

   (a) The frequency of the recessive allele: _____

   (b) The percentage that are heterozygous for this trait: _____

   (c) The percentage that exhibit the dominant trait: _____

   (d) The percentage that are homozygous for the dominant trait: _____

   (e) The percentage that has one or more recessive alleles: _____

Recessive allele:	q =	
Dominant allele:	p =	
Recessive phenotype:	q^2 =	
Homozygous dominant:	p^2 =	
Heterozygous:	2pq =	

7. Albinism is recessive to normal pigmentation in humans. The frequency of the albino allele was 10% in a population.
   Data: Frequency of recessive allele (10% albino allele).

   Determine the proportion of people that you would expect to be albino:

   _____

   _____

   _____

101 Analysis of a Squirrel Gene Pool

Key Idea: Allele frequencies for real populations can be calculated using the Hardy-Weinberg equation. Analysis of those allele frequencies can show how the population's gene pool changes over time.

In Olney, Illinois, there is a unique population of albino (white) and grey squirrels. Between 1977 and 1990, students at Olney Central College carried out a study of this population. They recorded the frequency of grey and albino squirrels. The albinos displayed a mutant allele expressed as an albino phenotype only in the homozygous recessive condition. The data they collected are provided in the table below. Using the **Hardy-Weinberg equation**, it was possible to estimate the frequency of the normal 'wild' allele (G) providing grey fur colouring, and the frequency of the mutant albino allele (g) producing white squirrels when homozygous.

Grey squirrel, usual colour form

Albino form of grey squirrel

Thanks to **Dr. John Stencel**, Olney Central College, Olney, Illinois, US, for providing the data for this exercise.

Population of grey and white squirrels in Olney, Illinois (1977-1990)

Year	Grey	White	Total	GG	Gg	gg	Freq. of g	Freq. of G
1977	602	182	784	26.85	49.93	23.21	48.18	51.82
1978	511	172	683	24.82	50.00	25.18	50.18	49.82
1979	482	134	616	28.47	49.77	21.75	46.64	53.36
1980	489	133	622	28.90	49.72	21.38	46.24	53.76
1981	536	163	699	26.74	49.94	23.32	48.29	51.71
1982	618	151	769	31.01	49.35	19.64	44.31	55.69
1983	419	141	560	24.82	50.00	25.18	50.18	49.82
1984	378	106	484	28.30	49.79	21.90	46.80	53.20
1985	448	125	573	28.40	49.78	21.82	46.71	53.29
1986	536	155	691	27.71	49.86	22.43	47.36	52.64
1987	No data collected this year							
1988	652	122	774	36.36	47.88	15.76	39.70	60.30
1989	552	146	698	29.45	49.64	20.92	45.74	54.26
1990	603	111	714	36.69	47.76	15.55	39.43	60.57

1. Graph population changes: Use the data in the first 3 columns of the table above to plot a line graph. This will show changes in the phenotypes: numbers of grey and white (albino) squirrels, as well as changes in the total population. Plot: grey, white, and total for each year:

(a) Determine by how much (as a %) total population numbers have fluctuated over the sampling period:

_____

(b) Describe the overall trend in total population numbers and any pattern that may exist:

_____

_____

_____

_____

_____

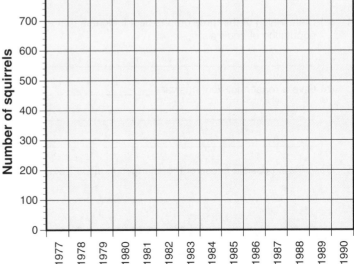

LINK
100

DATA

2. **Graph genotype changes:** Use the data in the genotype columns of the table on the opposite page to plot a line graph. This will show changes in the allele combinations (**GG**, **Gg**, **gg**). Plot: **GG**, **Gg**, and **gg** for each year:

Describe the overall trend in the frequency of:

(a) Homozygous dominant (**GG**) genotype:

_____

_____

(b) Heterozygous (**Gg**) genotype:

_____

_____

(c) Homozygous recessive (**gg**) genotype:

_____

_____

_____

Percentage frequency of genotype — vertical axis: 0, 10, 20, 30, 40, 50, 60

Year — horizontal axis: 1977, 1978, 1979, 1980, 1981, 1982, 1983, 1984, 1985, 1986, 1987, 1988, 1989, 1990

3. **Graph allele changes:** Use the data in the last two columns of the table on the previous page to plot a line graph. This will show changes in the allele frequencies for each of the dominant (**G**) and recessive (**g**) alleles. Plot: the frequency of **G** and the frequency of **g**:

(a) Describe the overall trend in the frequency of the dominant allele (**G**):

_____

_____

_____

(b) Describe the overall trend in the frequency of the recessive allele (**g**):

_____

_____

_____

_____

_____

Percentage frequency of allele — vertical axis: 0, 10, 20, 30, 40, 50, 60, 70

Year — horizontal axis: 1977, 1978, 1979, 1980, 1981, 1982, 1983, 1984, 1985, 1986, 1987, 1988, 1989, 1990

4. (a) State which of the three graphs best indicates that a significant change may be taking place in the gene pool of this population of squirrels:

_____

(b) Give a reason for your answer: _____

_____

_____

5. Describe a possible cause of the changes in allele frequencies over the sampling period: _____

_____

_____

_____

_____

© 2017 **BIOZONE** International
ISBN: 978-1-927309-26-1
Photocopying Prohibited

102 Gene Pool Model

The set of all the versions of all the genes in a population (it genetic make-up) is called the **gene pool**. Cut out the squares below and use them to model the events described in *Modelling Natural Selection*.

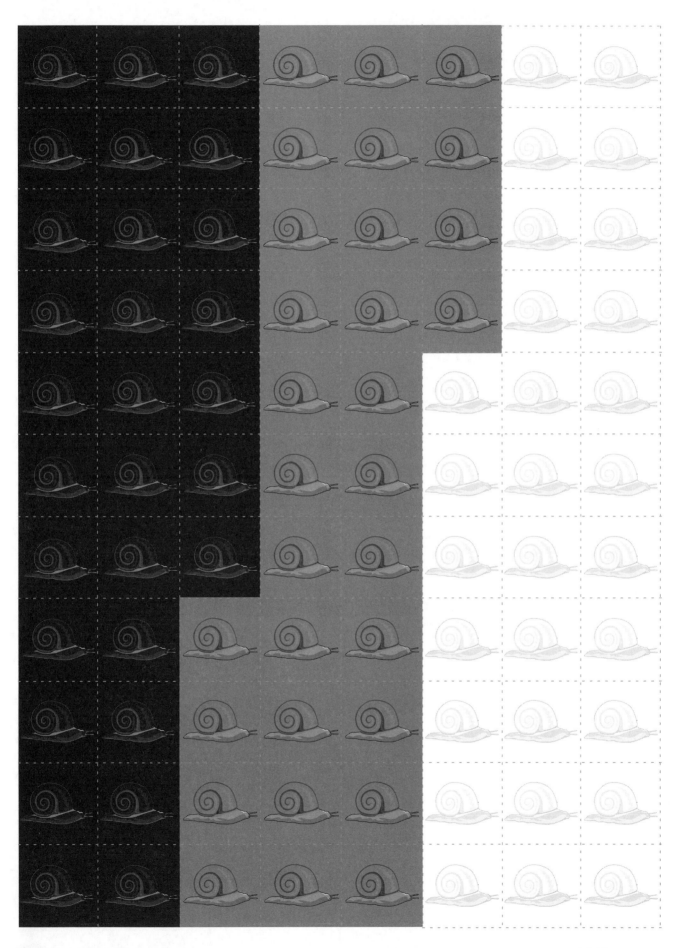

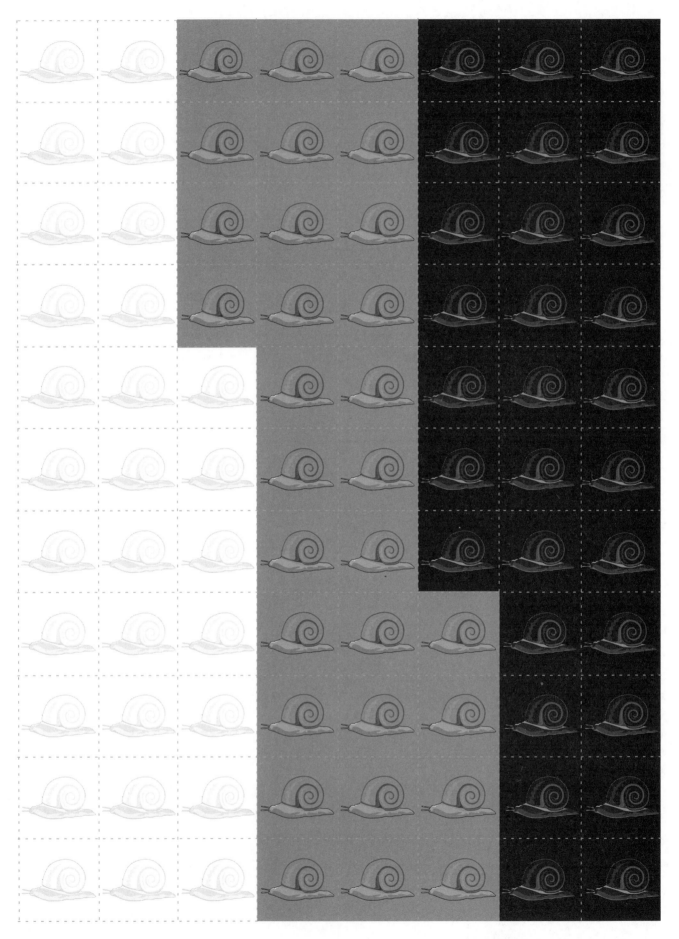

103 Modelling Natural Selection

Key Idea: The way that natural selection acts on phenotypes can be modelled for a hypothetical population in which individuals differ with respect to one phenotypic character.

Natural selection can be modelled in a simple activity based on predation. You can carry out the following activity by yourself, or work with a partner to increase the size of the population. The black, grey, and white squares on the preceding pages represent phenotypes of a population. Cut them out and follow the instructions below to model natural selection. You will also need a sheet of white paper and a sheet of black paper.

1. Cut out the squares on the preceding pages and record the number of black, grey, and white squares.

2. For the first half of the activity you will also need a black sheet of paper or material that will act as the environment (A3 is a good size). For the second half of the activity you will need a white sheet of paper.

3. Place 10 black, 10 white, and 22 grey squares in a bag and shake them up to mix them. Keep the other squares for making up population proportions later. Write the values in the numbers row of generation 1 below.

4. Work out the proportion of each phenotype in the population (e.g. 10/42 = 0.24) and place these values in the table below. This represents your starting population (you can combine populations with a partner to increase the population size for more reliable results).

5. Now take the squares out of the bag and randomly distribute them over the sheet of black paper (this works best if your partner does this while you aren't looking).

6. You will act the part of a predator on the snails. For 15 seconds, pick up the squares that stand out (are obvious) on the black paper using your thumb and forefinger. These squares represent animals in the population that have been preyed upon and killed. Place them to one side. The remaining squares represent the population that survived to reproduce.

7. Count the remaining phenotypes. In this population, black carries the alleles BB, grey the alleles Bb, and white the alleles bb. On a separate sheet, calculate the frequency of the B and b alleles in the remaining population (hint: if there are 5 black and 10 grey snails then there are 20 B alleles).

8. These frequencies are what is passed on to the next generation. To produce the next generation, the number of black, grey, and white snails must be calculated. This can be done using the original population number and Hardy - Weinberg equations ($p^2 + 2pq + q^2 = 1$ and $p + q = 1$).

9. For example. If there are 24 snails left with the numbers 5 black, 10 grey, and 9 white then the frequency of B (p) = (5 x 2 + 10) / (24 x 2) = 0.4167 and b (q) = 0.5833. The number of black snails in the next generation will therefore be p^2 x 42 = 0.4167^2 x 42 = 7.3 = 7 (you can't have 0.3 of a snail).

10. Record the number of black, grey, and white snails in the table below in generation 2, along with their phenotype frequencies.

11. Repeat steps 4 to 10 for generation 2, and 3 more generations (5 generations in total or more if you wish).

12. On separate graph paper, draw a line graph of the proportions of each colour over the five generations. Which colours have increased, which have decreased?

13. Now repeat the whole activity using a white sheet background instead of the black sheet. What do you notice about the proportions this time?

Generation		Black	Grey	White
1	Number			
	Proportion			
2	Number			
	Proportion			
3	Number			
	Proportion			
4	Number			
	Proportion			
5	Number			
	Proportion			

104 Types of Natural Selection

Key Idea: Natural selection is responsible for the differential survival of some phenotypes (and genotypes) over others. It is an important cause of genetic change in populations.

Natural selection operates on the phenotypes of individuals, produced by their particular combinations of alleles. It results in the differential survival of some genotypes over others. As a result, organisms with phenotypes most suited to the prevailing environment are more likely to survive and breed than those with less suited phenotypes. Favourable

phenotypes will become relatively more numerous than unfavourable phenotypes. Over time, natural selection may lead to a permanent change in the genetic makeup of a population. Natural selection is always linked to phenotypic suitability in the prevailing environment so it is a dynamic process. It may favour existing phenotypes or shift the phenotypic median, as is shown in the diagrams below. The top row of diagrams represents the population phenotypic spread before selection, and the bottom row the spread afterwards.

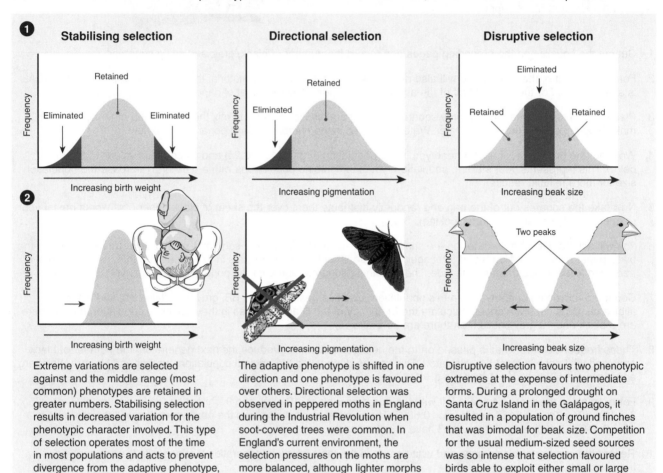

Stabilising selection

Extreme variations are selected against and the middle range (most common) phenotypes are retained in greater numbers. Stabilising selection results in decreased variation for the phenotypic character involved. This type of selection operates most of the time in most populations and acts to prevent divergence from the adaptive phenotype, e.g. birth weight of human infants. Stabilising selection predominates when environments are stable.

Directional selection

The adaptive phenotype is shifted in one direction and one phenotype is favoured over others. Directional selection was observed in peppered moths in England during the Industrial Revolution when soot-covered trees were common. In England's current environment, the selection pressures on the moths are more balanced, although lighter morphs predominate. Selection will be directional when there is a trend in environmental conditions, e.g. warm to cold.

Disruptive selection

Disruptive selection favours two phenotypic extremes at the expense of intermediate forms. During a prolonged drought on Santa Cruz Island in the Galápagos, it resulted in a population of ground finches that was bimodal for beak size. Competition for the usual medium-sized seed sources was so intense that selection favoured birds able to exploit either small or large seeds. Disruptive selection may occur when environments or resources are fluctuating or distinctly divergent.

1. Define the following, including a statement about the type of environment that favours each:

   (a) Stabilising selection: _____

   _____

   (b) Directional selection: _____

   _____

   (c) Disruptive selection: _____

   _____

2. Explain why fluctuating (as opposed to stable) environments favour disruptive (diversifying) selection: _____

   _____

   _____

   _____

© 2017 **BIOZONE** International
ISBN: 978-1-927309-26-1
Photocopying Prohibited

105 Stabilising Selection for Human Birth Weight

Key Idea: Stabilising selection operates to keep human birth weight within relatively narrow constraints.

Selection pressures operate on populations in such a way as to reduce mortality. For humans, selection pressures act to constrain birth weight to within narrow limits. This is a good example of **stabilising selection**. It is possible to document this effect by plotting birth weights for a large sample of the population. Carry out the steps below.

Step 1: For this activity, you will need a sample of 100 birth weights. You can search birth records online or use the data provided in the Model Answers booklet and weblinks.

Step 2: Group the weights into each of the 12 weight classes indicated on the graph template provided. Calculate the percentage in each weight class.

Step 3: Graph these in the form of a histogram for the 12 weight classes (use the graphing grid provided right). Be sure to use the scale provided on the left vertical (y) axis.

Step 4: Create a plot of percentage mortality of newborns in relation to their birth weight. Use the scale on the right y axis and data provided (below). Draw a line of best fit through the points.

Weight (kg)	Percent mortality
1.0	80
1.5	30
2.0	12
2.5	4
3.0	3
3.5	2
4.0	3
4.5	7
5.0	15

The size of the baby and the diameter and shape of the birth canal are the two crucial factors in determining whether a normal delivery is possible.

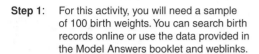

Percentage of births sampled (left y axis) / *Percent mortality* (right y axis) vs *Birth weight / kg*

DID YOU KNOW?

Evidence indicates that the phenotypic norm is shifting. Researchers estimate that cases where the baby cannot fit down the birth canal have increased from 30/1000 in the 1960s to 36/1000 births today, indicating that there is less selection against women with narrow pelves and babies with larger heads.

1. Describe the shape of the histogram for birth weights: _____

2. What is the optimum birth weight in terms of the lowest newborn mortality?_____

3. Describe the relationship between newborn mortality and birth weight: _____

   _____

4. Describe the selection pressures that are operating to control the range of birth weight: _____

   _____

   _____

5. How might modern medical intervention during pregnancy and childbirth have altered these selection pressures?

   _____

   _____

106 Directional Selection in Moths

Key Idea: Directional selection pressures on the peppered moth during the Industrial Revolution shifted the common phenotype from the grey form to the melanic (dark) form. Natural selection may act on the frequencies of phenotypes (and hence genotypes) in populations in one of three different ways (through stabilising, directional, or disruptive selection).

Colour change in the **peppered moth** (*Biston betularia*) during the Industrial Revolution is often used to show **directional selection** in a polymorphic population (polymorphic means having two or more forms). Intensive coal burning during this time caused trees to become dark with soot, and the dark form (morph) of peppered moth became dominant.

The gene controlling colour in the peppered moth, is located on a single locus. The allele for the melanic (dark) form (**M**) is dominant over the allele for the grey (light) form (**m**).

Olaf Leillinger

Melanic form
Genotype: MM or Mm

The peppered moth, *Biston betularia*, has two forms: a grey mottled form, and a dark melanic form. During the Industrial Revolution, the relative abundance of the two forms changed to favour the dark form. The change was thought to be the result of selective predation by birds. It was proposed that the grey form was more visible to birds in industrial areas where the trees were dark. As a result, birds preyed upon them more often, resulting in higher numbers of the dark form surviving.

Olaf Leillinger

Grey form
Genotype: mm

Museum collections of the peppered moth over the last 150 years show a marked change in the frequency of the melanic form (above right). Moths collected in 1850, prior to the major onset of the Industrial Revolution in England, were mostly the grey form (above left). Fifty years later the frequency of the darker melanic forms had increased.

In the 1940s and 1950s, coal burning was still at intense levels around the industrial centres of Manchester and Liverpool. During this time, the melanic form of the moth was still very dominant. In the rural areas further south and west of these industrial centres, the occurrence of the grey form increased dramatically. With the decline of coal burning factories and the introduction of the Clean Air Act in cities, air quality improved between 1960 and 1980. Sulfur dioxide and smoke levels dropped to a fraction of their previous levels. This coincided with a sharp fall in the relative numbers of melanic moths (right).

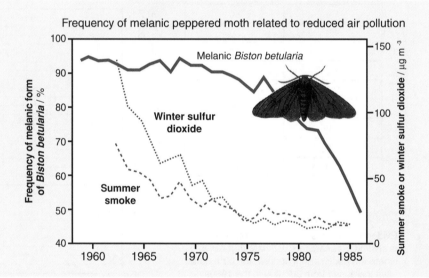

Frequency of melanic peppered moth related to reduced air pollution

1. The populations of peppered moth in England have undergone changes in the frequency of an obvious phenotypic character over the last 150 years. What is the phenotypic character?

_____

2. Describe how the selection pressure on the grey form has changed with change in environment over the last 150 years:

_____

_____

_____

3. Describe the relationship between allele frequency and phenotype frequency: _____

_____

_____

4. The level of pollution dropped around Manchester and Liverpool between 1960 and 1985. How did the frequency of the darker melanic form change during this period?

_____

WEB 106   LINK 104   LINK 107

KNOW

107 Directional Selection in Darwin's Finches

Key Idea: The effect of directional selection on a population can be verified by making measurements of phenotypic traits. Natural selection acts on the phenotypes of a population. Individuals with phenotypes that increase their fitness produce more offspring, increasing the proportion of the genes corresponding to that phenotype in the next generation. Many population studies have shown natural selection can cause phenotypic changes in a population relatively quickly.

The finches on the Galápagos island (Darwin's finches) are famous in that they are commonly used as examples of how evolution produces new species. In this activity you will analyse data from the measurement of beaks depths of the medium ground finch (*Geospiza fortis*) on the island of Daphne Major near the centre of the Galápagos Islands. The measurements were taken in 1976 before a major drought hit the island and in 1978 after the drought (survivors and survivors' offspring).

Beak depth / mm	No. 1976 birds	No. 1978 survivors	Beak depth of offspring / mm	Number of birds
7.30-7.79	1	0	7.30-7.79	2
7.80-8.29	12	1	7.80-8.29	2
8.30-8.79	30	3	8.30-8.79	5
8.80-9.29	47	3	8.80-9.29	21
9.30-9.79	45	6	9.30-9.79	34
9.80-10.29	40	9	9.80-10.29	37
10.30-10.79	25	10	10.30-10.79	19
10.80-11.29	3	1	10-80-11.29	15
11.30+	0	0	11.30+	2

1. Use the data above to draw two separate sets of histograms:

   (a) On the left hand grid draw side-by-side histograms for the number of 1976 birds per beak depth and the number of 1978 survivors per beak depth.

   (b) On the right hand grid draw a histogram of the beak depths of the offspring of the 1978 survivors.

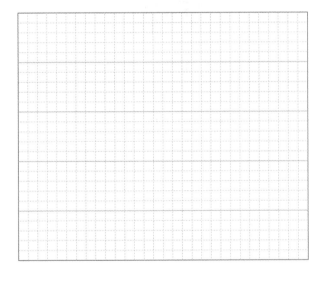

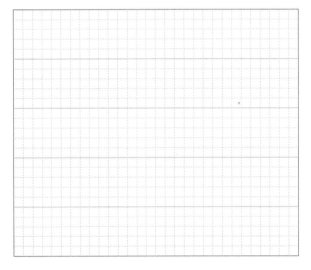

2. (a) Mark the approximate mean beak depth on the graphs of the 1976 beak depths and the 1978 offspring.

   (b) How much has the average moved from 1976 to 1978? _____

   (c) Is beak depth heritable? What does this mean for the process of natural selection in the finches?

   _____

   _____

3. The 1976 drought resulted in plants dying back and not producing seed. Based on the graphs, what can you say about competition between the birds for the remaining seeds, i.e. in what order were the seeds probably used up?

   _____

   _____

   _____

LINK 108 LINK 104 WEB 107

DATA

108 Disruptive Selection in Darwin's Finches

Key Idea: Disruptive selection in the finch *Geospiza fortis* produces a bimodal distribution for beak size.

The Galápagos Islands, 970 km west of Ecuador, are home to the finch species *Geospiza fortis*. A study during a prolonged drought on Santa Cruz Island showed how **disruptive selection** can change the distribution of genotypes in a population. During the drought, large and small seeds were more abundant than the preferred intermediate seed size.

Beak sizes of *G. fortis* were measured over a three year period (2004-2006), at the start and end of each year. At the start of the year, individuals were captured, banded, and their beaks were measured.

The presence or absence of banded individuals was recorded at the end of the year when the birds were recaptured. Recaptured individuals had their beaks measured.

The proportion of banded individuals in the population at the end of the year gave a measure of fitness. Absent individuals were presumed dead (fitness = 0).

Fitness related to beak size showed a bimodal distribution (left) typical of disruptive selection.

Beak size vs fitness in *Geospiza fortis*

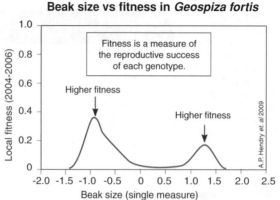

Fitness is a measure of the reproductive success of each genotype.

Higher fitness

Higher fitness

Fitness showed a **bimodal distribution** (arrowed) being highest for smaller and larger beak sizes.

Measurements of the beak length, width, and depth were combined into one **single measure**.

Beak size pairing in *Geospiza fortis*

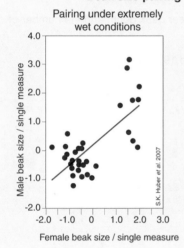

Pairing under extremely wet conditions

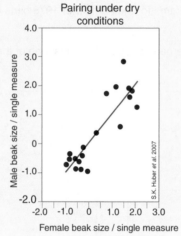

Pairing under dry conditions

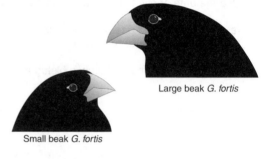

Large beak *G. fortis*

Small beak *G. fortis*

A 2007 study found that breeding pairs of birds had similar beak sizes. Male and females with small beaks tended to breed together, and males and females with large beaks tended to breed together. Mate selection maintained the biomodal distribution in the population during extremely wet conditions. If beak size wasn't a factor in mate selection, the beak size would even out.

1. (a) How did the drought affect seed size on Santa Cruz Island? _____

_____

(b) How did the change in seed size during the drought create a selection pressure for changes in beak size?

_____

_____

_____

2. How does beak size relate to fitness (differential reproductive success) in *G. fortis*? _____

_____

_____

_____

3. (a) Is mate selection in *G. fortis* random / non-random? (delete one)

(b) Give reasons for your answer: _____

_____

_____

© 2017 **BIOZONE** International
ISBN: 978-1-927309-26-1
Photocopying Prohibited

109 Genetic Drift Affects Gene Pools

Key Idea: Genetic drift is the change in allele frequencies in a population as a result of random events. It can be an important agent of evolution in small populations.

Genetic drift is the change in allele frequencies in a population due to random (chance) events. It may result in the loss (or fixation) of any allele, including beneficial ones. Genetic drift is effectively sampling error so its effects are greater when the population is small. In natural systems, small populations are

generally the result of the founder effect or a genetic bottleneck. In the founder effect, a small proportion of the population becomes isolated, e.g. through a colonisation event. Genetic bottlenecks occur when populations experience catastrophic losses so that only a small proportion of the population survives. Both these mechanisms are well documented in natural populations. In these small populations, genetic drift is an important agent of genetic change.

How does genetic drift reduce variation in populations?

The change in allele frequencies within a population through genetic drift is often illustrated using the random sampling of marbles from a jar. The diagram below represents a population of 20 individuals. The different alleles are represented by blue and grey marbles. The starting population contains an equal number of blue and grey marbles. Random mating is represented by selecting 10 marbles at random. Twenty marbles representing the new allele proportions are placed into a new jar to represent the second generation, and the process is repeated for subsequent generations.

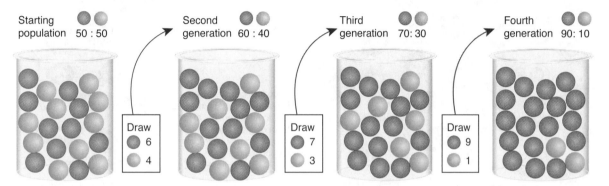

In the example above, the grey marbles are becoming less frequent within the population and the amount of genetic variation within the population is reducing. Unless the proportion of grey marbles increases, it will eventually be lost from the population altogether and the allele for the blue marble becomes fixed (the only variant).

If environmental conditions change so that the blue allele becomes detrimental, the population may become extinct (the potentially adaptive grey allele has been lost).

In small populations, genetic drift can be a major agent of rapid change because the loss of any one individual represents a greater proportion of the total population.

The graph on the right shows the effect of genetic drift on populations of various sizes. Fluctuations are minimal for a large population (2000) but more pronounced in smaller populations (200 and 20), which may lose alleles.

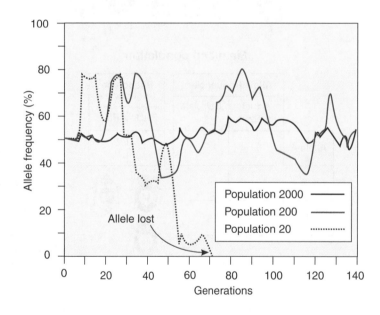

1. (a) Describe the effects of genetic drift: _____

   _____

   (b) Explain why the effects of genetic drift are more significant in small populations? _____

   _____

   _____

2. (a) Genetic drift in a small population would increase / decrease the number of heterozygotes (delete one):

   (b) How could this affect a population's long term viability? _____

   _____

   _____

LINK 111   LINK 110   LINK 98   WEB 109   **KNOW**

110 The Founder Effect

Key Idea: The founder effect can result in differences in allele frequencies between a parent and founder populations.

If a small number of individuals from a large population becomes isolated from their original parent population, their sample of alleles is unlikely to represent the allele proportions of the parent population. This phenomenon is called the **founder effect** and it can result in the colonising (founder) population evolving in a different direction to the parent population. This is particularly the case if the founder population is subjected to different selection pressures in a new environment and if the population is missing alleles that are present in the parent population.

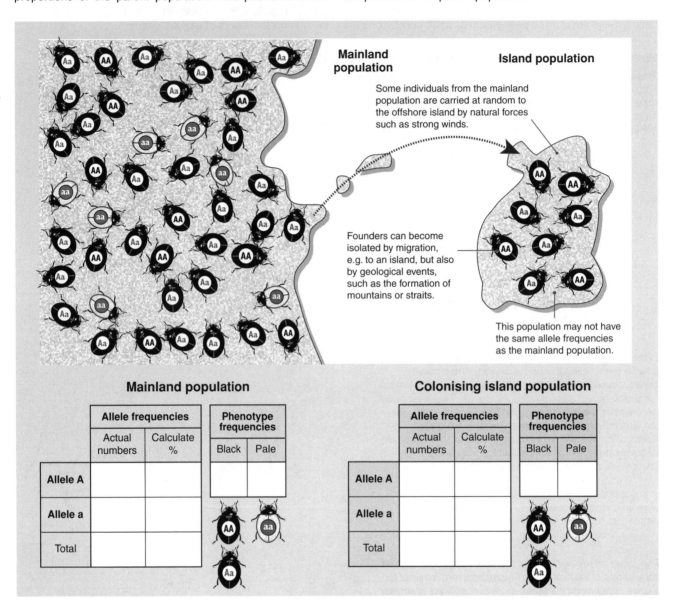

Mainland population

Some individuals from the mainland population are carried at random to the offshore island by natural forces such as strong winds.

Island population

Founders can become isolated by migration, e.g. to an island, but also by geological events, such as the formation of mountains or straits.

This population may not have the same allele frequencies as the mainland population.

Mainland population

| | Allele frequencies | | Phenotype frequencies | |
	Actual numbers	Calculate %	Black	Pale
Allele A				
Allele a				
Total				

Colonising island population

| | Allele frequencies | | Phenotype frequencies | |
	Actual numbers	Calculate %	Black	Pale
Allele A				
Allele a				
Total				

1. Compare the mainland population to the population which ended up on the island (use the spaces in the tables above):
   (a) Count the **phenotype** numbers for the two populations (i.e. the number of black and pale beetles).
   (b) Count the **allele** numbers for the two populations: the number of dominant alleles (A) and recessive alleles (a). Calculate these as a percentage of the total number of alleles for each population.

2. How are the allele frequencies of the two populations different? _____

_____

_____

3. Describe some possible ways in which various types of organism can be **carried** to an offshore island:

   (a) Plants: _____

   (b) Land animals: _____

   (c) Non-marine birds: _____

© 2017 **BIOZONE** International
ISBN: 978-1-927309-26-1
Photocopying Prohibited

Microgeographic isolation in garden snails

The European garden snail (*Cornu aspersum*, formerly *Helix aspersa*) is widely distributed throughout the world, both naturally and by human introduction. However because of its relatively slow locomotion and need for moist environments it can be limited in its habitat and this can lead to regional variation. The study below illustrates an investigation carried out on two snail populations in the city of Bryan, Texas. The snail populations covered two adjacent city blocks surrounded by tarmac roads.

The snails were found in several colonies in each block. Allele frequencies for the gene *MDH-1* (alleles A and a) were obtained and compared. Statistical analysis of the allele frequencies of the two populations showed them to be significantly different ($P \ll 0.05$). Note: A Mann-Whitney U test was used in this instance. It is similar to a Student's t test, but does not assume a normal distribution of data (it is non-parametric).

Block A **Block B**

Source: Evolution, Vol 29, No. 3, 1975

Road (not to sclae)

● Snail colony (circle size is proportional to colony size). ▢ Building

	Colony	1	2	3	4	5	6	7	8	9	10	11	12	13	14	15
Block A	*MDH-1* A %	39	39	36	42	39	47	32	42	44	42	44	50	50	58	75
	MDH-1 a %															
Block B	*MDH-1* A %	81	61	75	68	70	61	70	60	58	61	54	54	47		
	MDH-1 a %															

4. Complete the table above by filling in the frequencies of the *MDH-1* a allele:

5. Suggest why these snail populations are effectively geographically isolated: _____

_____

_____

6. Both the *MDH-1* alleles produce fully operative enzymes. Suggest why the frequencies of the alleles have become significantly different.

_____

_____

_____

_____

7. Identify the colony in block A that appears to be isolated from the rest of the block itself: _____

111 Genetic Bottlenecks

Key Idea: Genetic bottlenecks occur when population numbers and diversity fall dramatically. Although a population's numbers may recover, its genetic diversity often does not.

Populations may sometimes be reduced to low numbers by predation, disease, or periods of climatic change. These large scale reductions are called genetic (or population) bottlenecks. The sudden population decline is not necessarily selective and it may affect all phenotypes equally. Large scale catastrophic events, such as fire or volcanic eruptions, are examples of such

non-selective events. Affected populations may later recover, having squeezed through a 'bottleneck' of low numbers. The diagram below illustrates how population numbers may be reduced as a result of a catastrophic event. Following such an event, the gene pool of the surviving remnant population may be markedly different to that of the original gene pool. Genetic drift may cause further changes to allele frequencies. The small population may return to previous levels but with a reduced genetic diversity.

The effect of genetic bottlenecks on genetic diversity

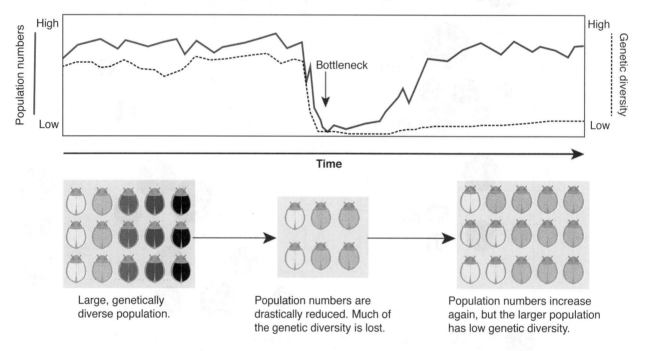

Large, genetically diverse population.

Population numbers are drastically reduced. Much of the genetic diversity is lost.

Population numbers increase again, but the larger population has low genetic diversity.

Genetic bottlenecks and low allelic diversity in Tasmanian devils

▶ Tasmanian devils are endemic to Australia and are the largest surviving marsupial carnivore. Although now restricted to the state of Tasmania, devils were once found throughout mainland Australia, but became locally extinct about 3000 years ago.

▶ Genetic evidence suggests that the devils went through at least two historic population crashes, one about 30 000 years ago and another about 3000 years ago. Coupled with these historic declines are modern declines as a result of trapping and disease (1850 to 1950) .

▶ These historic population crashes are likely to be responsible for the very low diversity in the major histocompatibility complex (MHC) I and II genes in devils. The MHC genes play an important role in immunity and the body's self recognition system.

▶ Low allelic diversity for MHC is implicated in the spread of devil facial tumour disease (DFTD), a contagious cancer that appeared in populations in the mid 1990s and has resulted in the loss of 80% of the devil population.

▶ The cancerous cells are transmitted when the devils fight. Ordinarily this foreign material would be recognised and destroyed by the immune system. In Tasmanian devils, the immune diversity is so low that tumours can spread without invoking an immune response.

▶ Recent evidence shows that some populations are developing immunity to DFTD. This may originate in individuals with MHC alleles distinctly different from the susceptible individuals.

Photos: Healthy Tasmanian devil (right, top) and devil infected with devil facial tumour disease (right, bottom).

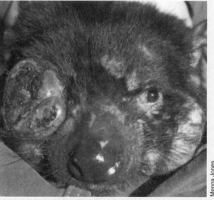

Cheetahs have undergone a genetic bottleneck

Cheetah mother with cub: they will be virtually genetically identical

▶ The world population of cheetahs currently stands at fewer than 8000. This is partially due to hunting and habitat loss, but also due to very low genetic diversity within the population.

▶ The low genetic variability in cheetahs is the result of past genetic bottlenecks, the first around 100 000 years ago and the second about 12 000 years ago. These bottlenecks were most likely associated with ice age migrations from North America into Africa and with a depletion of prey species at the end of the Pleistocene. The bottlenecks severely reduced genetic variability in the population and greatly increased the amount of inbreeding.

▶ Researchers measured genetic variation between seven individuals in two countries using a number of measures. They found cheetahs have very little genetic variation. In fact, their variation is so depleted, organs could be transplanted between individuals and not cause an immune response.

▶ A high level of inbreeding increases the incidence of harmful alleles and is associated with reproductive failures. Male cheetahs have a high occurrence of malformed sperm, which contributes to their poor reproductive success. In addition, the low allelic diversity means that the cheetahs are less able to respond to environmental changes or new pathogens, making extinction much more likely.

1. Define the term population bottleneck: _____

_____

_____

2. Explain how a population bottleneck can decrease genetic diversity in a population: _____

_____

_____

_____

_____

_____

3. What events might cause a population bottleneck? _____

_____

4. (a) What has been the genetic consequence of bottleneck events in the Tasmanian devil population?_____

_____

_____

_____

   (b) How has this led to increased susceptibility to disease, specifically infectious cancer? _____

_____

_____

_____

5. Endangered species are often subjected to genetic bottlenecks. Explain how genetic bottlenecks affect the ability of a population of an endangered species to recover from its plight:

_____

_____

_____

© 2017 **BIOZONE** International
ISBN: 978-1-927309-26-1
Photocopying Prohibited

112 Chapter Review

Summarise what you know about this topic under the headings and sub-headings provided. You can draw diagrams or mind maps, or write short notes to organise your thoughts. Use the images and hints to help you and refer back to the introduction to check the points covered:

Origins of genetic variation

HINT: Explain how mutation, meiosis, and random fertilisation bring about genetic variation.

Transfer of genetic information

HINT: Describe monohybrid inheritance involving dominant, recessive, and codominant alleles. Describe dihybrid inheritance, including the effect of linkage. Explain sex linkage and describe the inheritance of sex linked traits.

© 2017 **BIOZONE** International
ISBN: **978-1-927309-26-1**
Photocopying Prohibited

Gene pools

HINT: Define a gene pool. What factors affect allele frequencies in gene pools? How is Hardy-Weinberg used to monitor changes in allele frequencies?

Gene pools: natural selection

HINT: Distinguish between stabilising, directional, and disruptive selection and their effect on the phenotypic variation in a population.

113 KEY TERMS AND IDEAS: Did You Get It?

1. Test your vocabulary by matching each term to its definition, as identified by its preceding letter code.

allele frequency

continuous variation

dihybrid cross

dominant (of alleles)

founder effect

genetic bottleneck

genetic drift

genotype

independent assortment

monohybrid cross

mutation

natural selection

phenotype

recessive (of alleles)

recombination

sex linkage

A The process by which favourable heritable traits become more common in successive generations (differential survival of favourable phenotypes).

B An evolutionary event in which a significant proportion of a population's alleles are lost.

C Allele that will only express its trait in the absence of the dominant allele.

D Variation showing a large number of phenotypic variants approximating a bell shaped (normal) curve.

E The specific allele combination of an organism.

F The loss of genetic variation when a new colony is formed by a very small number of individuals from a larger population.

G The random alignment and distribution of chromosomes to gametes during meiosis.

H The observable characteristics in an organism.

I The recombination of genetic material between homologous chromosomes as a result of crossing over during meiosis.

J Genetic cross between two individuals that differ in one characteristic of interest.

K A change in the base sequence of DNA; the ultimate source of new alleles.

L The condition in which a gene responsible for a specific trait is located on a sex chromosome, resulting in sex-linked inheritance of the trait.

M Allele that expresses its trait irrespective of the other allele.

N A cross studying the inheritance pattern of two genes.

O The relative frequency of an allele at a particular locus in a population, expressed as a fraction or percentage.

P Variation in the relative frequency of alleles due to their chance loss from the population.

2. Using examples, contrast the characteristics of directional and stabilising selection and their effects:

_____

_____

_____

_____

3. Within a population of butterflies, brown colour (B) is dominant over white (b) and 40% of butterflies are white. Calculate:

(a) The percentage of butterflies that are heterozygous: _____

_____

(b) The frequency of homozygous dominant individuals: _____

_____

4. Blood samples of 1000 individuals were typed for the MN blood group, which can be detected because the alleles are codominant. Using the results (right) calculate the frequency of each allele in the population:

(a) Frequency of M: _____

_____

(b) Frequency of N: _____

_____

Blood type	Genotype	No. of individuals	Frequency
M	MM	490	0.49
MN	MN	420	0.42
N	NN	90	0.09

© 2017 **BIOZONE** International
ISBN: 978-1-927309-26-1
Photocopying Prohibited

Topic 9

Control Systems

9.1 Homeostasis

Learning outcomes

Activity number

☐ i Know that homeostasis is the maintenance of a state of dynamic equilibrium. — 114

☐ ii Explain the importance of maintaining a stable core temperature, stable blood pH, and stable water potential in the body. — 114

☐ iii Describe the role of feedback mechanisms in dynamic homeostasis, including:
   • negative feedback, counteracting departures from the steady state. — 115
   • positive feedback as a mechanism that escalates a physiological response. — 116

9.2 Chemical control in mammals

Learning outcomes

Activity number

☐ i Describe endocrine control in mammals to include production of hormones by endocrine glands and their mode of action involving receptors on target cells. — 117 118

☐ ii Describe the two main modes of hormone action with reference to:
   • Adrenaline, which attaches to receptors on the target cell and triggers the release of a second messenger that activates specific enzymes in the cell.
   • Oestrogen, which enters cells and binds directly to an intracellular receptor, forming a DNA binding complex (a transcription factor). — 118 119

9.3 Chemical control in plants

Learning outcomes

Activity number

☐ i Explain the basis of chemical control in plants with reference to plant growth substances such as auxins, cytokinins, and gibberellins. — 120

☐ **CP-14** ▸ Investigate the effect of gibberellin on the production of amylase in germinating cereals using a starch agar assay. — 124

☐ **AT** ▸ Safely and ethically use organisms to measure physiological functions. — 124

☐ ii Describe and explain the effects of auxins on cell elongation, apical dominance, and promotion of root growth. — 121 122

☐ iii Explain how plant growth substances can interact to produce differential responses in different tissues. Include reference to the antagonistic actions of cytokinin and auxin on apical dominance. — 120 123

☐ iv Explain the control of flowering and photomorphogenesis by phytochrome. — 125

☐ iii Describe the location and main functions of: **128**
  - the medulla oblongata to include the control of breathing and heart rate.
  - cerebellum to include the control of balance and coordination.
  - cerebrum to include the control of voluntary movement (motor cortex).
  - hypothalamus to include temperature regulation and osmoregulation.

☐ iv Describe the basic structure of the peripheral nervous system to include the **126**
autonomic nervous system (ANS) and the voluntary (somatic) nervous system.

☐ v Describe and explain the division of the autonomic nervous system into **127**
sympathetic and parasympathetic systems, which act antagonistically.

9.5 Nervous transmission
Learning outcomes Activity number

☐ i Identify the main regions of a motor neurone. Describe the properties of the **129 130**
axon membrane and explain how the resting potential is generated.

☐ ii Explain how an action potential is generated and propagated along an axon. **129 130**

☐ iii Explain why the speed of impulse transmission in myelinated axons is greater **129 130**
than in non-myelinated axons with reference to saltatory conduction.

☐ iv Describe the structure and function of a synapse, including the role of the **131**
neurotransmiters acetylcholine (ACh) and noradrenaline.

☐ v Describe and explain the effects of excitatory and inhibitory postsynaptic **132**
potentials, including reference to synaptic integration.

9.6 Effects of drugs on the nervous system
Learning outcomes Activity number

☐ i Explain the effects of drugs on synaptic transmission including: **132**
  - nicotine as an acetylcholine mimic (agonist).
  - lidocaine as an acetylcholine antagonist, binding and blocking the voltage
    gated sodium (Na^+) channels on the postsynaptic membrane (multiple targets).
  - cobra venom as an acetylcholine antagonist blocking acetylcholine receptors.

9.7 Detection of light by mammals
Learning outcomes Activity number

☐ i Know the basic structure of the human eye. Describe the structure of the human **135 136**
retina with reference to the rods and cones, bipolar neurones, and ganglion cells.

☐ ii Explain the role of rhodopsin in initiating generator potentials, which are **136**
converted to action potentials in the ganglion cells.

☐ iii Explain how the distribution of human rod and cone cells maintain vision in **136**
different light intensities.

9.8 Control of heart rate in mammals
Learning outcomes Activity number

☐ i Explain extrinsic control of heart rate by the ANS to include: **137**
  - aortic and carotid baroreceptors and chemoreceptors.
  - sympathetic nervous stimulation to release noradrenaline at the SAN.
  - parasympathetic nervous stimulation to release acetylcholine at the SAN.

☐ ii Describe the role of the ANS in the release of adrenaline to increase heart rate. **137**

9.9 Osmoregulation and temperature regulation
Learning outcomes Activity number

☐ i Describe the gross and microscopic structure of the mammalian kidney. **139 140**

☐ ii Outline how urea is produced in the liver from excess amino acids and how it is **138**
removed from the bloodstream by ultrafiltration.

☐ iii Explain how solutes are selectively reabsorbed in the proximal tubule and how the **140**
loop of Henle acts as a countercurrent multiplier to increase water reabsorption.

☐ iv Explain how the pituitary gland, hypothalamic osmoreceptors, and antidiuretic **141**
hormone (ADH) regulate plasma concentration through negative feedback.

☐ v Describe how the kidney of a kangaroo rat is adapted for life in a dry environment. **142**

☐ vi Distinguish between endotherms and ectotherms in their source of body heat. **143**

☐ vii Explain thermoregulation in an endotherm through behaviour and physiology. **144 145**
Include the role of the ANS, thermoreceptors, hypothalamus and skin.

114 Homeostasis

Key Idea: Homeostasis refers to the maintenance of a (relatively) constant physiological state of the body despite fluctuations in the external environment.

Organisms maintain a relatively constant physiological state, called **homeostasis**, despite changes in their environment. Any change in the environment to which an organism responds is called a **stimulus** and, because environmental stimuli are not static, organisms must also adjust their behaviour and physiology constantly to maintain homeostasis. This requires the coordinated activity of the body's organ systems.

Homeostatic mechanisms prevent deviations from the steady state and keep the body's internal conditions within the strict limits needed to maintain the metabolic reactions that sustain life. Body temperature, blood glucose level, blood pressure, and pH and water potential of the body's fluids are all factors that must be regulated to within narrow limits. Deviations from these limits can cause a fatal loss of metabolic function. For example, during exercise, the body must maintain a constant temperature of ~37.0°C despite the increased heat generated by activity. Heart and breathing rates must increase to meet the energy demands of muscle contraction, and blood pH must be maintained at 7.35-7.45 despite increased production and transport of CO_2.

To maintain homeostasis, the body must detect stimuli through receptors, process this sensory information, and respond to it appropriately via effectors. The responses provide new feedback to the receptor (below).

How homeostasis is maintained

Muscles and glands

Sense organ (e.g. eye)

Receptor	**Effector**
Detects change and sends a message to the control centre.	Responds to the output from the control centre.

Brain and spinal cord

Control centre
Receives the message and coordinates a response. Sends an output message to an effector.

The analogy of a thermostat on a heater is a good way to understand how homeostasis is maintained. A heater has sensors (a receptor) to monitor room temperature. It also has a control centre to receive and process the data from the sensors. Depending on the data it receives, the control centre activates the effector (heating unit), switching it on or off. When the room is too cold, the heater switches on. When it is too hot, the heater switches off. This maintains a constant temperature.

1. What is homeostasis and why is it important? _____

_____

_____

_____

2. What is the role of the following components in maintaining homeostasis:

(a) Receptor: _____

(b) Control centre: _____

_____

(c) Effector: _____

© 2017 **BIOZONE** International
ISBN: 978-1-927309-26-1
Photocopying Prohibited

LINK 144   LINK 141   WEB 114   **KNOW**

115 Negative Feedback

Key Idea: Negative feedback mechanisms detect departures from a set point norm and act to restore the steady state.

Most physiological systems achieve homeostasis through negative feedback. In negative feedback systems, movement away from a steady state is detected and triggers a mechanism to counteract that change. **Negative feedback** has a stabilising effect, dampening variations from a set point and returning internal conditions to a steady state. This steady state provides the specific conditions of temperature, pH, and osmolarity required for the billions of enzyme-catalysed reactions that constitute metabolism. Enzymes work correctly within very narrow limits. Outside those limits they break down or denature and are unable to catalyse reactions in the body. For example, most enzymes in the body denature above 40°C. If the body's internal environment reaches this temperature for any prolonged time it may result in death.

Negative feedback and control systems

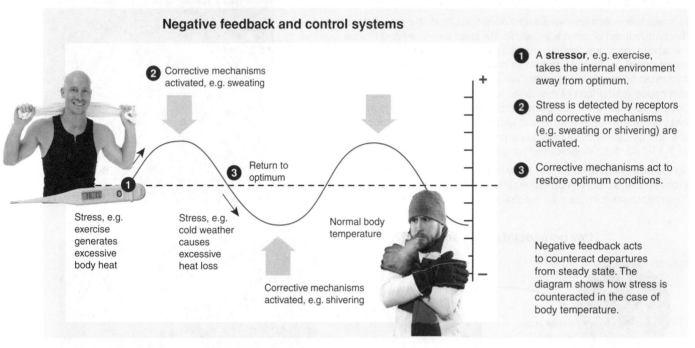

1 A **stressor**, e.g. exercise, takes the internal environment away from optimum.

2 Stress is detected by receptors and corrective mechanisms (e.g. sweating or shivering) are activated.

3 Corrective mechanisms act to restore optimum conditions.

2 Corrective mechanisms activated, e.g. sweating

3 Return to optimum

Stress, e.g. exercise generates excessive body heat

Stress, e.g. cold weather causes excessive heat loss

Normal body temperature

Corrective mechanisms activated, e.g. shivering

Negative feedback acts to counteract departures from steady state. The diagram shows how stress is counteracted in the case of body temperature.

Negative feedback in blood pH

Regulation of ventilation rate helps to maintain blood pH between 7.35 and 7.45. Low blood pH stimulates increased breathing rate, which reduces H^+ via exhalation. This reduces sensory input to the medulla and breathing returns to normal.

High H^+ (low pH) in blood

Chemoreceptors in the medulla oblongata detect changes in H^+ and send impulses to the lungs.

H^+ level in blood falls

Lung ventilation rate increases.

More CO_2 is exhaled, reducing H_2CO_3 in the blood and therefore reducing H^+.

Negative feedback in stomach emptying

Empty stomach. Stomach wall is relaxed.

Stretch receptors are deactivated

A

Food is eaten

Food enters the stomach, stretching the stomach wall.

Stretch receptors are activated

Smooth muscle in the stomach wall contracts. Food is mixed and emptied from the stomach.

B

1. How do negative feedback mechanisms maintain homeostasis in a variable environment? _____

_____

_____

2. On the diagram of stomach emptying, state:

The stimulus at: A: _____   The response at B: _____

© 2017 **BIOZONE** International
ISBN: 978-1-927309-26-1
Photocopying Prohibited

116 Positive Feedback

Key Idea: Positive feedback results in the escalation of a response to a stimulus. It causes system instability and occurs when a particular outcome or resolution is required. Positive feedback mechanisms amplify a physiological response in order to achieve a particular result. Labour, fever, blood clotting, and fruit ripening all involve positive feedback. Normally, a positive feedback loop is ended when the natural resolution is reached (e.g. baby is born, pathogen is destroyed). Positive feedback is relatively rare because such mechanisms are unstable and potentially damaging.

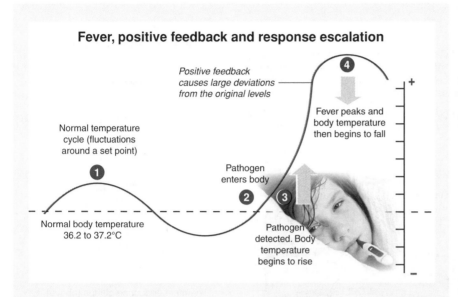

Fever, positive feedback and response escalation

Positive feedback causes large deviations from the original levels

Normal temperature cycle (fluctuations around a set point)

Normal body temperature 36.2 to 37.2°C

Pathogen enters body

Pathogen detected. Body temperature begins to rise

Fever peaks and body temperature then begins to fall

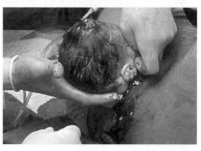

Labour and lactation: During childbirth (above), the release of oxytocin intensifies the contractions of the uterus so that labour proceeds to its conclusion. The birth itself restores the system by removing the initiating stimulus. After birth, levels of the milk-production hormone prolactin increase. Suckling maintains prolactin secretion and causes the release of oxytocin, resulting in milk release. The more an infant suckles, the more these hormones are produced.

1. Body temperature fluctuates on a normal, regular basis around a narrow set point.

2. Pathogen enters the body.

3. The body detects the pathogen and macrophages attack it. Macrophages release interleukins which stimulate the hypothalamus to increase prostaglandin production and reset the body's thermostat to a higher 'fever' level by shivering (the chill phase).

4. The fever breaks when the infection subsides. Levels of circulating interleukins (and other fever-associated chemicals) fall, and the body's thermostat is reset to normal. This ends the positive feedback escalation and normal controls resume. If the infection persists, the escalation may continue, and the fever may intensify. Body temperatures in excess of 43°C are often fatal or result in brain damage.

Ethylene is a gaseous plant hormone involved in fruit ripening. It accelerates the ripening of fruit in its vicinity so nearby fruit also ripens, releasing more ethylene. Over-exposure to ethylene causes fruit to over-ripen (rot).

1. (a) What is the biological role of positive feedback loops? Describe an example: _____

_____

_____

_____

(b) Why is positive feedback inherently unstable (contrast with negative feedback)? _____

_____

_____

_____

(c) How is a positive feedback loop normally stopped? _____

_____

(d) Describe a situation in which this might not happen. What would be the result? _____

_____

_____

_____

117 Hormonal Regulatory Systems

Key Idea: The endocrine system regulates physiological processes by releasing hormones which interact with target cells to bring about a specific cellular response.

The endocrine system consists of endocrine cells (organised into endocrine glands) and the hormones (blood-borne chemical messengers) they produce. Endocrine glands located throughout the body secrete hormones directly into the bloodstream rather than through a duct. Hormones are produced in very small quantities but can exert a very large effect on their target cells. They regulate the activity of cells or organs, thus maintaining homeostasis or regulating metabolism. The major endocrine organs are shown below.

How hormones work

▶ Endocrine cells produce hormones and secrete them into the bloodstream where they are distributed throughout the body. Although hormones are sent throughout the body, they affect only specific target cells. These target cells have **receptors** on the plasma membrane which recognise and bind the hormone (inset, below).

▶ The binding of hormone and receptor triggers the response in the target cell. Cells are unresponsive to a hormone if they do not have the appropriate receptors.

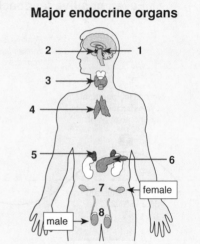

Major endocrine organs

The main endocrine glands (above) regulate the body's growth, metabolism, sexual development, and function.

1. Pineal gland
2. Pituitary gland
3. Thyroid gland
4. Thymus
5. Adrenal gland
6. Pancreas
7. Ovary (female)
8. Testis (male)

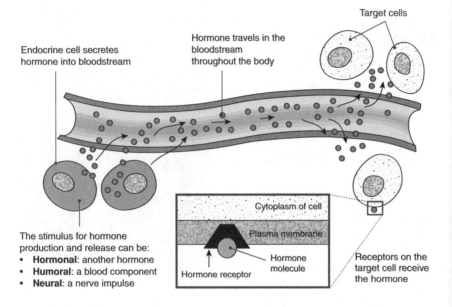

The stimulus for hormone production and release can be:
• **Hormonal**: another hormone
• **Humoral**: a blood component
• **Neural**: a nerve impulse

1. (a) What is a hormone? _____

_____

(b) What are the functions of hormones? _____

_____

_____

(c) How are hormones distributed throughout the body? _____

_____

_____

(d) Given that hormones are transported widely throughout the body, why is it that hormones only affect certain cells?

_____

_____

2. Describe the three types of stimuli for the production and release of hormones:

(a) _____

(b) _____

(c) _____

© 2017 **BIOZONE** International
ISBN: **978-1-927309-26-1**
Photocopying Prohibited

118 What is Signal Transduction?

Key Idea: Signal transduction is the conversion of an external signal (e.g. from a hormone) to a functional change within the cell through a series of biochemical reactions.

Signal transduction (or cell signalling) is the process by which a physical or chemical signal (such as from a hormone) is transmitted through a cell as a series of biochemical reactions, which result in a cellular response. The series of reactions is often called a cascade and usually involves phosphorylation (charging) of a number of molecules in a sequence. Signal transduction pathways often involve amplification of the signal so that one signal molecule can produce a large net effect in the cell. Responses vary from change in metabolism (activating a pathway), to changes in gene expression or membrane permeability.

An overview of signal transduction

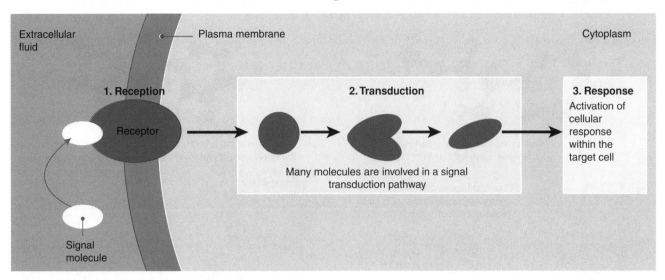

Signal transduction can be broken into three main steps:

▶ **Reception**: An extracellular signal molecule, such as a hormone, binds to its receptor on a target cell.

▶ **Transduction**: The activated receptor triggers a chain of biochemical events within the cell. Many different enzymes are involved, and the entire reaction is often called a signalling cascade.

▶ **Response**: The signal cascade results in a specific cellular response.

Gibberellic acid activation of α-amylase: An example of a cellular response

In plants, the hormone gibberellic acid (GA) is involved in seed germination. GA acts as a signal molecule to stimulate the production of the enzyme α-amylase. The α-amylase hydrolyses (breaks down) starch into simple sugars, which the plant can use.

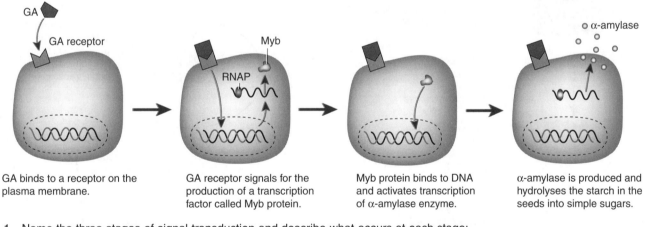

GA binds to a receptor on the plasma membrane.

GA receptor signals for the production of a transcription factor called Myb protein.

Myb protein binds to DNA and activates transcription of α-amylase enzyme.

α-amylase is produced and hydrolyses the starch in the seeds into simple sugars.

1. Name the three stages of signal transduction and describe what occurs at each stage:

(a) _____

(b) _____

(c) _____

LINK 119 WEB 118 **KNOW**

119 Modes of Hormone Action

Key Idea: Hormones may bind to extracellular receptors and exert their effects through a second messenger, or they may cross the plasma membrane, binding to intracellular receptors and acting directly at the level of gene transcription. Hormones have two broadly different modes of action. Hydrophilic hormones (e.g. peptide hormones) interact with extracellular receptors on the target cell membrane and exert their effects through activation of a second messenger signalling system. Hydrophobic hormones (e.g. steroids) can cross the plasma membrane, entering the cell and interacting with intracellular receptors to form a hormone-receptor complex that directly regulates transcription of genes.

Hydrophilic signal molecules are received by extracellular receptors

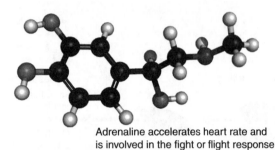

Adrenaline accelerates heart rate and is involved in the fight or flight response

Hydrophobic signal molecules are received by intracellular receptors

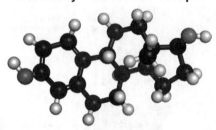

Oestrogen is the primary female sex hormone. It is involved in the development and maintenance of female characteristics.

Extracellular fluid

The first messenger (hormone) binds to the receptor protein

Membrane-bound enzyme

Receptor protein

Plasma membrane

Protein subunit from the receptor protein activates the enzyme

Second messenger — Active enzyme produces a second messenger, e.g. cyclic AMP

The second messenger triggers a cascade of phosphorylation events leading to a cellular response

P

Cytoplasm

Cell response

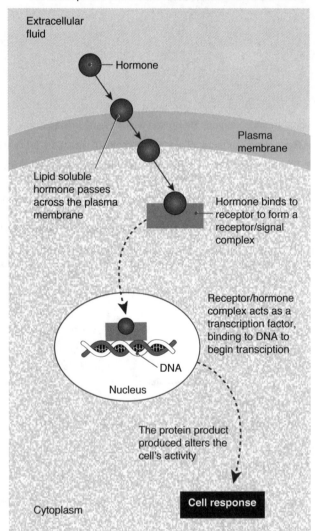

Extracellular fluid

Hormone

Plasma membrane

Lipid soluble hormone passes across the plasma membrane

Hormone binds to receptor to form a receptor/signal complex

Receptor/hormone complex acts as a transcription factor, binding to DNA to begin transciption

DNA

Nucleus

The protein product produced alters the cell's activity

Cytoplasm

Cell response

Hydrophilic hormones, such as amines (e.g. adrenaline) and peptides (e.g. insulin), are water soluble and cannot cross the plasma membrane. They require the aid of an extracellular receptor and activation of a second messenger system to exert their effect. The hormone is called the first messenger. When it binds to the extracellular receptor, it triggers a sequence of biochemical reactions, including activation of a second messenger. As a consequence of these sequential reactions, the original signal is amplified, bringing about a cellular response.

Hydrophobic hormones, such as steroids (e.g. oestrogen), diffuse freely across the plasma membrane and into the cytoplasm of target cells. Once inside the cell, they bind to intracellular receptors in the cytoplasm to form a receptor-signal complex. The complex moves to the cell nucleus where it binds directly to the DNA and acts as a **transcription factor**, resulting in the transcription of a one or more specific genes. Concentrations of the different gene products (proteins) change as a result (a phenotypic change).

© 2017 **BIOZONE** International
ISBN: 978-1-927309-26-1
Photocopying Prohibited

1. Describe the differences between an intracellular receptor and an extracellular receptor: _____

_____

_____

_____

2. What must a hormone do in order to activate a receptor? _____

_____

3. In terms of their ability to cross the plasma membrane, distinguish between hydrophobic and hydrophilic hormones:

_____

_____

_____

4. (a) Giving an example, outline signal transduction involving a hydrophilic hormone: _____

_____

_____

_____

_____

(b) Distinguish between a first messenger and a second messenger: _____

_____

_____

_____

5. Giving an example, outline signal transduction involving a hydrophobic hormone: _____

_____

_____

_____

_____

6. The diagram on the right represents a cell signalling process.

(a) Does this diagram represent an extracellular or intracellular
signalling process? Explain your answer:

_____

_____

_____

_____

Plasma membrane

Cell response

A B

(b) What type of receptor is B? _____

(c) What does A represent? _____

(d) Would A be hydrophobic or hydrophilic? Explain your answer: _____

_____

_____

_____

120 Auxins, Gibberellins, and Cytokinins

Key Idea: Plant hormones, such as auxins, gibberellins, and cytokinins, regulate plant growth, often acting in opposition to bring about specific growth responses at specific times.

Plant hormones (phytohormones) regulate the growth and developmental responses of vascular plants. Most often, regulation is achieved through the interactions of more than one hormone. **Auxins** are a group of hormones involved in a wide range of processes including elongation, bud formation, and initiation of root growth. **Gibberellins** are involved in stem and leaf elongation, as well as breaking dormancy in seeds. Specifically, they stimulate cell division and cell elongation. **Cytokinins** promote axillary bud growth and cell division in plant roots and shoots. They also moderate the effects of auxin on apical dominance and delay leaf fall.

Auxin (indole-acetic acid or IAA) is required for fruit growth. The maturing seed releases auxin, inducing the surrounding flower parts to develop into fruit.

Gibberellins cause stem and leaf elongation by stimulating cell division and cell elongation. They are responsible for bolting in brassicas (e.g. cabbage, above).

Cytokinin is found at the highest concentrations in meristematic (growth) regions of plants such as the roots, young leaves, developing fruits, and seeds.

Differential auxin transport, and therefore differential growth, is responsible for phototropism. Auxins are also responsible apical dominance in shoots. Auxin is produced in the shoot tip and diffuses down the stem to inhibit the development of the lateral buds.

Gibberellins are responsible for breaking dormancy in seeds and promote the growth of the embryo and emergence of the seedling. Auxin is known to affect gibberellin signalling and its synthesis. For example, gibberellin-stimulated root elongation requires auxin to be present.

Hormones can work antagonistically to cause responses. The stimulatory effect of auxin on apical dominance (upward growth) can be countered by cytokinin. Under certain ratios of auxin/cytokinin, lateral (side) growth can be stimulated even in the presence of a growing shoot tip.

1. Summarise the main roles of the each of the following plant hormones:

   (a) Auxins: _____

   _____

   (b) Gibberellins: _____

   _____

   (c) Cytokinins: _____

   _____

2. What evidence is there that plant hormones work antagonistically (against) each other? _____

   _____

   _____

121 Plant Hormones as Signal Molecules

Key Idea: Auxin is a plant hormone involved in the differential growth responses of plants to environmental stimuli.

Auxins are plant hormones with a central role in a range of growth and developmental responses in plants. Indole-acetic acid (IAA) is the most potent native auxin in intact plants.

The response of a plant tissue to IAA depends on the tissue itself, the hormone concentration, the timing of its release, and the presence of other hormones. Gradients in auxin concentration during growth prompt differential responses in specific tissues and contribute to directional growth.

Light is an important growth requirement for all plants. Most plants show an adaptive response of growing towards the light. This growth response is called phototropism.

The bending of the plants shown on the right is a phototropism in response to light shining from the left and is caused by the plant hormone **auxin**. Auxin causes the elongation of cells on the shaded side of the stem, causing it to bend (photo right).

Auxin is produced in the shoot tip and is responsible for apical dominance by suppressing growth of the lateral (side) buds.

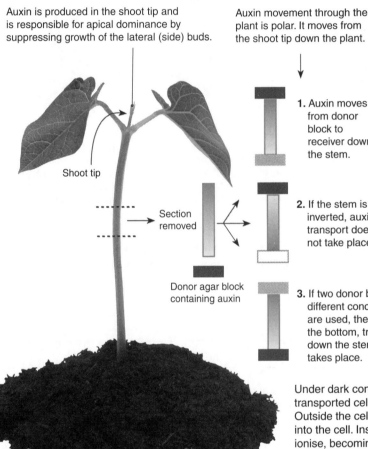

Shoot tip

Section removed

Donor agar block containing auxin

Auxin movement through the plant is polar. It moves from the shoot tip down the plant.

1. Auxin moves from donor block to receiver down the stem.

2. If the stem is inverted, auxin transport does not take place.

3. If two donor blocks of different concentration are used, the higher at the bottom, transport down the stem still takes place.

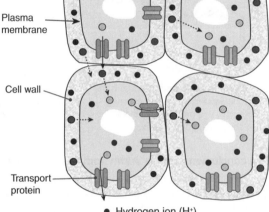

Plasma membrane

Cell wall

Transport protein

- ● Hydrogen ion (H⁺)
- ● Non-ionised auxin (AH)
- ● Ionised auxin (A⁻)
- ····▶ Diffusion
- —▶ Active transport

Under dark conditions auxin moves evenly down the stem. It is transported cell to cell by diffusion and transport proteins (above right). Outside the cell auxin is a non-ionised molecule (AH) which can diffuse into the cell. Inside the cell the pH of the cytoplasm causes auxin to ionise, becoming A⁻ and H⁺. Transport proteins at the basal end of the cell then transport A⁻ out of the cell where it reacquires an H⁺ ion and reforms AH. In this way auxin is transported in one direction through the plant. When plant cells are illuminated by light from one direction transport proteins in the plasma membrane on the shaded side of the cell are activated and auxin is transported to the shaded side of the plant.

1. What is the term given to the tropism being displayed in the photo (top right)? _____

2. Describe one piece of evidence that demonstrates the transport of auxin is polar: _____

_____

_____

_____

3. What is the effect of auxin on cell growth? _____

_____

122 The Role of Auxins in Apical Dominance

Key Idea: Auxin promotes apical growth in plants and inhibits the growth of lateral (side) buds.

Auxins are responsible for apical dominance in shoots. Auxin is produced in the shoot tip and diffuses down to inhibit the development of the lateral (side) buds. The effect of auxin on preventing the development of lateral buds can be demonstrated by removing the source of the auxin and examining the outcome (below).

▶ In many plants the growth of the shoot apex inhibits the growth of side (lateral) buds. As a result, plants tend to grow a single main stem upwards, which dominates over lateral branches.

▶ This response is called **apical dominance**.

▶ The hormone responsible for this response is **auxin**. It acts by stimulating cell elongation.

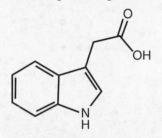

Indole-acetic acid (above) is the only known naturally occurring auxin. It is produced in the apical shoot and young leaves.

No treatment
Apical bud is left intact.

Apical bud

Inhibited lateral bud

In an intact plant, the plant stem elongates and the lateral buds remain inactive. No side growth occurs.

Treatment one
Apical bud is removed; no auxin is applied.

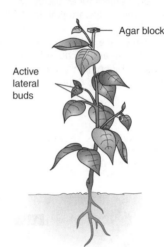

Agar block

Active lateral buds

The apical bud is removed and an agar block without auxin is placed on the cut surface. The seedling begins to develop lateral buds.

Treatment two
Apical bud is removed; auxin is applied.

Agar block

Inhibited lateral bud

The apical bud is removed and an agar block containing auxin is placed on the cut surface. Lateral bud development is inhibited.

Two conclusions can be drawn from this experiment:

(1) The apical bud contains a hormone that inhibits lateral growth because its removal promoted lateral growth.

(2) The presence of auxin in the apical bud inhibits lateral growth because auxin applied to a cut stem tip could inhibit lateral growth and mimic the effect of an intact apical bud.

1. Describe the role of auxins in apical dominance: _____

_____

_____

2. Outline the experimental evidence supporting the role of auxins in apical dominance: _____

_____

_____

_____

_____

3. Study the photo (right) and then answer the following questions:

(a) Label the apical bud.   (b) Label the lateral bud(s).

(c) Which buds are the largest? _____

(d) Why would this be important? _____

_____

NASA

4. If you were a gardener, how would you make your plants bushier?_____

_____

_____

LINK **120**   LINK **121**

KNOW

© 2017 **BIOZONE** International
ISBN: 978-1-927309-26-1
Photocopying Prohibited

123 | How Gibberellins Affect Growth

Key Idea: The effect of gibberellins on plant growth can be tested experimentally by comparing the growth of gibberellin treated plants to plants with no hormonal treatment.

Gibberellins (GA) are a group of plant hormones that affect stem growth. Gibberellic acid is a type of gibberellin. Dwarf pea plants are a selected variety with a mutation that results in impaired GA synthesis. By applying GA to them, the effect of GA on plant growth can easily be demonstrated. The experiment below was performed by a group of students to determine the effect of GA on dwarf pea stem growth.

The aim

To investigate the effect of gibberellic acid (GA) on stem growth in dwarf pea plants.

Hypothesis

If GA promotes stem elongation, dwarf pea plants treated with GA will grow taller than untreated dwarf pea plants.

Method

Students soaked 10 dwarf pea seeds (*Pisum sativum*) overnight in distilled water (seeds must absorb water in order to activate the metabolic functions needed for germination and growth). The seeds were divided into two groups of five seeds each. The test group received GA treatment and the control group did not. The seeds were planted into two separate containers filled with potting mix. Once the seeds had germinated, the test group had GA paste (500 ppm) painted on them. Both seed groups were watered daily with distilled water. The heights of the germinating shoots were recorded every few days for 20 days (except for one break in recording between days 11 and 18 when students were away).

Background

Japanese rice farmers documented rapid stem elongation in the 1800s. This process, called **bolting**, resulted in tall, spindly rice plants that set no seed. In 1934, two Japanese scientists isolated the plant hormone responsible for the rapid growth. That hormone was **gibberellin** and it acts by stimulating cell division and cell elongation.

Chemical analysis has revealed that bolting plants contain higher levels of gibberellin than non-bolting plants. The link between gibberellin and bolting can be tested experimentally by applying gibberellin to one group of plants but not to a control group. Both groups are grown in the same conditions and the differences in stem length are measured at the end of set period.

Plants treated with gibberellins have longer stems than the plants in the control group.

The results from the experiment are described in tables 1 and 2.

1. For each table (control and treatment), calculate the mean seedling height for each day and record it in the space provided.

2. For each table (control and treatment), calculate the standard deviation for each day and record it in the space provided.

   Remember: The standard deviation (s) is a measure of the variability (spread) in a set of data. Calculate standard deviation using either of the equations provided, right (they give the same answer). The first is simpler if calculating by hand. In general, if the standard deviation is small, the mean will more accurately represent the data than if the standard deviation is large.

① $$S = \sqrt{\frac{\sum x^2 - ((\sum x)^2 / n)}{n-1}}$$

where $(\sum x)$ = sum of value x
$\sum x^2$ = sum of value x^2
n = sample size

② $$S = \sqrt{\frac{\sum (x - \bar{x})^2}{n-1}}$$

where $\bar{x}$ = mean

Seed number	Table 1: Height (in cm) of control dwarf pea plants						
	Days after germination						
	2	4	6	9	11	18	20
1	1.2	3.1	4.4	6.1	8.3	12.3	16.1
2	1.8	3.6	5.1	7.1	8.8	15.9	19.0
3	1.3	3.3	4.6	6.4	8.9	15.4	18.1
4	0.4	2.9	4.2	6.3	9.5	12.0	13.4
5	1.2	3.7	5.1	6.9	7.2	10.8	12.3
Mean height / cm							
Standard deviation							

LINK
120

DATA

Table 2: Height (in cm) of gibberellin treated dwarf pea plants							
Seed number	Days after germination						
	2	4	6	9	11	18	20
1	1.1	5.5	12.1	22.4	25.9	37.5	38.5
2	0.6	5.4	14.6	24.7	28.1	35.8	30.1
3	1.1	6.6	15.0	24.5	26.8	34.8	30.0
4	0.9	6.7	14.2	21.7	26.5	30.2	38.2
5	0.4	4.8	14.1	23.6	25.9	29.0	39.2
Mean height / cm							
Standard deviation							

3. (a) Use the grid below to plot a line graph showing the mean plant heights for the two groups of dwarf peas. Plot the standard deviation for each mean as error bars either side of the mean. Include a title and correctly labelled axes.

    (b) Describe the effect of gibberellin on the growth of dwarf pea plants:

    _____

    _____

    _____

    (c) Do the results support the hypothesis?

    _____

    (d) Based on the spread of data around the two means at day 20, do you think that the difference between the control and treatment plants is significant? Explain.

    _____

    _____

    _____

    (e) If you were to use a statistical test to test this, what test could you use and why?

    _____

    _____

    _____

    (f) As extension, perform this test and report the result. Staple it to this page.

5. Why did the students use mutant dwarf peas?

    _____

    _____

6. In a second experiment, students treated one group of dwarf pea seeds with gibberellin and another group with gibberellin plus gibberellin inhibitor. Predict the result of this experiment:

    _____

    _____

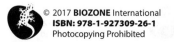

124 The Effect of Gibberellin on Amylase Production

Key Idea: The effect of gibberellin on the amylase produced by a seedling can be investigated using a starch agar assay. Amylase is an enzyme found in germinating seeds. Amylase is produced in the aleurone layer of the endosperm in response to gibberellin produced by the embryo. It hydrolyses starch molecules into smaller sugar molecules, which can then be converted to glucose. Gibberellins control the breaking of seed dormancy by controlling the synthesis of amylase in seeds. Investigations into the effect of gibberellins can be carried out using starch agar plates.

Using a starch agar plate

A starch agar plate is an agar plate infused with starch. Amylase-producing organisms are placed on the plate and, after a set time, they are removed and the plate is flooded with iodine. The starch reacts with the iodine and turns blue-black. Areas where amylase has hydrolysed the starch appear clear. The level of amylase activity can be related to the size of the clear area. The larger the clear area the greater the level of activity.

Does gibberellin affect amylase?

A student wished to find out if gibberellin affects amylase production. The student picked out eight maize grains. Four were soaked in distilled water for 24 hours. Four were soaked in a 1 μmol dm^{-3} solution of gibberellin for 24 hours to ensure gibberellin was absorbed by the seed.

The maize grains were then rinsed in hypochlorite solution to surface sterilise them. They were then cut in half and the half containing the embryo discarded.

The half grains containing the endosperm were then placed on a starch agar plate cut side down. Seeds soaked in water and seeds soaked in gibberellin were placed on different agar plates (four halves per plate) (right).

The plates were then incubated in the dark at room temperature for 24 hours.

After 24 hours the seeds were removed and ten drops of iodine added to the plates and spread over the agar. The results are shown below:

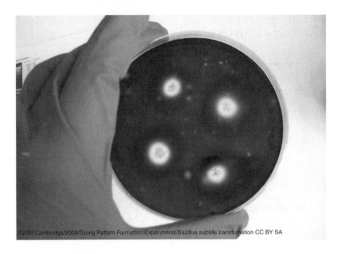

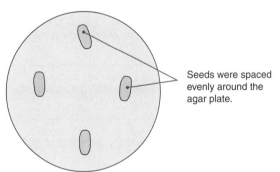

Seeds were spaced evenly around the agar plate.

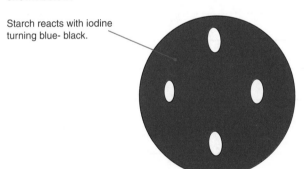

Starch reacts with iodine turning blue-black.

Seeds soaked in water

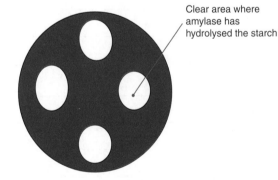

Clear area where amylase has hydrolysed the starch

Seeds soaked in gibberellin

1. Why were four of the seeds soaked in distilled water? _____

_____

2. Why were the halves of the seeds containing the embryo discarded? _____

_____

_____

3. Describe the results of the experiment and what can be concluded from it: _____

_____

_____

_____

LINK
123

PRAC

Quantifying the effect of gibberellin on amylase production

Different levels of gibberellin produce different activation levels of amylase. Use the information on the previous page and the questions below to plan an experiment to show how different concentrations of gibberellin affect amylase production.

4. What is the aim of your investigation? _____

_____

5. Produce a hypothesis for the investigation: _____

_____

_____

6. (a) Starting with a stock solution of 1 μmol^{-1} dm^3 of gibberellin how many gibberellin solutions of different concentrations will you produce?

_____

_____

(b) What will you use as a control? _____

7. How will you ensure the seeds are not contaminated? _____

_____

8. How will you ensure the embryo will not affect the concentration of gibberellin in your solution? _____

_____

9. How many seeds will you use for each gibberellin solution? _____

_____

10. How will you measure and quantify the effect of gibberellin on amylase production? _____

_____

_____

_____

11. Write your full method below: _____

_____

_____

_____

_____

_____

_____

_____

_____

_____

_____

_____

_____

_____

_____

125 Photoperiodism in Plants

Key Idea: Photoperiodism is the response of a plant to the relative lengths of light and dark. It is controlled by the pigment phytochrome, which occurs in two forms Pr and Pfr. Many plant growth patterns are photomorphogenic, meaning they are affected by light. Flowering is a photoperiodic activity that is dependent on the species' response to light. It is controlled through the action of a pigment called **phytochrome**. Phytochrome acts as a signal for some biological clocks in plants and exists in two forms, Pr and Pfr. It is important in initiating flowering in long-day and short-day plants, but is also involved in other light initiated responses, such as germination and shoot growth.

Phytochrome

Phytochrome is a blue-green pigment that acts as a photoreceptor for detection of night and day in plants and is universal in vascular plants. It has two forms: **Pr** (inactive) and **Pfr** (active). Pr is readily converted to Pfr under natural light. Pfr converts back to Pr in the dark but more slowly. Pfr predominates in daylight. The plant measures daylength (or rather night length) by the amount of phytochrome in each form.

In **daylight** or **red light** (660 nm), Pr converts rapidly, but reversibly, to Pfr.

Pfr is the physiologically active form of phytochrome. It promotes flowering in long-day plants and inhibits flowering in short-day plants.

Phytochrome interacts with genes collectively called "clock genes" that maintain the plant's biological clock.

In the **dark** or in **far red light** (730 nm) Pfr reverts slowly, but spontaneously, back to the inactive form of phytochrome Pr.

Sunlight

Pr — Rapid conversion → Pfr

Slowly in darkness

Physiologically active

"Clock genes"

Flowering hormone

There is still uncertainty over what the flowering hormone (commonly called **florigen**) is. Recent studies suggested it may be the protein product of the gene FLOWERING LOCUS T (FT) (in long day plants at least) which appears to influence gene expression that includes the gene LEAFY (LFY) in the apical meristem and causes flowering.

The hormone is transported to the apical meristem where it causes a change in gene expression that leads to flowering.

1. (a) Identify the two forms of phytochrome and the wavelengths of light they absorb: _____

    _____

   (b) Identify the biologically active form of phytochrome and how it behaves in long day plants and short day plants with respect to flowering:

    _____

    _____

2. (a) Discuss the role of phytochrome in a plant's ability to measure daylength: _____

    _____

    _____

    _____

    _____

   (b) Explain how this helps to coordinate flower production in a plant species? _____

    _____

    _____

    _____

Long day vs short day plants

1. Long-day plants (LDP) flower when the photoperiod is greater than a critical day length. Short-day plants (SDP) flower when the photoperiod is less than a critical day length.

2. Interruption of the long dark period inhibits flowering in SDP but promotes flowering in LDP.

3. Dark must be continuous in SDP but not in LDP.

4. Interruption of the light period inhibits flowering in LDP but not in SDP.

5. Alternating cycles of short light and short dark inhibit flowering in SDP.

6. Plants that do not use daylength to initiate flowering are called day-neutral (e.g. cucumber, tomato).

Chrysanthemums

Manipulating flowering in plants

Controlling the light-dark régime has allowed flower growers and horticulturists to produce flowers out of season or to coincide flowering with specific dates.

Plants kept in greenhouses can be subjected to artificial lighting or covered to control the amount of light they receive. To be totally effective at controlling flowering, temperature must also be controlled, as this is also an important flowering cue.

For the example of the *Chrysanthemum*, a short-day plant, flowering is can be controlled under the following conditions. The temperature is kept between 16 - 25 °C. The light-dark regime is controlled at 13 hours of light and 11 hours of dark for 4-5 weeks from planting to ensure vegetative growth. Then the regime changes to 10 hours light and 14 hours darkness to induce flowering.

Long-day plants

When subjected to the light regimes on the right, the 'long-day' plants below flowered as indicated:

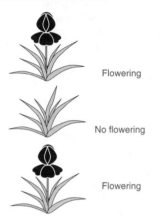

Flowering

No flowering

Flowering

Examples: *lettuce, clover, delphinium, gladiolus, beets, corn, coreopsis*

Photoperiodism in plants

An experiment was carried out to determine the environmental cue that triggers flowering in 'long-day' and 'short-day' plants. The diagram below shows 3 different light regimes to which a variety of long-day and short-day plants were exposed.

```
0 ◄─────── hours ───────► 24
┌──────────────────┬──────────────┐
│    Long-day      │  Short night │
└──────────────────┴──────────────┘

┌───────────┬──────────────────────┐
│ Short-day │      Long night      │
└───────────┴──────────────────────┘

┌───────────┬──────────┬┬──────────┐
│ Short-day │   Long   ││  night   │
└───────────┴──────────┴┴──────────┘
```

Long night interrupted by a short period exposed to light

Short-day plants

When subjected to the light regimes on the left, the 'short-day' plants below flowered as indicated:

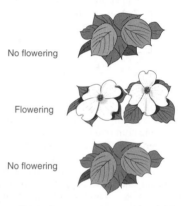

No flowering

Flowering

No flowering

Examples: *potatoes, asters, dahlias, cosmos, chrysanthemums, pointsettias*

3. (a) What is the environmental cue that synchronises flowering in plants? _____

(b) What is a biological advantage of this synchronisation to the plants? _____

_____

_____

_____

4. Study the three light regimes above and the responses of short-day and long-day flowering plants to that light. From this observation, describe the most important factor controlling the onset of flowering in:

(a) Short-day plants:_____

(b) Long-day plants: _____

5. What evidence is there for the idea that short-day plants are best described as "long-night plants": _____

_____

_____

_____

_____

_____

© 2017 **BIOZONE** International
ISBN: 978-1-927309-26-1
Photocopying Prohibited

126 The Mammalian Nervous System

Key Idea: The mammalian nervous system consists of the central and peripheral nervous systems. The peripheral nervous system comprises sensory and motor pathways. It is the motor pathways that control the voluntary and autonomic responses of the body to sensory information.

The nervous system is the body's control and communication centre. Its roles are to detect stimuli, interpret them, and coordinate appropriate responses, even those that occur unconsciously. These roles are performed by the central and peripheral nervous systems (below).

The human nervous system

The nervous system has two major divisions, the central nervous system (CNS) and the peripheral nervous system (PNS).

The **central nervous system** comprises the brain and spinal cord. The spinal cord is a cylinder of nervous tissue extending from the base of the brain down the back, protected by the spinal column. It transmits messages to and from the brain, and controls spinal reflexes.

The **peripheral nervous system** comprises all the nerves and sensory receptors outside the central nervous system.

Structure of the spinal cord

The **spinal cord** has an H shaped central area of grey matter, made up of the cell bodies and dendrites of nerve cells (neurones) and synapses, around a central canal filled with cerebrospinal fluid. The area of white matter contains the nerve fibres (neurone axons).

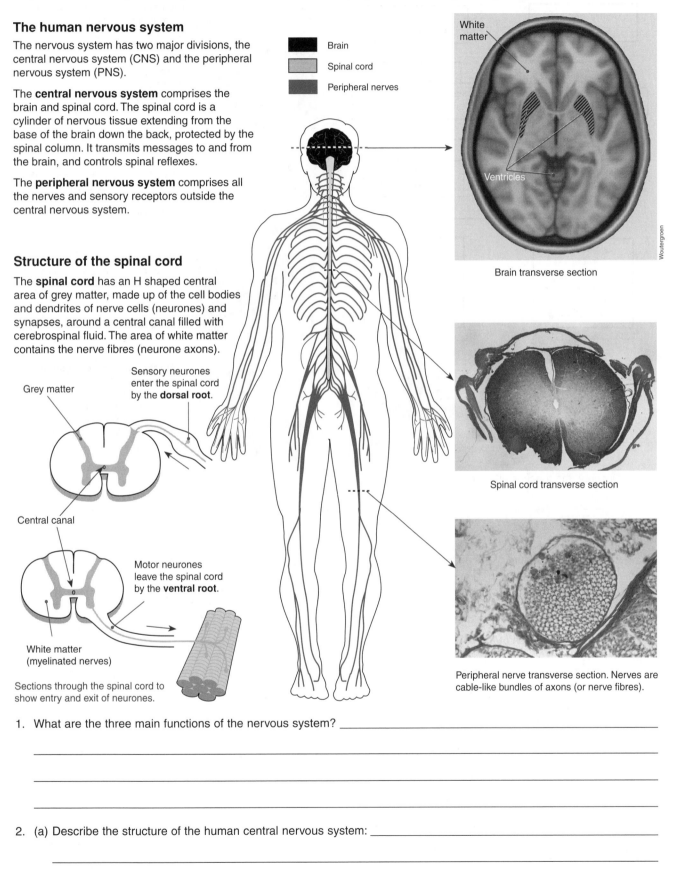

■ Brain

▨ Spinal cord

▨ Peripheral nerves

White matter

Ventricles

Brain transverse section

Woutergroen

Grey matter

Sensory neurones enter the spinal cord by the **dorsal root**.

Central canal

Motor neurones leave the spinal cord by the **ventral root**.

White matter (myelinated nerves)

Sections through the spinal cord to show entry and exit of neurones.

Spinal cord transverse section

Peripheral nerve transverse section. Nerves are cable-like bundles of axons (or nerve fibres).

1. What are the three main functions of the nervous system? _____

_____

_____

_____

2. (a) Describe the structure of the human central nervous system: _____

_____

_____

© 2017 **BIOZONE** International
ISBN: 978-1-927309-26-1
Photocopying Prohibited

LINK 129   LINK 128   WEB 126   **KNOW**

The divisions of the nervous system

The nervous system

- **Central nervous system**
  - Brain
  - Spinal cord
  - **Somatic (voluntary) nervous system**
    - Sympathetic division
      Prepares the body for emergencies or strenuous activity (flight or flight)
- **Peripheral nervous system**
  - Motor pathways
  - Sensory pathways
  - **Autonomic nervous system**
    - Parasympathetic division
      Maintains involuntary processes and conserves energy (rest and digest)

The peripheral nervous system (PNS)

The PNS comprises sensory and motor divisions. Peripheral nerves all enter or leave the CNS, either from the spinal cord (the spinal nerves) or the brain (cranial nerves). They can be **sensory** (from sensory receptors), **motor** (running to a muscle or gland), or **mixed** (containing sensory and motor neurones). Cranial nerves are numbered in roman numerals, I-XII. They include the vagus (X), a mixed nerve with an important role in regulating bodily functions, including heart rate and digestion.

Sensory division
Sensory nerves arise from **sensory receptors** and carry messages to the central nervous system for processing.
The sensory system keeps the central nervous system aware of the external and internal environments. This division includes the familiar sense organs such as ears, eyes (A), and taste buds as well as internal receptors that monitor pressure (B), thirst, hunger, body position, movement and pain.

Motor division
Motor nerves carry impulses from the CNS to effectors: muscles and glands. The motor division comprises two parts:

Somatic nervous system: the neurones that carry impulses to voluntary (skeletal) muscles (C).

Autonomic nervous system: regulates visceral functions over which there is generally no conscious control, e.g. heart rate, gut peristalsis involving smooth muscle (D), pupil reflex, and sweating.

(b) Describe the function of the human central nervous system: _____

_____

_____

3. (a) Describe the structure of the peripheral nervous system: _____

_____

_____

(b) Describe the function of the peripheral nervous system: _____

_____

_____

4. Explain the significance of the separation of the motor division of the PNS into somatic and autonomic divisions:

_____

_____

_____

5. Describe the two different functions of the sympathetic and parasympathetic divisions of the autonomic nervous system:

_____

_____

© 2017 **BIOZONE** International
ISBN: 978-1-927309-26-1
Photocopying Prohibited

127 The Autonomic Nervous System

Key Idea: The autonomic nervous system regulates the body's involuntary activities through the parasympathetic and sympathetic divisions, which have generally opposing effects. The **autonomic nervous system** (ANS) regulates involuntary organ functions, mainly through unconscious reflexes. The ANS has two divisions (**sympathetic** and **parasympathetic**) and their actions on the organs they control are generally antagonistic (opposing). The sympathetic division stimulates the body's fight or flight response at times of stress, whereas the parasympathetic division predominates when the body is at rest. Nerves in the parasympathetic division release the neurotransmitter acetylcholine which is rapidly deactivated and its effects are short lived and localised. Most sympathetic postganglionic nerves release noradrenaline, but sympathetic stimulation of the adrenal glands also causes the release of noradrenaline into the bloodstream (as a hormone). Sympathetic stimulation can therefore affect a wider range of tissues for a longer time. The ANS structure and function are illustrated below. Arrows indicate nervous output to organs or ganglia (concentrations of nerve cell bodies).

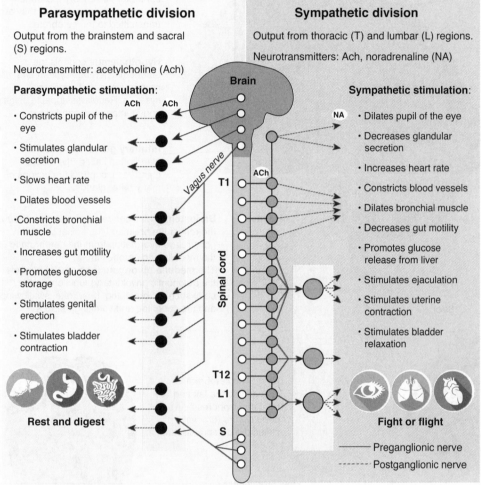

Parasympathetic division

Output from the brainstem and sacral (S) regions.

Neurotransmitter: acetylcholine (Ach)

Parasympathetic stimulation:

- Constricts pupil of the eye
- Stimulates glandular secretion
- Slows heart rate
- Dilates blood vessels
- Constricts bronchial muscle
- Increases gut motility
- Promotes glucose storage
- Stimulates genital erection
- Stimulates bladder contraction

Rest and digest

Sympathetic division

Output from thoracic (T) and lumbar (L) regions.

Neurotransmitters: Ach, noradrenaline (NA)

Sympathetic stimulation:

- Dilates pupil of the eye
- Decreases glandular secretion
- Increases heart rate
- Constricts blood vessels
- Dilates bronchial muscle
- Decreases gut motility
- Promotes glucose release from liver
- Stimulates ejaculation
- Stimulates uterine contraction
- Stimulates bladder relaxation

Fight or flight

——— Preganglionic nerve
------- Postganglionic nerve

As part of the fight or flight response, the sympathetic nervous system dilates the pupils and the arteries and increases the rate and force at which the heart contracts.

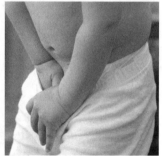

Parasympathetic stimulation is responsible for bladder emptying through contraction of the bladder wall and relaxation of the urethral sphincter. This reflex activity can be inhibited by conscious control, but this ability does not develop until 2-4 years of age.

1. Explain why the sympathetic and parasympathetic divisions of the ANS are described as being antagonistic in function:

_____

_____

_____

2. Explain why autonomic bodily functions are regulated through the activity of two opposing systems: _____

_____

_____

_____

3. Explain why the effects of sympathetic stimulation tend to be more widespread and longer lasting than the effects of parasympathetic stimulation:

_____

_____

© 2017 **BIOZONE** International
ISBN: 978-1-927309-26-1
Photocopying Prohibited

LINK 126 WEB 127

KNOW

128 The Human Brain

Key Idea: The brain is the body's control centre. It comprises several distinct but communicating regions, each with a specialised role in physiology or behaviour.

The brain is constantly receiving, processing, and prioritising information, and coordinating appropriate responses to stimuli. The human brain consists of four main regions: the **cerebrum**, **diencephalon** (thalamus and hypothalamus), **brainstem** (midbrain, pons, and medulla oblongata), and **cerebellum**. The **cerebrum** is divided into two hemispheres, each of which has four lobes. The cerebrum is responsible for higher thought processes, whereas reflex activity is mainly the job of the cerebellum and medulla.

Primary structural regions of the brain

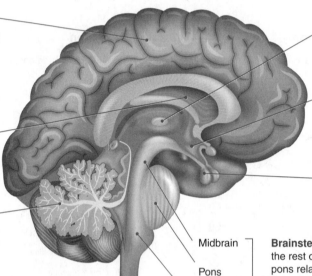

Cerebrum: Divided into the left and right cerebral hemispheres. It has many, complex roles including initiating voluntary (conscious) body movements. It contains sensory, motor, and association areas, and is involved in memory, emotion, language, reasoning, and sensory processing.

Ventricles: Cavities containing the CSF, which absorbs shocks and delivers nutritive substances.

Cerebellum: Part of the hindbrain that coordinates body movements, posture, and balance.

Thalamus acts as the main relay centre for all sensory messages that enter the brain, before they are transmitted to the cerebrum.

Hypothalamus controls the autonomic nervous system and links nervous and endocrine systems. Regulates appetite, thirst, body temperature, and sleep.

Pituitary gland: An endocrine gland often called "the master gland" as it controls the actions of many other glands.

Midbrain

Pons

Medulla oblongata

Brainstem: Relay centre for impulses between the rest of the brain and the spinal cord. The pons relays information from the cerebrum to the medulla and cerebellum.
The **medulla oblongata** (or medulla) controls the autonomic (involuntary) functions in the body such as breathing, heart rate, swallowing, and the coughing and vomiting reflexes.

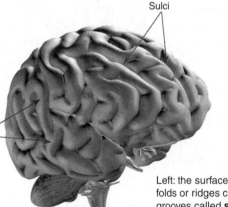

Sulci

Gyri

Left: the surface of the cerebrum has prominent folds or ridges called **gyri**. The gyri are separated by grooves called **sulci**. Folding increases the surface area of the brain (and therefore the number of neurones) without greatly increasing its size.

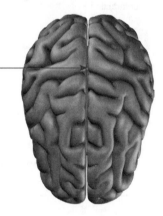

Right: The cerebrum is divided into the left and right hemispheres by a deep fissure (groove) called the cerebral fissure.

1. Identify the regions labelled on the diagram of the human brain (right) and state their function:

A: _____

_____

B: _____

_____

C: _____

_____

D: _____

_____

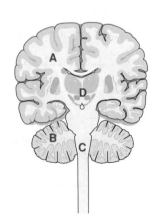

© 2017 **BIOZONE** International
ISBN: 978-1-927309-26-1
Photocopying Prohibited

Sensory and motor regions in the cerebrum

Primary somatic sensory area receives sensations from receptors in the skin, muscles and viscera, allowing recognition of pain, temperature, or touch. Sensory information from receptors on one side of the body crosses to the opposite side of the cerebral cortex where conscious sensations are produced. The size of the sensory region for different body parts depends on the number of receptors in that particular body part.

Visual areas within the occipital lobe receive, interpret, and evaluate visual stimuli. In vision, each eye views both sides of the visual field but the brain receives impulses from left and right visual fields separately. The visual cortex combines the images into a single impression or perception of the image.

Olfactory area interprets signals relating to smell (chemicals in air)

Primary motor area controls muscle movement. Stimulation of a point one side of the motor area results in muscular contraction on the opposite side of the body.

Primary gustatory area interprets sensations related to taste (chemicals in fluid).

Language areas: The motor speech area (Broca's area) is concerned with speech production. The sensory speech area (Wernicke's area) is concerned with speech recognition and coherence.

Auditory areas interpret the basic characteristics and meaning of sounds.

Touch is interpreted in the primary somatic sensory area. The lips and fingertips have a relatively large amount of area devoted to them.

Humans rely heavily on vision. The importance of this sense in humans is indicated by the large occipital region of the brain.

The olfactory tract connects the olfactory bulb with the cerebral hemispheres where olfactory information is interpreted.

The endothelial tight junctions of the capillaries supplying the brain form a protective **blood-brain barrier** against toxins and infection.

2. Why is damage to the medulla oblongata likely to result in death? _____

3. What is the function of the primary somatic area? _____

4. What is the function of the primary motor area? _____

5. For each of the following bodily functions, identify the region(s) of the brain involved in its control:

   (a) Breathing and heartbeat: _____

   (b) Memory and emotion: _____

   (c) Posture and balance: _____

   (d) Autonomic functions: _____

   (e) Visual processing: _____

   (f) Body temperature: _____

   (g) Language: _____

   (h) Muscular movement: _____

© 2017 **BIOZONE** International
ISBN: 978-1-927309-26-1
Photocopying Prohibited

129 Neurones

Key Idea: Neurones are electrically excitable cells that are specialised to process and transmit information via electrical and chemical signals.

Neurones are cells specialised to transmit information in the form of electrochemical signals from receptors (in the CNS) to effectors (muscles or glands). Neurones consist of a cell body and long processes (dendrites and axons). Signals between neurones and effectors not involving higher brain functions produce involuntary actions called reflexes. Many autonomic nervous system responses involve reflexes.

Motor (efferent) neurones transmit impulses from the CNS to effectors

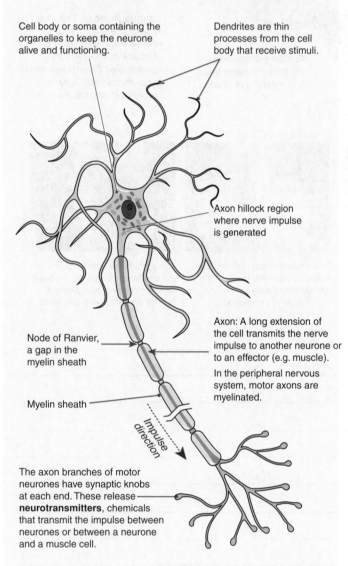

Cell body or soma containing the organelles to keep the neurone alive and functioning.

Dendrites are thin processes from the cell body that receive stimuli.

Axon hillock region where nerve impulse is generated

Node of Ranvier, a gap in the myelin sheath

Axon: A long extension of the cell transmits the nerve impulse to another neurone or to an effector (e.g. muscle).

In the peripheral nervous system, motor axons are myelinated.

Myelin sheath

Impulse direction

The axon branches of motor neurones have synaptic knobs at each end. These release **neurotransmitters**, chemicals that transmit the impulse between neurones or between a neurone and a muscle cell.

Reflexes are unconscious responses to stimuli

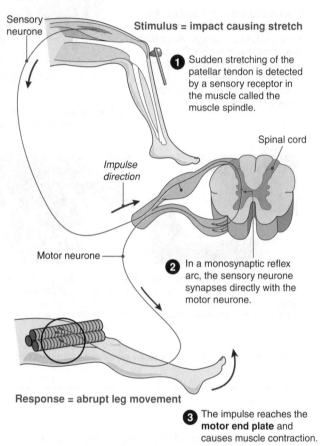

Sensory neurone

Stimulus = impact causing stretch

1 Sudden stretching of the patellar tendon is detected by a sensory receptor in the muscle called the muscle spindle.

Spinal cord

Impulse direction

Motor neurone

2 In a monosynaptic reflex arc, the sensory neurone synapses directly with the motor neurone.

Response = abrupt leg movement

3 The impulse reaches the **motor end plate** and causes muscle contraction.

A reflex is an automatic response to a stimulus and does not involve higher brain functions. A reflex ensures a fast response to a stimulus and are adaptive in that they aid survival (e.g. pain withdrawal reflex). A reflex involves a small number of neurones and a central nervous system processing point (usually the spinal cord, but sometimes the brain stem). This type of circuit is called a **reflex arc**. Changes in breathing rate or heart rate are reflexes instigated by the autonomic nervous system in response to a changes in stimuli. The diagram shows a common monosynaptic reflex, the knee-jerk reflex.

1. (a) Describe the basic structure of a motor neurone: _____

    _____

    (b) How is the structure related to the neurone's function? _____

    _____

    _____

2. (a) What is a reflex? _____

    (b) In what way are reflexes adaptive? _____

    _____

    _____

© 2017 **BIOZONE** International
ISBN: 978-1-927309-26-1
Photocopying Prohibited

Where conduction speed is important, the axons of neurones are sheathed within a lipid-rich substance called myelin. Myelin is produced by oligodendrocytes in the CNS and by Schwann cells in the PNS.

At intervals along the axons of myelinated neurones, there are gaps between neighbouring Schwann cells and their sheaths called nodes of Ranvier. Myelin acts as an insulator, increasing the speed at which nerve impulses travel because it forces the current to "jump" along the axon from node to node.

Myelinated neurones
Diameter: 1-25 µm
Conduction speed: 6-120 ms^{-1}

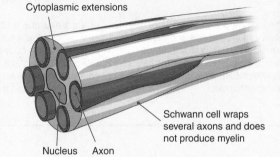

Node of Ranvier

Axon

Myelin layers wrapped around axon

Schwann cell wraps only one axon and produces myelin

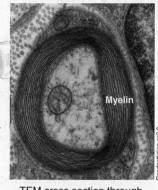

Myelin

TEM cross section through a myelinated axon

Roadnottaken cc3.0

Non-myelinated axons are relatively more common in the CNS where the distances travelled are less than in the PNS. Here, the axons are encased within the cytoplasmic extensions of oligodendrocytes or Schwann cells, rather than within a myelin sheath.

Impulses travel more slowly because the nerve impulse is propagated along the entire axon membrane, rather than jumping from node to node as occurs in myelinated neurones.

Non-myelinated neurones
Diameter: <1 µm
Conduction speed: 0.2-0.5 ms^{-1}

Cytoplasmic extensions

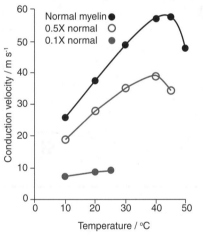

Schwann cell wraps several axons and does not produce myelin

Nucleus   Axon

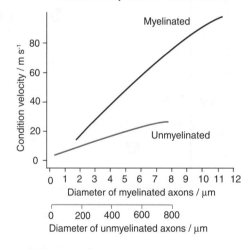

Unmyelinated pyramidal neurons of the cerebral cortex

UC Regents David campus

Effect of temperature and diameter on conduction speed

Temperature and neurone diameter have a direct effect on the speed of signal conduction. Signal conduction increases as temperature increases (to a peak). Conduction also increases as axon diameter increases. In non-myelinated neurones, conduction velocity is proportional to the square root of neurone diameter.

Conduction speed and temperature

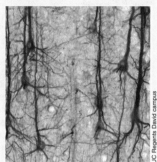

Normal myelin ●
0.5X normal ○
0.1X normal ●

Conduction velocity / m s^{-1}

Temperature / °C

Conduction speed and axon diameter

Myelinated

Condition velocity / m s^{-1}

Unmyelinated

Diameter of myelinated axons / µm

Diameter of unmyelinated axons / µm

3. (a) What is the function of myelination in neurones? _____

_____

(b) How does myelination increase the speed of nerve impulse conduction? _____

_____

_____

_____

(c) Describe the adaptive advantage of faster conduction of nerve impulses: _____

_____

(d) For what diameter neurones is conduction in non-myelinated neurones faster than myelinated neurones?

_____

130 Transmission of Nerve Impulses

Key Idea: A nerve impulse involves the movement of an action potential along a neurone as a series of electrical depolarisation events in response to a stimulus.

The plasma membranes of cells, including neurones, contain **sodium-potassium ion pumps** which actively pump sodium ions (Na⁺) out of the cell and potassium ions (K⁺) into the cell. The action of these ion pumps in neurones creates a separation of charge (a potential difference or voltage) either side of the membrane and makes the cells **electrically**

excitable. It is this property that enables neurones to transmit electrical impulses. The **resting state** of a neurone, with a net negative charge inside, is maintained by the sodium-potassium pumps, which actively move two K⁺ into the neurone for every three Na⁺ moved out (below left). When a nerve is stimulated, a brief increase in membrane permeability to Na⁺ temporarily reverses the membrane polarity (a **depolarisation**). After the nerve impulse passes, the sodium-potassium pump restores the resting potential.

The resting neurone

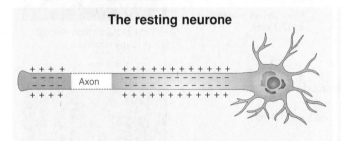

When a neurone is not transmitting an impulse, the inside of the cell is negatively charged relative to the outside and the cell is said to be electrically polarised. The potential difference (voltage) across the membrane is called the **resting potential**. For most nerve cells this is about -70 mV. Nerve transmission is possible because this membrane potential exists.

The nerve impulse

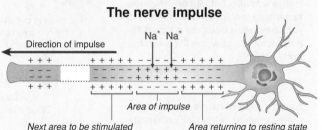

When a neurone is stimulated, the distribution of charges on each side of the membrane briefly reverses. This process of **depolarisation** causes a burst of electrical activity to pass along the axon of the neurone as an **action potential**. As the charge reversal reaches one region, local currents depolarise the next region and the impulse spreads along the axon.

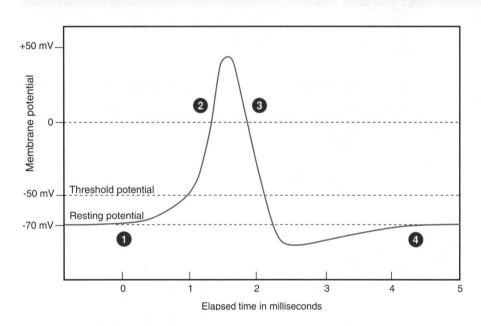

The depolarisation in an axon can be shown as a change in membrane potential (in millivolts). A stimulus must be strong enough to reach the **threshold potential** before an action potential is generated. This is the voltage at which the depolarisation of the membrane becomes unstoppable.

The action potential is **all or nothing** in its generation and because of this, impulses (once generated) always reach threshold and move along the axon without attenuation. The resting potential is restored by the movement of potassium ions (K⁺) out of the cell. During this **refractory period**, the nerve cannot respond, so nerve impulses are discrete.

Voltage-gated ion channels and the course of an action potential

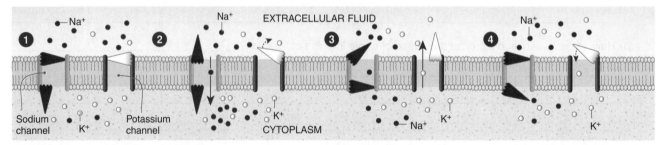

Resting state:

Voltage activated Na⁺ and K⁺ channels are closed.

Depolarisation:

Voltage activated Na⁺ channels open and there is a rapid influx of Na⁺ ions. The interior of the neurone becomes positive relative to the outside.

Repolarisation:

Voltage activated Na⁺ channels close and the K⁺ channels open; K⁺ moves out of the cell, restoring the negative charge to the cell interior.

Returning to resting state:

Voltage activated Na⁺ and K⁺ channels close to return the neurone to the resting state.

© 2017 **BIOZONE** International
ISBN: 978-1-927309-26-1

Axon myelination is a feature of vertebrate nervous systems and it enables them to achieve very rapid speeds of nerve conduction. Myelinated neurones conduct impulses by **saltatory conduction**, a term that describes how the impulse jumps along the fibre. In a myelinated neurone, **action potentials are generated only at the nodes**, which is where the voltage gated channels occur. The axon is insulated so the action potential at one node is sufficient to trigger an action potential in the next node and the impulse jumps along the fibre. Contrast this with a non-myelinated neurone in which voltage-gated channels occur along the entire length of the axon.

As well as increasing the speed of conduction, the myelin sheath reduces energy expenditure because the area over which depolarisation occurs is less (and therefore also the number of sodium and potassium ions that need to be pumped to restore the resting potential).

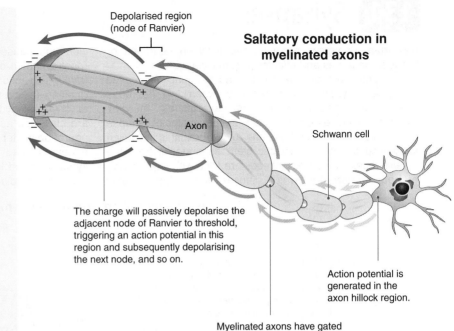

Depolarised region
(node of Ranvier)

Saltatory conduction in myelinated axons

Axon

Schwann cell

The charge will passively depolarise the adjacent node of Ranvier to threshold, triggering an action potential in this region and subsequently depolarising the next node, and so on.

Action potential is generated in the axon hillock region.

Myelinated axons have gated channels only at their nodes.

1. In your own words, explain what an action potential is: _____

_____

2. (a) Identify the defining functional feature of neurones: _____

_____

(b) How does this differ from the supporting tissue (e.g. Schwann cells) of the nervous system? _____

_____

3. Describe the movement of voltage-gated channels and ions associated with:

(a) Depolarisation of the neurone: _____

(b) Repolarisation of the neurone: _____

4. Summarise the sequence of events in a neurone when it receives a stimulus sufficient to reach threshold:

_____

_____

_____

_____

_____

5. How is the resting potential restored in a neurone after an action potential has passed?_____

_____

6. (a) Explain how an action potential travels in a myelinated neurone: _____

_____

(b) How does this differ from its travel in a non-myelinated neurone? _____

_____

7. Explain how the refractory period influences the direction in which an impulse will travel: _____

_____

_____

131 Synapses

Key Idea: Synapses are junctions between neurones or between neurones and effector (e.g. muscle) cells.

Action potentials are transmitted across junctions called **synapses**. Synapses can occur between two neurones or between a neurone and an effector cell (e.g. muscle). Chemical synapses are the most widespread type of synapse in nervous systems. In these, the axon terminal is a swollen knob, and a gap (or synaptic cleft) separates it from the receiving cell. The synaptic knobs are filled with tiny vesicles of **neurotransmitter**, which diffuses across the synaptic cleft and causes an electrical response in the receiving (post-synaptic) cell. This response may be a depolarisation (making an action potential more likely) or a hyperpolarisation (making an action potential less likely). However transmission at chemical synapses is always unidirectional. Synapses are classified as cholinergic or adrenergic according to the neurotransmitter involved (opposite). The junction between a neurone and a muscle cell is a specialised cholinergic synapse called the motor end plate but it is functionally no different. The diagram below depicts an excitatory synapse.

The structure of an excitatory chemical synapse

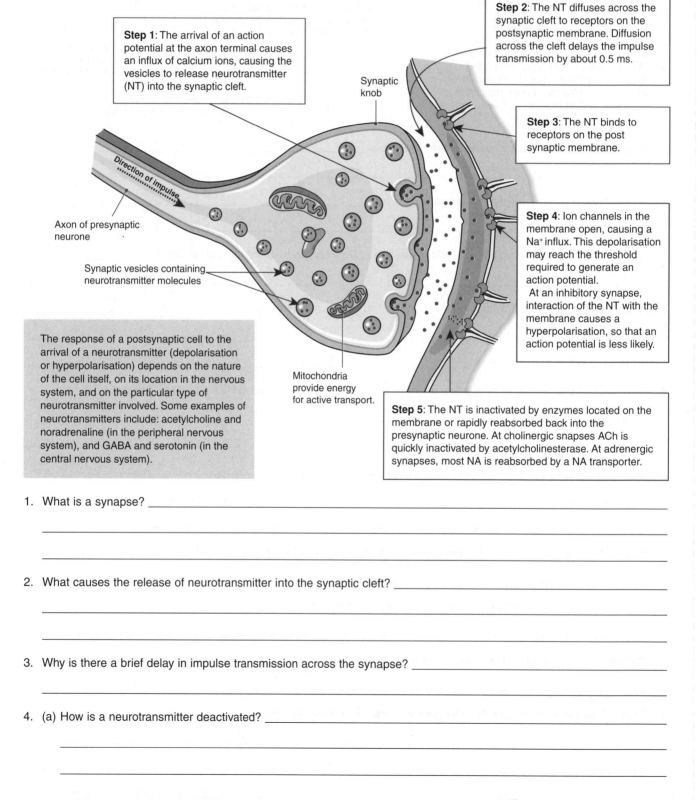

Step 1: The arrival of an action potential at the axon terminal causes an influx of calcium ions, causing the vesicles to release neurotransmitter (NT) into the synaptic cleft.

Step 2: The NT diffuses across the synaptic cleft to receptors on the postsynaptic membrane. Diffusion across the cleft delays the impulse transmission by about 0.5 ms.

Step 3: The NT binds to receptors on the post synaptic membrane.

Step 4: Ion channels in the membrane open, causing a Na+ influx. This depolarisation may reach the threshold required to generate an action potential.
At an inhibitory synapse, interaction of the NT with the membrane causes a hyperpolarisation, so that an action potential is less likely.

Step 5: The NT is inactivated by enzymes located on the membrane or rapidly reabsorbed back into the presynaptic neurone. At cholinergic snapses ACh is quickly inactivated by acetylcholinesterase. At adrenergic synapses, most NA is reabsorbed by a NA transporter.

Direction of impulse

Synaptic knob

Axon of presynaptic neurone

Synaptic vesicles containing neurotransmitter molecules

Mitochondria provide energy for active transport.

The response of a postsynaptic cell to the arrival of a neurotransmitter (depolarisation or hyperpolarisation) depends on the nature of the cell itself, on its location in the nervous system, and on the particular type of neurotransmitter involved. Some examples of neurotransmitters include: acetylcholine and noradrenaline (in the peripheral nervous system), and GABA and serotonin (in the central nervous system).

1. What is a synapse? _____

_____

_____

2. What causes the release of neurotransmitter into the synaptic cleft? _____

_____

_____

3. Why is there a brief delay in impulse transmission across the synapse? _____

_____

4. (a) How is a neurotransmitter deactivated? _____

_____

_____

© 2017 **BIOZONE** International
ISBN: 978-1-927309-26-1
Photocopying Prohibited

Acetylcholine and noradrenaline are neurotransmitters

Neurotransmitters (NT) are chemicals that transmit signals between neurones. There are many different types and their effects (excitatory or inhibitory) depend on the NT and properties of the cell receiving them. Excitatory NTs increase the chance of an action potential being propagated, whereas inhibitory NTs have the opposite effect. The table below summarises the properties of two common NTs, acetylcholine (ACh) and noradrenaline (NA).

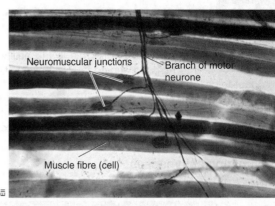

	Acetylcholine	Noradrenaline
Structure		
Synapse	Cholinergic	Adrenergic
Effect	Excitatory/inhibitory	Excitatory
Targets	The NT in all autonomic ganglia and the only NT in the somatic nervous system. Skeletal muscle, brain, many organs.	Body wide. The primary NT in the sympathetic nervous system.
Action	Wide range of effects, including stimulation of muscles, memory, alertness, arousal, learning, and control of many organs.	Alerts the nervous system for fight or flight response, e.g. increases heart rate and blood pressure.

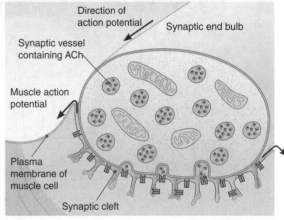

Diagrammatic representation of part of a motor end plate.

(b) Why do you think it is important for the neurotransmitter to be deactivated soon after its release? _____

_____

_____

(c) Why is transmission at chemical synapses unidirectional and what is the significance of this? _____

_____

_____

_____

5. In what way is the motor end plate like any other cholinergic synapse: _____

_____

6. (a) What is the response of the postsynaptic membrane at an excitatory synapse? _____

(b) What is the response of the postsynaptic membrane at an inhibitory synapse? _____

(c) What factors determine the response of the post-synaptic cell? _____

_____

_____

7. Contrast the effect and roles of acetylcholine and noradrenaline as neurotransmitters: _____

_____

_____

_____

_____

_____

132 Integration at Synapses

Key Idea: Synapses play a pivotal role in the ability of the nervous system to respond appropriately to stimulation and to adapt to change by integrating all inputs.

The nature of synaptic transmission in the nervous system allows the **integration** (interpretation and coordination) of inputs from many sources. These inputs can be excitatory (causing depolarisation) or inhibitory (making an action potential less likely). It is the sum of all excitatory and inhibitory inputs that leads to the final response in a post-synaptic cell. Synaptic integration is behind all the various responses we have to stimuli. It is also the most probable mechanism by which learning and memory are achieved.

Summation at synapses

Graded postsynaptic responses may sum to produce an action potential.

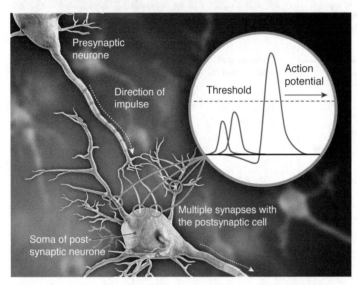

Nerve transmission across chemical synapses has several advantages, despite the delay caused by neurotransmitter diffusion. Chemical synapses transmit impulses in one direction to a precise location and, because they rely on a limited supply of neurotransmitter, they are subject to fatigue (inability to respond to repeated stimulation). This protects the system against overstimulation.

Synapses also act as centres for the **integration of inputs** from many sources. The response of a postsynaptic cell is often not strong enough on its own to generate an action potential. However, because the strength of the response is related to the amount of neurotransmitter released, subthreshold responses can sum together to produce a response in the post-synaptic cell. This additive effect is called summation. Summation can be temporal or spatial (right).

① Temporal summation

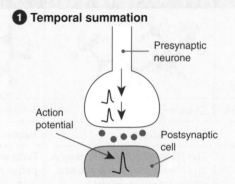

Several impulses may arrive at the synapse in quick succession from a single axon. The individual responses are so close in time that they sum to reach threshold and produce an action potential in the postsynaptic neurone.

② Spatial summation

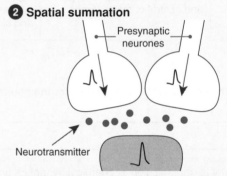

Impulses from spatially separated axon terminals may arrive simultaneously at different regions of the same postsynaptic neurone. The responses from the different places sum to produce an action potential.

1. Explain the purpose of nervous system integration: _____

_____

_____

2. Describe two advantages of chemical synapses:

(a) _____

_____

(b) _____

_____

3. (a) Explain what is meant by summation: _____

_____

_____

(b) In simple terms, distinguish between temporal and spatial summation: _____

_____

© 2017 **BIOZONE** International
ISBN: 978-1-927309-26-1
Photocopying Prohibited

133 Drugs at Synapses

Key Idea: Drugs may increase or decrease the effect of neurotransmitters at synapses.

Drugs may act at synapses either mimicking or blocking the usual effect of a neurotransmitter (whether it be excitatory or inhibitory). Drugs that increase the usual effect of a neurotransmitter are called **agonists** while those that decrease their effect are called **antagonists**. Many recreational and therapeutic drugs work through their action at synapses, controlling the response of the receiving cell to incoming action potentials.

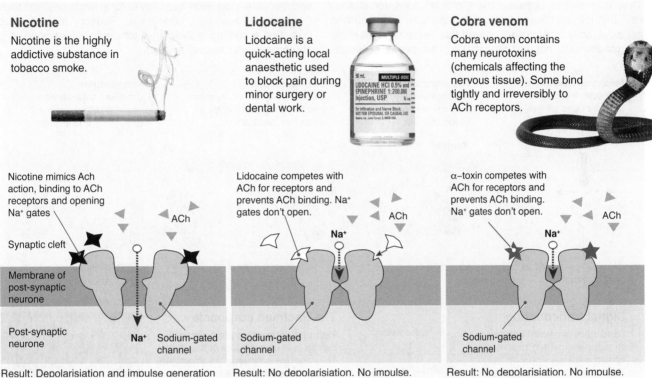

Nicotine
Nicotine is the highly addictive substance in tobacco smoke.

Nicotine mimics ACh action, binding to ACh receptors and opening Na⁺ gates

Synaptic cleft

Membrane of post-synaptic neurone

Post-synaptic neurone

Na^+ Sodium-gated channel

Result: Depolarisation and impulse generation

Effect: Agonistic
Result: Action potential generation
Nicotine acts as an agonist at nicotinic synapses (autonomic ganglia and the motor end plate). It binds to and activates ACh receptors on the postsynaptic membrane (e.g. of a muscle cell). This opens sodium gates, leading to a sodium influx and membrane depolarisation.

Lidocaine
Liodcaine is a quick-acting local anaesthetic used to block pain during minor surgery or dental work.

Lidocaine competes with ACh for receptors and prevents ACh binding. Na⁺ gates don't open.

Na^+

Sodium-gated channel

Result: No depolarisation. No impulse.

Effect: Antagonistic
Result: Sensory inhibition
Lidocaine binds to the ACh receptors on sensory neurones and prevents ACh binding. No depolarisation occurs, so no action potential is generated on the post-synaptic neurone. Pain signals are not generated.

Cobra venom
Cobra venom contains many neurotoxins (chemicals affecting the nervous tissue). Some bind tightly and irreversibly to ACh receptors.

α–toxin competes with ACh for receptors and prevents ACh binding. Na⁺ gates don't open.

Na^+

Sodium-gated channel

Result: No depolarisation. No impulse.

Effect: Antagonistic
Result: Muscular paralysis
Toxins in cobra venom bind to ACh receptors and prevent ACh binding to receptors on the plasma membrane of muscle cells. As a result, sodium channels remain closed and no action potentials are produced. They can cause muscular paralysis, respiratory failure, and death.

1. Explain the difference between an agonistic and antagonistic drug: _____

_____

_____

2. Nicotine and cobra venom both bind to acetylcholine receptors. Explain why their effects are different: _____

_____

_____

_____

_____

3. Explain why lidocaine is used as a local anaesthetic: _____

_____

_____

LINK
131
WEB
133

KNOW

134 The Basis of Sensory Reception

Key Idea: Sensory receptors act as transducers, detecting stimuli and converting them to an electrochemical signal.

Sensory receptors are specialised to detect stimuli and respond by producing an electrical (or chemical) discharge. In this way they act as **biological transducers**, converting the energy from a stimulus into an electrochemical signal. They can do this because the stimulus opens (or closes) ion channels and leads to localised changes in membrane potential called **receptor potentials**. Receptor potentials are graded and not self-propagating, but sense cells can

amplify them, generating action potentials directly or inducing the release of a neurotransmitter. Whether or not the sensory cell itself fires action potentials, ultimately the stimulus is transduced into action potentials whose frequency is dependent on stimulus strength. The simplest sensory receptors consist of a single sensory neurone (e.g. nerve endings). More complex sense cells form synapses with their sensory neurones (e.g. taste buds). Sensory receptors are classified according to the stimuli to which they respond (e.g. photoreceptors respond to light).

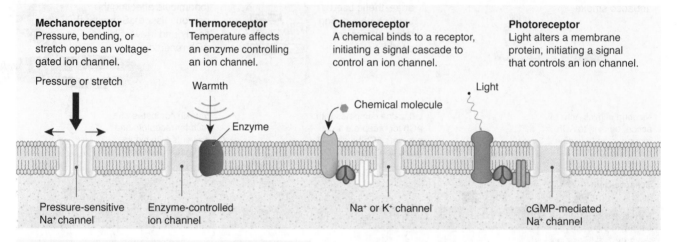

Mechanoreceptor
Pressure, bending, or stretch opens an voltage-gated ion channel.

Pressure or stretch

Pressure-sensitive Na⁺ channel

Thermoreceptor
Temperature affects an enzyme controlling an ion channel.

Warmth

Enzyme

Enzyme-controlled ion channel

Chemoreceptor
A chemical binds to a receptor, initiating a signal cascade to control an ion channel.

Chemical molecule

Na⁺ or K⁺ channel

Photoreceptor
Light alters a membrane protein, initiating a signal that controls an ion channel.

Light

cGMP-mediated Na⁺ channel

Signal transduction

Sensory cells convert one type of stimulus energy (e.g. pressure) into an electrical signal by altering the flow of ions across the plasma membrane and generating receptor potentials. In many cases (as in the Pacinian corpuscle), this leads directly to action potentials which are generated in the voltage-gated region of the sensory cell.

In some receptor cells, the receptor potential leads to neurotransmitter release, which then directly or indirectly leads to action potentials in a post-synaptic cell.

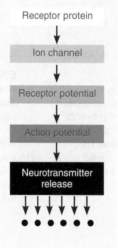

Receptor protein
↓
Ion channel
↓
Receptor potential
↓
Action potential
↓
Neurotransmitter release
↓↓↓↓↓↓
●●●●●●

The Pacinian corpuscle

Pacinian corpuscles are pressure receptors in deep tissues of the body. They are relatively large but structurally simple, consisting of a sensory nerve ending (dendrite) surrounded by a capsule of connective tissue layers. Pressure deforms the capsule, stretching the nerve ending and leading to a localised depolarisation called a **receptor potential**. Receptor potentials are graded and do not spread far, although they may sum together and increase in amplitude.

The sense cell converts the receptor potentials to action potentials at the start of the axon (where there are voltage-gated channels). The action potential is then propagated along the axon.

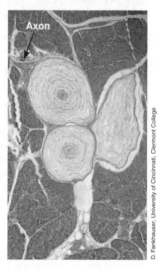

Axon

D. Fankhauser, University of Cincinnati, Clermont College

1. Explain why sensory receptors are termed 'biological transducers': _____

_____

_____

2. Identify one feature that all sensory receptors have in common: _____

_____

3. Explain how a stimulus received by a sensory receptor is converted into an electrical response: _____

_____

_____

_____

4. Describe the properties of receptor potentials: _____

_____

© 2017 **BIOZONE** International
ISBN: 978-1-927309-26-1
Photocopying Prohibited

135 The Structure of the Eye

Key Idea: The eye is a sensory organ that converts light into nerve impulses resulting in the formation of a visual image. The human eye is a complex and highly sophisticated sense organ specialised to detect light and translate images into nerve signals to conduct to the brain. Photoreceptor cells detect and respond to light. In the human eye they are specialised for different light levels, allowing us to see in both bright and low light. The eye has many structures and features associated with achieving the best possible visual image in varying conditions.

The structure and function of the human eye

The human eye is a three layered sense organ made up of an outer fibrous layer, a middle vascular layer, and an inner retina of photoreceptor cell.

For vision to occur, light reaching the photoreceptor cells must form an image on the retina. This requires refraction (bending) of the incoming light, accommodation (adjustment for distance of the object) and constriction of the pupil to regulate the light level entering the eye. The shape of the eye is maintained by the fluid filled cavities which also assist in light refraction. Some structures are labelled below.

Light striking the photoreceptor cells initiates a series of reactions that ultimately trigger nerve impulses to the brain resulting in the formation of a visual image. The image on the retina is upside down and reversed. We 'see' it in its correct orientation because the visual processing area of the brain interprets the nerve impulses it recieves and corrects the orientation of the image.

Central fovea is a pit where the cone cells are concentrated. Cones provide sharp, colour vision and work best in bright light.

Blind spot occurs where the optic nerve enters the retina. There are no photoreceptor cells here.

Optic nerve transmits visual information from the retina to the brain

Retina contains neurones and the photoreceptor cells (rods and cones). The rod cells are more numerous than cones and specialised for vision in low-light. Rod cells are located on the outer edges of the retina.

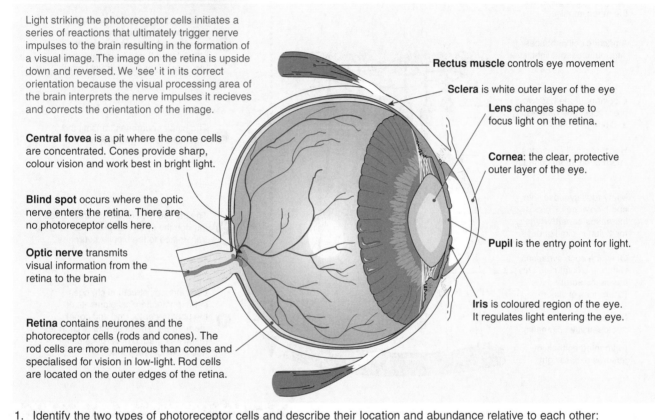

Rectus muscle controls eye movement

Sclera is white outer layer of the eye

Lens changes shape to focus light on the retina.

Cornea: the clear, protective outer layer of the eye.

Pupil is the entry point for light.

Iris is coloured region of the eye. It regulates light entering the eye.

1. Identify the two types of photoreceptor cells and describe their location and abundance relative to each other:

_____

_____

2. The first stage of vision involves forming an image on the retina. In simple terms, explain what this involves: _____

_____

_____

_____

3. (a) In basic terms, how is light converted into a chemical signal? _____

_____

_____

(b) The image formed on the retina is upside down. How is it that we see images the right way up? _____

_____

_____

© 2017 **BIOZONE** International
ISBN: 978-1-927309-26-1
Photocopying Prohibited

136 The Physiology of Vision

Key Idea: The retina of the eye is a multilayered structure, which detects light and generates electrical responses. These are converted to action potentials in the optic nerve.

Vision in mammals is achieved by focussing light through a lens to form an image on the retina at the back of the eye. Light reaching the retina is absorbed by the photosensitive pigments associated with the membranes of the **photoreceptor cells** (the rods and cones). The pigment molecules are altered by the absorption of light and this causes them to produce electrical responses. These initial responses are converted to action potentials, which are transmitted via the **optic nerve** to the visual cortex of the brain, where the information is interpreted. The retina is not uniform. The **central fovea** is an area where there is a high density of cones and virtually no rods. It is the region of highest acuity.

Structure and function of the retina

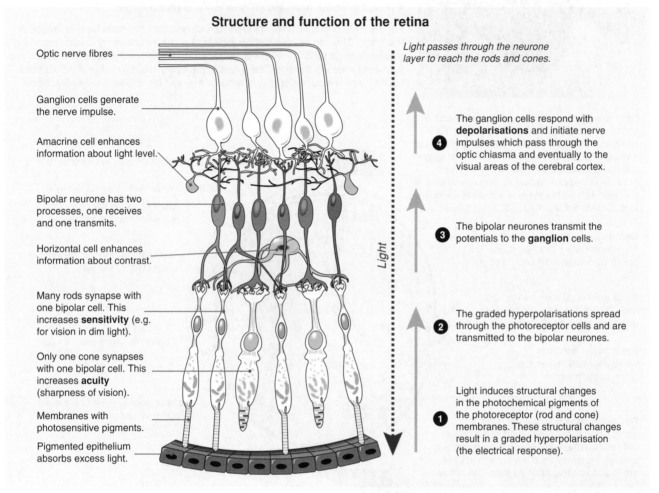

Optic nerve fibres

Ganglion cells generate the nerve impulse.

Amacrine cell enhances information about light level.

Bipolar neurone has two processes, one receives and one transmits.

Horizontal cell enhances information about contrast.

Many rods synapse with one bipolar cell. This increases **sensitivity** (e.g. for vision in dim light).

Only one cone synapses with one bipolar cell. This increases **acuity** (sharpness of vision).

Membranes with photosensitive pigments.

Pigmented epithelium absorbs excess light.

Light passes through the neurone layer to reach the rods and cones.

Light

4 The ganglion cells respond with **depolarisations** and initiate nerve impulses which pass through the optic chiasma and eventually to the visual areas of the cerebral cortex.

3 The bipolar neurones transmit the potentials to the **ganglion** cells.

2 The graded hyperpolarisations spread through the photoreceptor cells and are transmitted to the bipolar neurones.

1 Light induces structural changes in the photochemical pigments of the photoreceptor (rod and cone) membranes. These structural changes result in a graded hyperpolarisation (the electrical response).

1. Describe the role of each of the following in human vision:

   (a) Retina: _____

   _____

   _____

   _____

   (b) Optic nerve: _____

   _____

   _____

   _____

   (c) Central fovea: _____

   _____

   _____

   _____

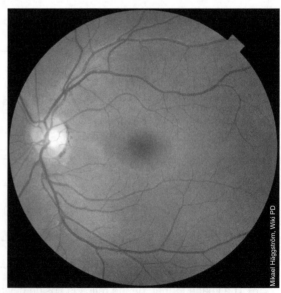

Mikael Häggström, Wiki PD

Photograph through the eye of a normal retina. The blind spot, where the where ganglion cell axons exit the eye to form the optic nerve, is seen as the bright area to the left of the image. The central fovea, where cone density is highest, is in the darker region at the centre of the image. Note the rich blood supply.

© 2017 **BIOZONE** International
ISBN: 978-1-927309-26-1
Photocopying Prohibited

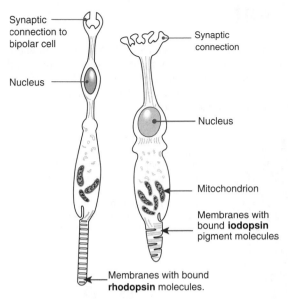

Synaptic connection to bipolar cell

Nucleus

Synaptic connection

Nucleus

Mitochondrion

Membranes with bound **iodopsin** pigment molecules

Membranes with bound **rhodopsin** molecules.

Structure of rod (left) and cone (right) photoreceptor cells

The basis of trichromatic vision

There are three classes of cones, each with a maximal response in either short (blue), intermediate (green) or long (yellow-green) wavelength light (below). The yellow-green cone is also sensitive to the red part of the spectrum and is often called the red cone. The differential responses of the cones to light of different wavelengths provides the basis of trichromatic colour vision.

Cone response to light wavelengths

| Violet | Blue | Green | Yellow | Orange |

Electrical response

B   G   R

Wavelength (nm)
450   500   550   600   650   700

2. Complete the table below, comparing the features of rod and cone cells:

Feature	Rod cells	Cone cells
Visual pigment(s):		
Visual acuity:		
Overall function:		

3. Identify the three major types of neurone making up the retina and describe their basic function:

(a) _____

(b) _____

(c) _____

4. Identify two types of accessory neurones in the retina and describe their basic function:

(a) _____

(b) _____

5. Account for the differences in acuity (sharpness of vision) and sensitivity (to light level) between rod and cone cells:

_____

_____

6. (a) What is meant by the term photochemical pigment (photopigment)? _____

_____

_____

(b) Identify two photopigments and their location: _____

_____

7. In your own words, explain how light is able to produce a nerve impulse in the ganglion cells: _____

_____

_____

_____

_____

137 Extrinsic Control of Heartbeat

Key Idea: The heart's basic rhythm is regulated via the cardiovascular control centre in response to hormones and input from sympathetic and parasympathetic nerves.
The pacemaker sets the basic rhythm of the heart, but this rate is influenced by the cardiovascular control centre,

primarily in response to sensory information from pressure receptors in the walls of the blood vessels entering and leaving the heart. The main trigger for changing the basic rate of heart beat is change in blood pressure. The responses are mediated though simple reflexes.

While most control is autonomic, the higher brain centres influence the cardiovascular centre, e.g. excitement or anticipation of an event.

Cardiovascular control	
Increase in rate	**+**
Decrease in rate	**−**

Baroreceptors in aorta, carotid arteries, and vena cava give feedback to cardiovascular centre on **blood pressure**. Blood pressure is directly related to the pumping action of the heart.
Chemoreceptors provide feedback on the blood chemistry (H^+ or CO_2 concentrations in blood).

Cardiovascular centre responds directly to noradrenaline and to low pH (high CO_2). It sends output to the sinoatrial node (SAN) to increase heart rate. Changing the rate and force of heart contraction is the main mechanism for controlling cardiac output in order to meet changing demands.

+ or **−**

Sympathetic output to heart via **cardiac nerve** increases heart rate. **+** Sympathetic output predominates during exercise or stress. Noradrenaline released at SAN.

Parasympathetic output to heart via **vagus nerve** decreases heart rate. Parasympathetic (vagal) **−** output predominates during rest. Acetylcholine released at SAN.

Influences on heart rate

Increase	Decrease
Increased physical activity	Decreased physical activity
Decrease in blood pressure	Increase in blood pressure
Secretion of adrenaline or noradrenaline	Re-uptake and metabolism of adrenaline or noradrenaline
Increase in H^+ or CO_2 concentrations in blood	Decrease in H^+ or CO_2 concentrations in blood

Extrinsic input to SAN

Reflex responses to changes in blood pressure

Reflex	Receptor	Stimulus	Response
Bainbridge reflex	Pressure receptors in vena cava and atrium	Stretch caused by increased venous return	Increase heart rate
Carotid reflex	Pressure receptors in the carotid arteries	Stretch caused by increased arterial flow	Decrease heart rate
Aortic reflex	Pressure receptors in the aorta	Stretch caused by increased arterial flow	Decrease heart rate

Opposing actions keep blood pressure within narrow limits

The intrinsic rhythm of the heart is influenced by the cardiovascular centre, which receives input from sensory neurones and hormones.

1. Explain how each of the following extrinsic factors influences the basic intrinsic rhythm of the heart:

    (a) Increased venous return: _____

    (b) Release of adrenaline in anticipation of an event: _____

    (c) Increase in blood CO_2: _____

2. How do these extrinsic factors bring about their effects? _____
_____

3. What type of activity might cause increased venous return? _____

4. (a) Identify the nerve that brings about increased heart rate: _____

    (b) Identify the nerve that brings about decreased heart rate: _____

5. (a) What do baroreceptors respond to? _____

    (b) What do chemoreceptors respond to? _____

© 2017 **BIOZONE** International
ISBN: 978-1-927309-26-1
Photocopying Prohibited

138 The Liver's Role in Protein Metabolism

Key Idea: The liver has a crucial role in the metabolism of proteins and the storage and detoxification of hormones and ingested or absorbed poisons (including alcohol).

The most critical aspects of protein metabolism occurring in the liver are deamination and transamination of amino acids, removal of ammonia from the body by synthesis of urea, and synthesis of non-essential amino acids. Liver cells are responsible for synthesis of most of the plasma proteins, including albumins, globulins, and blood clotting proteins. Urea formation via the ornithine cycle occurs primarily in the liver. The urea is formed from ammonia and carbon dioxide by condensation with the amino acid ornithine, which is recycled through a series of enzyme-controlled steps. Urea is transported in the blood to the kidneys and excreted.

Storage and detoxification

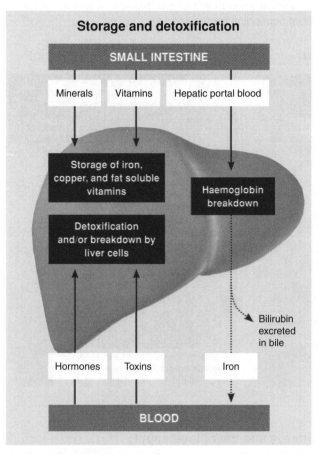

Protein metabolism

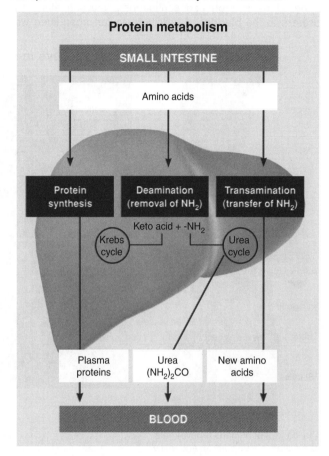

1. Describe three aspects of protein metabolism in the liver:

   (a) _____

   _____

   (b) _____

   _____

   (c) _____

   _____

2. Identify the waste products arising from deamination of amino acids and describe their fate:

   _____

   _____

   _____

3. (a) Why must ammonia be removed from the body? _____

   _____

   (b) How is this achieved? _____

   _____

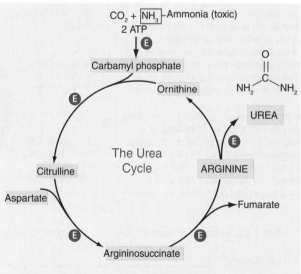

Ammonia (NH_3), the product of protein metabolism, is toxic in even small amounts and must be removed. It is converted to the less toxic urea via the ornithine cycle and is excreted from the body by the kidneys. The liver contains a system of carrier molecules and enzymes (**E**) which quickly convert the ammonia (and CO_2) into urea. One turn of the cycle consumes two molecules of ammonia (one comes from aspartate) and one molecule of CO_2, creates one molecule of urea, and regenerates a molecule of ornithine.

© 2017 **BIOZONE** International
ISBN: 978-1-927309-26-1
Photocopying Prohibited

LINK
139

KNOW

139 The Urinary System

Key Idea: The urinary system filters the blood and removes wastes, producing urine. The functional unit of the kidney is a selective filter element called the nephron.

The urinary system consists of the kidneys and bladder, and their associated blood vessels and ducts. The **kidneys** have a plentiful blood supply from the renal artery. The blood plasma is filtered by the **kidney nephrons** to form urine. Urine is produced continuously, passing along the **ureters** to the **bladder**, a hollow muscular organ lined with

smooth muscle and stretchable epithelium, which stores the urine before it is voided. Each day the kidneys filter about 180 dm^3 of plasma. Most of this is reabsorbed, leaving a daily urine output of about 1 dm^3. By adjusting the volume and composition of the fluid excreted, a process called **osmoregulation**, the kidneys help to maintain the body's internal chemical balance. Human kidneys are very efficient, producing a urine that is concentrated to a greater or lesser extent depending on requirements.

Urinary system

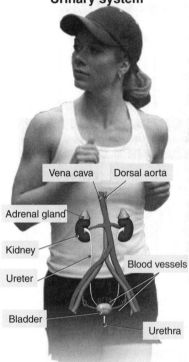

Kidneys *in-situ* (rat)

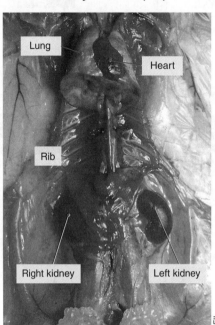

Sagittal section of kidney (pig)

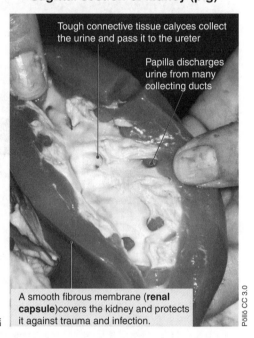

Tough connective tissue calyces collect the urine and pass it to the ureter

Papilla discharges urine from many collecting ducts

A smooth fibrous membrane (**renal capsule**) covers the kidney and protects it against trauma and infection.

The kidneys of humans (above), rats (dissection, above centre), and many other mammals (e.g. pig above right) are distinctive, bean shaped organs that lie at the back of the abdominal cavity to either side of the spine. The kidneys lie outside the peritoneum of the abdominal cavity (**retroperitoneal**) and are partly protected by the lower ribs (see kidneys *in-situ* above centre).

Human kidneys are ~100-120 mm long and 25 mm thick. A cut through in a sagittal plane (see photo above right), reveals numerous tough connective tissue calyces. These collect the urine from the papillae where it is discharged and drain it into the ureter.

The kidneys and their blood supply

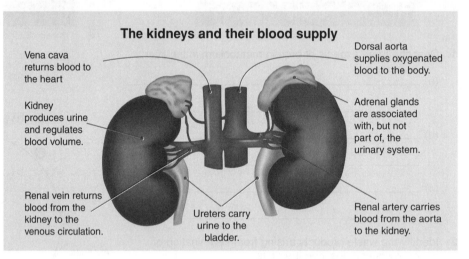

Vena cava returns blood to the heart

Kidney produces urine and regulates blood volume.

Renal vein returns blood from the kidney to the venous circulation.

Ureters carry urine to the bladder.

Dorsal aorta supplies oxygenated blood to the body.

Adrenal glands are associated with, but not part of, the urinary system.

Renal artery carries blood from the aorta to the kidney.

1. State the function of each of the following components of the urinary system:

   (a) Kidney: _____

   _____

   (b) Ureters: _____

   _____

   (c) Bladder: _____

   _____

© 2017 **BIOZONE** International
ISBN: 978-1-927309-26-1
Photocopying Prohibited

Internal structure of the human kidney

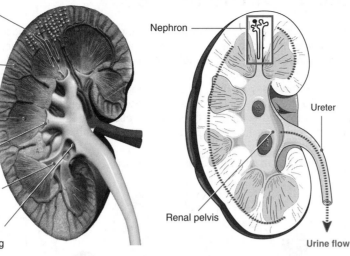

Nephrons are arranged with all the collecting ducts pointing towards the renal pelvis.

Outer cortex contains the renal corpuscles and convoluted tubules.

Inner medulla is organised into pyramids.

Each pyramid ends in a papilla or opening.

Urine enters the **calyces**

Urine collects in a space near the ureter called the renal pelvis, before leaving the kidney via the ureter.

Nephron —

Ureter

Renal pelvis

Urine flow

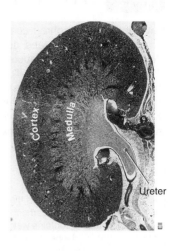

Cortex

Medulla

Ureter

The functional units of the kidney are selective filter elements called **nephrons**. Each kidney contains more than 1 million nephrons and they are precisely aligned so that urine is concentrated as it flows towards the ureter (model and diagram above). The alignment gives the kidney tissue a striated (striped) appearance and makes it possible to accommodate all the filtering units needed.

The outer cortex and inner medulla can be seen in a low power LM of the kidney. The ureter is seen extending into the fat and connective tissue surrounding and protecting the kidney.

(d) Urethra: _____

_____

(e) Renal artery: _____

_____

(f) Renal vein: _____

_____

(g) Renal capsule: _____

2. Calculate the percentage of the plasma reabsorbed by the kidneys: _____

3. (a) What is a nephron? _____

(b) What is its role in excretion? _____

_____

4. Complete a biological drawing of the kidney shown below, identifying the renal pelvis, renal capsule, ureter, medulla, and cortex. At this level of detail, the layers of the kidney can be seen but no cellular detail is evident.

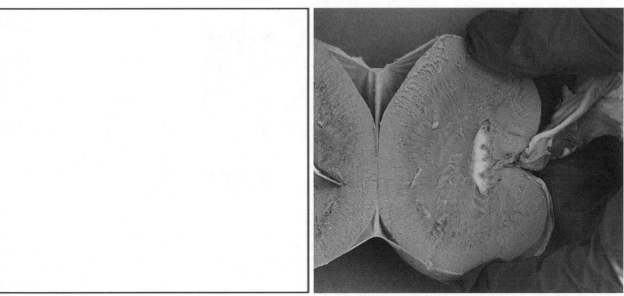

140 The Physiology of the Kidney

Key Idea: Each nephron comprises a renal corpuscle and its associated tubules and ducts. It produces the urine by ultrafiltration, selective reabsorption, and secretion.

Ultrafiltration, i.e. forcing fluid and dissolved substances through a membrane by pressure, occurs in the first part of the nephron, across the membranes of the capillaries and the glomerular capsule. The passage of water and solutes into the nephron and the formation of the glomerular filtrate depends on the pressure of the blood entering the afferent arteriole (below). If it increases, filtration rate increases. When it falls, glomerular filtration rate also falls. This process is so precisely regulated that, in spite of fluctuations in arteriolar pressure, glomerular filtration rate per day stays constant. After formation of the initial filtrate, the **urine** is modified through secretion and tubular reabsorption according to physiological needs at the time.

Nephron structure and function

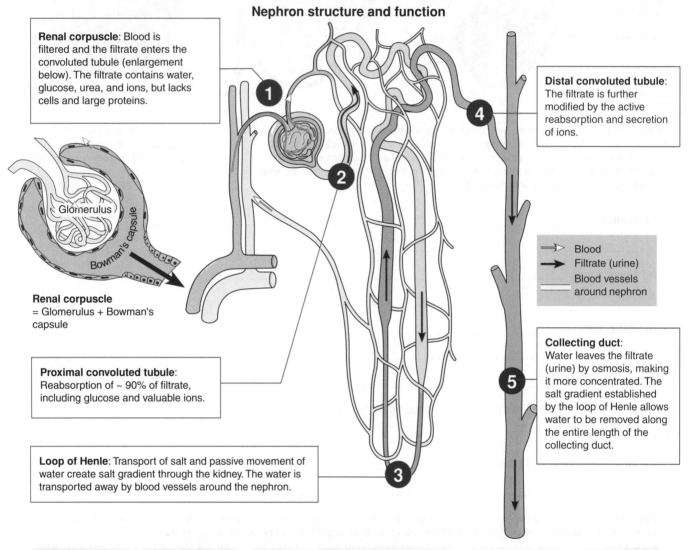

Renal corpuscle: Blood is filtered and the filtrate enters the convoluted tubule (enlargement below). The filtrate contains water, glucose, urea, and ions, but lacks cells and large proteins.

Glomerulus

Bowman's capsule

Renal corpuscle
= Glomerulus + Bowman's capsule

Proximal convoluted tubule:
Reabsorption of ~ 90% of filtrate, including glucose and valuable ions.

Loop of Henle: Transport of salt and passive movement of water create salt gradient through the kidney. The water is transported away by blood vessels around the nephron.

Distal convoluted tubule:
The filtrate is further modified by the active reabsorption and secretion of ions.

→ Blood
→ Filtrate (urine)
— Blood vessels around nephron

Collecting duct:
Water leaves the filtrate (urine) by osmosis, making it more concentrated. The salt gradient established by the loop of Henle allows water to be removed along the entire length of the collecting duct.

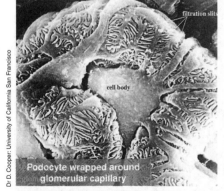

Dr D. Cooper: University of California San Francisco

filtration slits

cell body

Podocyte wrapped around glomerular capillary

The epithelium of Bowman's capsule is made up of specialised cells called **podocytes**. The finger-like cellular processes of the podocytes wrap around the capillaries of the glomerulus, and the plasma filtrate passes through the filtration slits between them.

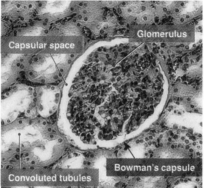

Capsular space

Glomerulus

Bowman's capsule

Convoluted tubules

Bowman's capsule is a double walled cup, lying in the cortex of the kidney. It encloses a dense capillary network called the **glomerulus**. The capsule and its enclosed glomerulus form a **renal corpuscle**. In this section, the convoluted tubules can be seen surrounding the renal corpuscle.

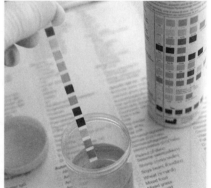

Normal, fresh urine is clear and pale to dark yellow or amber in colour. A urine dipstick test is a fast and convenient way to make a qualitative analysis of urine to diagnose a medical problem. The presence of specific molecules in the urine (e.g. glucose) are indicated by a colour change on the dipstick.

© 2017 **BIOZONE** International
ISBN: 978-1-927309-26-1
Photocopying Prohibited

Summary of activities in the kidney nephron

Urine formation begins by **ultrafiltration** of the blood, as fluid is forced through the capillaries of the glomerulus, forming a filtrate similar to blood but lacking cells and proteins. The filtrate is then modified by **secretion** and **reabsorption** to add or remove substances (e.g. ions). The processes involved in urine formation are summarised below for each region of the nephron: glomerulus, proximal convoluted tubule, loop of Henle, distal convoluted tubule, and collecting duct.

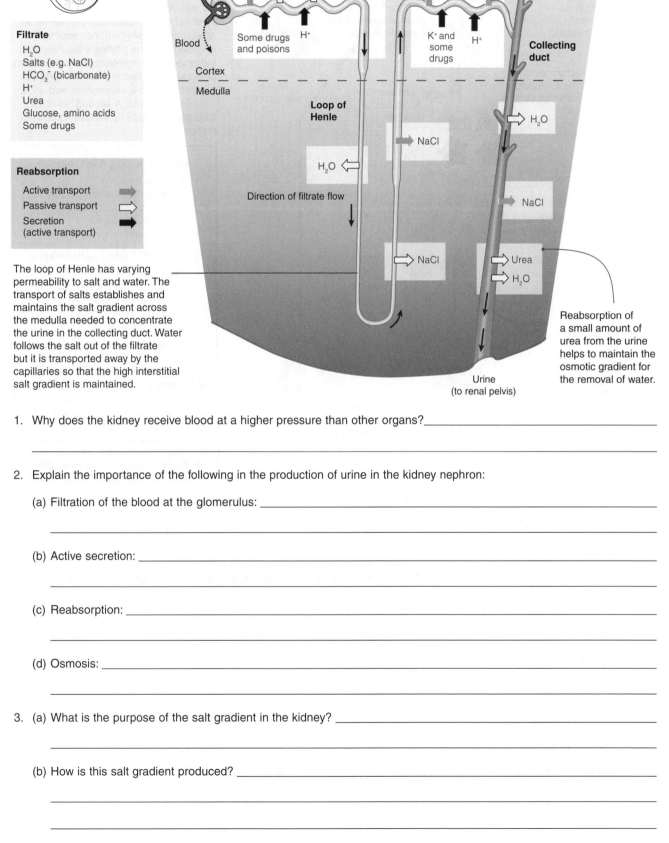

Filtrate

H_2O
Salts (e.g. NaCl)
HCO_3^- (bicarbonate)
H^+
Urea
Glucose, amino acids
Some drugs

Reabsorption

Active transport ➡
Passive transport ⇨
Secretion ➡
(active transport)

The loop of Henle has varying permeability to salt and water. The transport of salts establishes and maintains the salt gradient across the medulla needed to concentrate the urine in the collecting duct. Water follows the salt out of the filtrate but it is transported away by the capillaries so that the high interstitial salt gradient is maintained.

Reabsorption of a small amount of urea from the urine helps to maintain the osmotic gradient for the removal of water.

Urine
(to renal pelvis)

1. Why does the kidney receive blood at a higher pressure than other organs? _____

_____

2. Explain the importance of the following in the production of urine in the kidney nephron:

(a) Filtration of the blood at the glomerulus: _____

_____

(b) Active secretion: _____

_____

(c) Reabsorption: _____

_____

(d) Osmosis: _____

_____

3. (a) What is the purpose of the salt gradient in the kidney? _____

_____

(b) How is this salt gradient produced? _____

_____

_____

141 Control of Urine Output

Key Idea: The body's balance of fluid and electrolytes is regulated by varying the composition and volume of urine. This is achieved through the action of the hormones antidiuretic hormone (ADH) and aldosterone.

The body regulates the composition and volume of the blood to compensate for variations in salt and water intake, and environmental conditions. This is achieved by varying the volume and composition of the urine and is under hormonal control. Antidiuretic hormone (ADH), from the posterior pituitary, regulates water reabsorption from the kidney collecting duct. Aldosterone, from the adrenal cortex, regulates sodium absorption from the kidney tubules.

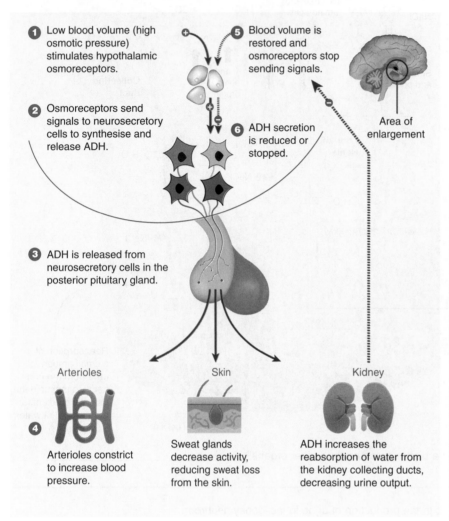

1. Low blood volume (high osmotic pressure) stimulates hypothalamic osmoreceptors.

2. Osmoreceptors send signals to neurosecretory cells to synthesise and release ADH.

3. ADH is released from neurosecretory cells in the posterior pituitary gland.

5. Blood volume is restored and osmoreceptors stop sending signals.

6. ADH secretion is reduced or stopped.

Area of enlargement

Arterioles

4. Arterioles constrict to increase blood pressure.

Skin
Sweat glands decrease activity, reducing sweat loss from the skin.

Kidney
ADH increases the reabsorption of water from the kidney collecting ducts, decreasing urine output.

Osmoreceptors in the **hypothalamus** of the brain respond to changes in blood volume. A blood volume stimulates the synthesis and secretion of the hormone ADH (antidiuretic hormone), which is released from the posterior pituitary into the blood. ADH increases the permeability of the kidney collecting duct to water so that more water is reabsorbed and urine volume decreases. A second hormone, aldosterone, helps by increasing sodium reabsorption.

Factors causing ADH release
▸ Low blood volume
   = More negative water potential
   = High blood sodium levels
   = Low fluid intake
▸ Nicotine and morphine

Factors inhibiting ADH release
▸ High blood volume
   = Less negative water potential
   = Low blood sodium levels
▸ High fluid intake
▸ Alcohol consumption

Factors causing the release of aldosterone
Low blood volumes also stimulate secretion of aldosterone from the adrenal cortex. This is mediated through a complex pathway involving osmoreceptors near the kidney glomeruli and the hormone renin from the kidney.

1. State what happens to urine volume and blood volume when:

   (a) ADH secretion increases: _____

   (b) ADH secretion decreases: _____

2. Diabetes insipidus is caused by a lack of ADH. From what you know about ADH, describe the symptoms of this disease:

   _____

   _____

3. Explain why alcohol consumption (especially to excess) causes dehydration and thirst: _____

   _____

4. (a) State the effect of aldosterone on the kidney nephron: _____

   (b) What would be the net result of this effect: _____

5. Explain the role of negative feedback in the regulation of blood volume and urine output: _____

   _____

   _____

© 2017 **BIOZONE** International
ISBN: 978-1-927309-26-1
Photocopying Prohibited

142 Adaptations for Conserving Water

Key Idea: Desert mammals have adaptations to conserve water or reduce water intake requirements.

Water loss is a major problem for most mammals. The adaptations of mammals in arid regions enables them to minimise water losses and reduce the amount of water they need to drink. Arid-adapted species typically produce very concentrated urine, so lose very little water this way. In addition, the metabolic breakdown of food contributes a large proportion of daily water needs. Some, like kangaroo rats, do not drink at all, and obtain most of their water metabolically.

Adaptations of arid adapted rodents

Most desert-dwelling mammals are able to tolerate a low water intake. Arid adapted rodents, such as kangaroo rats, conserve water by reducing losses to the environment and obtain the balance of their water needs from the oxidation of dry foods (respiratory metabolism). The table below shows the water balance in a kangaroo rat after eating 100 g of dry pearl barley. Note the high urine to plasma concentration ratio (17) which is more than four times that of a human (4).

Water balance in a kangaroo rat
(*Dipodomys spectablis*)

Water gains / cm^3		Water losses / cm^3	
Absorbed from food	6.0	Breathing	43.9
From metabolism	54.0	Urination	13.5
		Defaecation	2.6

Urine/plasma concentration ratio = 17

Adaptations of kangaroo rats

Kangaroo rats, and other arid-adapted rodents, tolerate long periods without drinking, meeting their water requirements from the metabolism of dry foods. They dispose of nitrogenous wastes with very little output of water. They do not sweat or pant to keep cool, but are nocturnal and remain underground during the day.

Daily water transfers in an adult human

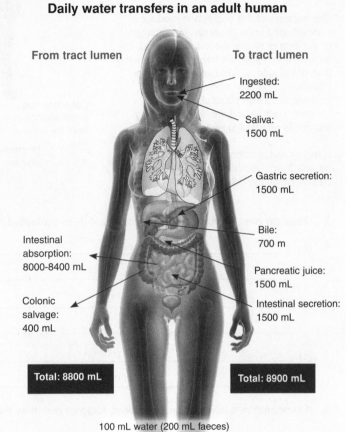

From tract lumen / To tract lumen

Ingested: 2200 mL
Saliva: 1500 mL
Gastric secretion: 1500 mL
Bile: 700 m
Pancreatic juice: 1500 mL
Intestinal secretion: 1500 mL
Intestinal absorption: 8000-8400 mL
Colonic salvage: 400 mL

Total: 8800 mL   Total: 8900 mL

100 mL water (200 mL faeces)

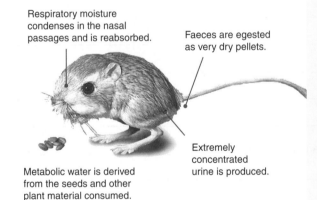

Respiratory moisture condenses in the nasal passages and is reabsorbed.

Faeces are egested as very dry pellets.

Extremely concentrated urine is produced.

Metabolic water is derived from the seeds and other plant material consumed.

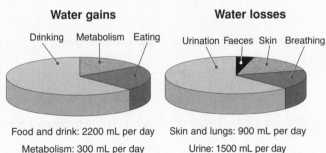

Water gains

Drinking   Metabolism   Eating

Food and drink: 2200 mL per day
Metabolism: 300 mL per day

Water losses

Urination   Faeces   Skin   Breathing

Skin and lungs: 900 mL per day
Urine: 1500 mL per day
Faeces: 100 mL per day

1. (a) Using the tabulated data for the kangaroo rat (above) plot a pie chart of the water gains and losses in the spaces provided right:

   (b) What are the main differences between humans and kangaroo rats in the way each obtains water?

   _____

   _____

   (c) Suggest why kangaroo rats lose much less water through urine than humans:

   _____

   _____

   _____

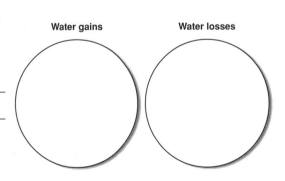

Water gains   Water losses

Each percentage point = 3.6°

LINK
140

KNOW

The Loop of Henle and water conservation

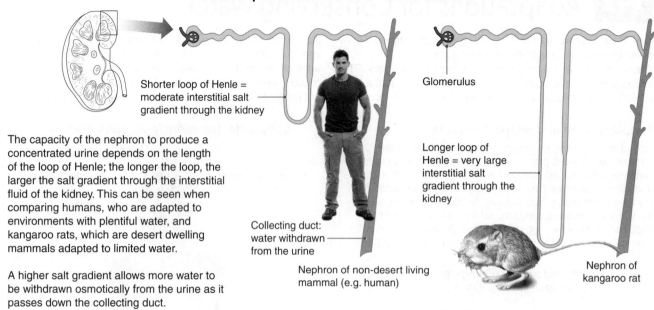

Shorter loop of Henle = moderate interstitial salt gradient through the kidney

Glomerulus

Longer loop of Henle = very large interstitial salt gradient through the kidney

The capacity of the nephron to produce a concentrated urine depends on the length of the loop of Henle; the longer the loop, the larger the salt gradient through the interstitial fluid of the kidney. This can be seen when comparing humans, who are adapted to environments with plentiful water, and kangaroo rats, which are desert dwelling mammals adapted to limited water.

A higher salt gradient allows more water to be withdrawn osmotically from the urine as it passes down the collecting duct.

Collecting duct: water withdrawn from the urine

Nephron of non-desert living mammal (e.g. human)

Nephron of kangaroo rat

2. Describe three physiological adaptations of desert adapted rodents to low water availability:

(a) _____

_____

(b) _____

_____

(c) _____

_____

3. If kangaroo rats neither pant nor sweat, suggest how they might keep cool during the heat of the day:

_____

_____

4. Suggest why most mammals need to drink regularly: _____

_____

_____

5. (a) Compare the length of the loop of Henle between a human and kangaroo rat: _____

_____

_____

(b) Explain the relationship between the length of the loop of Henle and the ability to concentrate the urine: _____

_____

_____

_____

_____

(c) What is the purpose of the salt gradient in the kidney? _____

_____

_____

_____

© 2017 BIOZONE International
ISBN: 978-1-927309-26-1
Photocopying Prohibited

143 Endothermy vs Ectothermy

Key Idea: Ectotherms depend on heat from the environment whereas endotherms generate heat through metabolic activity. Both endotherms and ectotherms may thermoregulate to maintain an optimum temperature for functioning.

Animals are classified into two broad groups based on the source of their body heat. **Ectotherms** depend on the environment for their heat energy (e.g. heat from the sun)

whereas **endotherms** generate most of their body heat from internal metabolic processes. All endotherms and many ectotherms **thermoregulate** (control body temperature) in order to maintain an optimum temperature for the functioning of their metabolic pathways. Ectotherms rely on behavioural mechanisms to do this, whereas in endotherms both behavioural and physiological responses are involved.

Most fish and all amphibians are ectothermic. Unlike many reptiles, they do not thermoregulate, so their body temperature fluctuates with the environment (they are poikilothermic) and they are usually restricted to thermally stable environments.

Reptiles, such as snakes, lizards, and crocodiles, depend on environmental sources of heat energy and regulate body temperature using behaviour. They bask and use body positioning to raise their body temperature for activity. Some larger reptiles maintain a relatively elevated body temperature for a lot of the time.

Birds and mammals achieve a high body temperature through metabolic activity and reduction of heat exchanges. They can function independently of the environmental temperature (within the species-specific tolerance range) and maintain high metabolic rates. Their body temperature remains stable (they are homeothermic).

Daily temperature variations in ectotherms and endotherms

Ectotherm: Diurnal lizard
Body temperature is regulated by behaviour so that it does not rise above 40°C. Basking increases heat uptake from the sun. Activity occurs when body temperature is high. Underground burrows are used for retreat.

Endotherm: Human
Body temperature fluctuates within narrow limits over a 24 hour period. Exercise and eating increase body temperature for a short time. Body temperature falls during rest and is partly controlled by an internal rhythm.

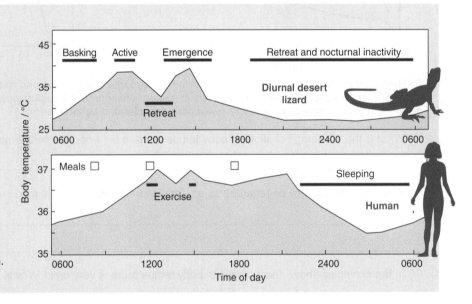

1. Distinguish between ectotherms and endotherms in terms of their sources of body heat: _____

_____

_____

2. The diagrams above show daily temperature variations in an ectotherm and an endotherm.

(a) Which animal has the largest temperature variation? _____

(b) How does the lizard regulate its body temperature? _____

_____

_____

(c) Describe the effect of eating and exercise on the temperature in humans: _____

_____

(d) What effect does sleeping have on human body temperature? _____

_____

LINK 144   WEB 143   KNOW

Liolaemus

The Peruvian mountain lizard (*Liolaemus*) emerges in the morning when the air temperature is below freezing. By exposing itself to the sun, it rapidly heats up to a body temperature that enables it to be fully active. Once warm, the lizard maintains its preferred body temperature of around 35°C by changing posture and orientation to the sun and thereby controlling the amount of heat energy absorbed.

Sauromalus

When the desert lizard, the chuckawalla (*Sauromalus*) is moved from 15°C to 45°C, cloacal and brain temperatures increase rapidly. At ~41°C, these temperatures diverge and the brain stays at ~2°C below the cloacal temperature* and 3°C below air temperature. The chuckawalla achieves this by panting. Its carotid arteries supplying the brain run close to the surface of the pharynx and heat is lost there by evaporative cooling.

*Cloacal temperature measures deep body temperature through the cloaca (equivalent to rectal temperature in mammals)

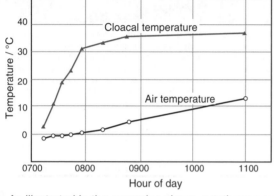

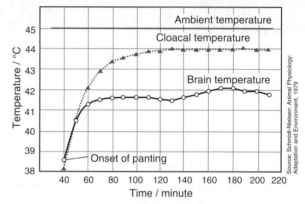

Source: Schmidt-Nielsen: Animal Physiology: Adaptation and Environment, 1979

3. As illustrated in the examples above, ectotherms are capable of achieving and maintaining high, relatively constant body temperatures for relatively long periods in spite of environmental fluctuations. However, they also tolerate marked declines in body temperature to levels lower than are tolerated by endotherms.

(a) What is the advantage of allowing body temperature to fall when ambient temperature drops? _____

_____

(b) Why might ectothermy be regarded as an adaptation to low or variable food supplies?_____

_____

_____

4. (a) In the examples above, the increase in body temperature is very rapid. Why is this important for an ectotherm?

_____

(b) What is the purpose of 'panting' in the chuckawalla? _____

_____

5. (a) In the generalised graph right, identify the optimum temperature range for an endotherm:

_____

(b) Describe the energetic costs of thermoregulation (as measured by oxygen consumption) in an endotherm:

_____

_____

(c) Explain why this is the case: _____

_____

_____

_____

Body temperature and oxygen consumption in an endotherm at different ambient temperatures

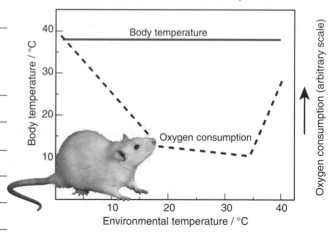

144 Thermoregulation in Humans

Key Idea: In humans, the temperature regulation centre is in the hypothalamus. Thermoregulation relies on negative feedback mechanisms and involves several body systems.

In humans and other mammals, the temperature regulation centre of the body is in the hypothalamus. The hypothalamus responds directly to changes in core temperature and to nerve impulses from receptors in the skin. It then coordinates appropriate nervous and hormonal responses to counteract any deviations from its 'set point' temperature of 36.7°C. Like a thermostat, the hypothalamus detects a return to normal temperature and the corrective mechanisms are switched off (negative feedback regulation).

The hypothalamus regulates temperature

▶ The hypothalamus acts as a thermostat. It detects changes in core body temperature and also receives information about temperature change from thermoreceptors in the skin. It then coordinates nervous and hormonal responses to counteract changes and restore normal body temperature (illustrated in the diagram below).

▶ When normal temperature is restored, the corrective mechanisms are switched off. This is an example of a negative feedback regulation.

▶ Infection can reset the set-point of the hypothalamus to a higher temperature. Homeostatic mechanisms then act to raise the body temperature to the new set point, resulting in a fever (right). This speeds up the body's immune response to infection.

Fever is an important defence against infection, but if the body temperature rises much above 42°C, a dangerous positive feedback loop can begin, making the body produce heat faster than it can get rid of it.

Blood vessels in the skin dilate. Heat is lost from the warm blood at the skin surface.

Sweat glands are activated. Sweating cools the body by evaporation. Hairs on the skin are flattened reducing insulating layer and promoting heat loss.

Body temperature decreases and the hypothalamus heat-loss centre shuts off.

Activates heat-loss centre in hypothalamus

Body temperature too high

Body temperature restored

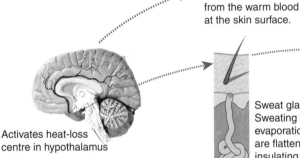

Imbalance

Normal body temperature, 35.6-37.8°C

Imbalance

Stimulus: Increased body temperature, e.g. when exercising or in a hot climate.

Stimulus: Decreased body temperature, e.g. cold environments.

Body temperature restored

Body temperature too low

Body temperature increases and the hypothalamus heat-promoting centre shuts off.

Thyroid gland releases hormones to increase metabolic rate.

Rapid contractions of the skeletal muscles causes reflex shivering, which expends energy to generate heat.

Activates heat-promoting centre in hypothalamus

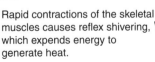

Blood vessels in the skin constrict. Blood is diverted from the skin so heat is not lost.

LINK **145**   LINK **115**   WEB **144**   **KNOW**

Adorabutton CC 4.0

Factors causing heat loss

▸ Wind chill factor accelerates heat loss through conduction.

▸ Heat loss due to temperature difference between the body and the environment.

▸ The rate of heat loss from the body is increased by being wet, by inactivity, dehydration, inadequate clothing, or shock.

Factors causing heat gain

▸ Gain of heat directly from the environment through radiation and conduction.

▸ Excessive fat deposits make it harder to lose the heat that is generated through activity.

▸ Heavy exercise, especially with excessive clothing.

1. (a) Where is the temperature regulation centre in humans located? _____

(b) How does it carry out this role? _____

_____

_____

2. Describe the role of the following in maintaining a constant body temperature in humans:

(a) The skin: _____

_____

(b) The muscles: _____

_____

(c) The thyroid gland: _____

_____

3. How is negative feedback involved in keeping body temperature within narrow limits? _____

_____

_____

_____

4. (a) Why does infection result in an elevated core body temperature? _____

_____

_____

(b) What is the purpose of this? _____

_____

_____

(c) Explain why a prolonged fever can be fatal: _____

_____

_____

5. Identify two factors that cause heat loss: _____

_____

6. Identify two factors that cause heat gain: _____

_____

145 The Role of the Skin in Thermoregulation

Key Idea: The skin plays an important part in regulating body temperature due to its large surface area from which heat from the environment is gained or lost.

The skin is made of two layers. The outer epidermis is made up of layers of simple cells that protect the deeper cell layers from wear and tear. The lower dermis contains the skin's sensory receptors and hairs. Blood vessels in the layer immediately below the skin (the hypodermis) help to regulate body temperature by promoting heat loss or retention through vasodilation or vasoconstriction respectively.

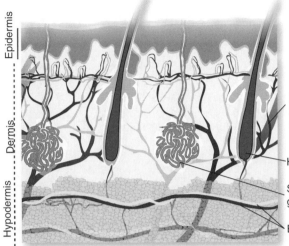

Epidermis
Dermis
Hypodermis

Hair erector muscle raises and lowers hair

Hair root

Sweat (eccrine) gland

Blood vessels

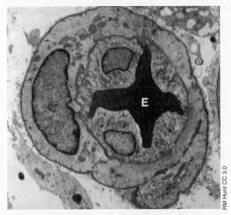

Constriction of a small blood vessel. An erythrocyte (E) (red blood cell) is in the centre of the vessel.

Thermoreceptors (free nerve endings) in the dermis detect changes in skin temperature and send nerve impulses to the hypothalamus, which mediates an appropriate response. Hot thermoreceptors detect an increase in skin temperature above 37.5°C. Cold thermoreceptors detect a fall below 35.8°C.

The skin provides a large surface area for heat loss or gain. To regulate this, the blood vessels beneath the surface constrict (**vasoconstriction**) to reduce blood flow or dilate (**vasodilation**) to increase the blood flow. When blood vessels are fully constricted there may be as much as a 10°C temperature gradient from the outer to inner layers of the skin. Extremities such as the hands and feet have additional vascular controls which can reduce their blood flow in severe cold.

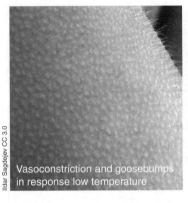

Vasoconstriction and goosebumps in response low temperature

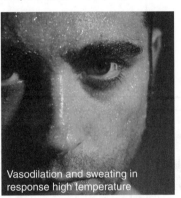

Vasodilation and sweating in response high temperature

Vanuatu boy

The hair erector muscles, sweat glands, and blood vessels are the effectors for mediating a response to information from thermoreceptors. Temperature regulation by the skin involves **negative feedback** because the output is fed back to the skin receptors and becomes part of a new stimulus-response cycle.

People are born with an excess of sweat glands, but if they spend the first years of their life in a cold climate most of these become permanently inactive. People acclimatised to a warm climate (right) produce sweat in a more uniformly distributed way than those who are not, and they may sweat up to 3 dm³ h⁻¹. This increases the efficiency of heat loss. People not acclimatised to warm climates often only sweat up to 1 dm³ h⁻¹ and the sweat usually beads up and drips off the body.

1. How do the blood vessels help to regulate the amount of heat lost from the skin and body? _____

_____

_____

_____

2. Why is a person from a cool climate and exposed to a tropical climate unable to regulate their body temperature as easily as someone who is native to that climate?

_____

_____

LINK 144 WEB 145 KNOW

146 Chapter Review

Summarise what you know about this topic under the headings and sub-headings provided. You can draw diagrams or mind maps, or write short notes to organise your thoughts. Use the images and hints to help you and refer back to the introduction to check the points covered:

Chemical control in mammals

HINT: Define hormone and target cell. Describe the modes of hormone action.

Principles of homeostasis

HINT: Using examples, explain how homeostasis is maintained through feedback mechanisms.

Chemical control in plants

HINT: Discuss the role of auxins, cytokinins, and gibberellins on plant growth.

The mammalian nervous system

HINT: Describe the structure and function of the mammalian nervous system.

REVISE

Nervous transmission

HINT: Neurones, neurotransmitters, and synapses, including the effects of drugs on synaptic transmission.

Extrinsic control of heart rate in mammals

HINT: Describe the role of the ANS (including reflexes) in controlling heart rate.

Osmoregulation

HINT: How do the kidneys maintain fluid and electrolyte balance?

Sensory perception and detection of light

HINT: Describe the structure and function of the human retina.

Thermoregulation

HINT: Distinguish between and ectotherms and endotherms. How do humans thermoregulate?

147 KEY TERMS AND IDEAS: Did You Get It?

1. Match each term to its definition, as identified by its preceding letter code.

acetylcholine _____

autonomic nervous system _____

auxin _____

central nervous system _____

cerebrum _____

gibberellin _____

homeostasis _____

hormones _____

hypothalamus _____

parasympathetic nervous system _____

retina _____

second messenger _____

stimulus _____

sympathetic nervous system _____

thermoregulation _____

A A molecule that relays signals from receptors on the cell surface to target molecules inside the cell.

B The division of the nervous system comprising the brain and spinal cord.

C A neurotransmitter found in both the somatic and autonomic nervous systems. It is rapidly broken down at the synapse.

D Any change in the environment that is capable of generating a response in an organisms.

E This division of the ANS controls activities occurring when the body is at rest, e.g. sexual arousal, salivation, tear production, urination, digestion and defecation.

F The largest region of the brain. It controls and integrates motor, sensory, and higher mental functions (e.g reason and emotion).

G This division of the ANS is responsible for the body's fight-or-flight response.

H The regulation of body temperature.

I The photosensitive layer at the back of the eye containing the photoreceptor cells.

J A division of the peripheral nervous system. It controls visceral functions, for example heart rate, breathing, and digestive functions.

K Area of the brain that controls the autonomic nervous system and links nervous and endocrine systems.

L Regulation of the internal environment to maintain a stable, constant condition.

M A class of plant hormones involved in stem elongation and breaking seed dormancy.

N A plant hormone responsible for apical dominance, phototropism, and cell elongation.

O A signalling molecule, produced by an endocrine gland, that is secreted into the blood and affects the metabolism of specific target cells.

2. (a) Label the components of this neurone (right) using the following word list: *cell body, axon, dendrites, node of Ranvier.*

   (b) Is this neurone myelinated or unmyelinated?(delete one)

   (c) Explain your answer: _____

   _____

   _____

3. (a) Name the excretory organ of vertebrates: _____

   (b) Name the selective filtering element of the kidney: _____

   (c) The structure associated with the creation of a salt gradient in the kidney: _____

   (d) Name the hormone involved in controlling urine output: _____

4. Study the graph and answer the following questions. Use biological terms appropriately to show your understanding.

   (a) Type of feedback mechanism: _____

   _____

   (b) Outcome: _____

   _____

   _____

TEST

© 2017 **BIOZONE** International
ISBN: 978-1-927309-26-1
Photocopying Prohibited

Ecosystems

Key terms

abiotic factor

ACFOR scale

biotic factor

carbon cycle

chi squared

CITES

climate change

climax community

competition

conservation

ecological pyramid

ecological succession

ecosystem

exploitation

greenhouse effect

gross primary
productivity

habitat

net primary
productivity

nitrogen cycle

nutrient cycle

overfishing

Pearson linear
correlation

percentage cover

predation

primary succession

quadrat

sample

secondary succession

Spearman's rank
correlation

Student's t test

sustainability

transect

trophic level

10.1 The nature of ecosystems

Learning outcomes

		Activity number
☐	i Define the term ecosystem, including reference to the terms biotic factor, abiotic factor, and community. Describe the range of ecosystem sizes.	148-150
☐	ii Define the term trophic level and give examples.	151 152
☐	iii Identify types of ecological pyramids and explain how they are used to represent ecosystem structure and energy and biomass transfers. Explain advantages and disadvantages of pyramids of numbers, energy, and biomass.	153
☐	iv Describe ecological techniques to assess abundance and distribution of organisms in a natural habitat including quadrats, transects, ACFOR scales, percentage cover, and individual counts.	154-159
	MATH A.1.5: Understand the principles of sampling as applied to scientific data.	154-157
☐	v Select appropriate ecological techniques according to the ecosystem and the organisms to be studied.	154-159
☐	**CP-15** Investigate the effect of different sampling methods on estimates of population size, taking into account the safe and ethical use of organisms.	159
	AT Use sampling techniques in field work.	159
☐	vi Use statistical tests to analyse data, including:	
	• Student's t test (to test for a difference between two groups)	160 161
	• Pearson's correlation coefficient (to test the strength of a linear relationship between two continuous variables where the data have a normal distribution)	162
	• Spearman' rank correlation (to test for a correlation in non-normal data, suitable for both continuous and discrete variables, including ordinal variables).	163
	• Chi-squared for goodness of fit (to test for departures from an expected theoretical outcome).	178-180
	MATH A.1.7: Use a scatter plot to identify a correlation between two variables.	162 163
	MATH A.1.9: Select and use a statistical test.	160-163 178-180

10.2 Energy transfer through ecosystems

Learning outcomes

		Activity number
☐	i Explain how energy is transferred between trophic levels including reference to net primary productivity and gross primary productivity.	164-167
☐	ii Calculate the efficiency of energy transfer between different trophic levels and account for the loss of energy at each level.	166 167
	MATH A.0.3: Use ratios, fractions, and percentages.	166
☐	iii Explain the role of microorganisms in recycling nutrients in ecosystems.	168-170

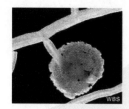

10.3 Changes in ecosystems

Learning outcomes

☐ i Explain how ecosystems develop and change over time including reference to colonisation, succession, and types of climax communities. 171-175

☐ ii Explain the effects of biotic and abiotic factors on population size. Abiotic factors could include temperature, humidity, salinity etc. Biotic factors could include predation and other forms of exploitation and competition. 176 177 181-185

☐ **CP-16** ▶Investigate the effect of one abiotic factor on the distribution or morphology of a species, taking into account the safe and ethical use of organisms. 180

☐ **AT** ▶Use sampling techniques in field work. 180

☐ **MATH** ▶A.1.9: Select and use a statistical test. 178-180

10.4 Human effects on ecosystems

Activity number

Learning outcomes

☐ i Interpret data relating to human influences on ecosystems, including reference to climate change and depletion of resources as exemplified by overfishing. 188 189 191-199

☐ ii Explain the effect that treaties such as CITES have had on global biodiversity. What are their goals and how effective are they in their implementation? 201

☐ iii With reference to conservation of fish stocks and climate change mitigation, explain how the sustainability of resources depends on effective management of conflicts between human needs and demands and conservation. 186 187 190 200

☐ iv Explain the role of scientific journals, the peer review process, and scientific conferences in validating evidence related to the climate change debate. 193 194

148 Components of an Ecosystem

Key Idea: An ecosystem consists of all the organisms living in a particular area and their physical environment.

An **ecosystem** is a community of living organisms and the physical (non-living) components of their environment. The community (living component of the ecosystem) is in turn made up of a number of **populations**, these being organisms of the same species living in the same geographical area. The structure and function of an ecosystem is determined by the physical (abiotic) and the living (biotic) factors, which determine species distribution and survival.

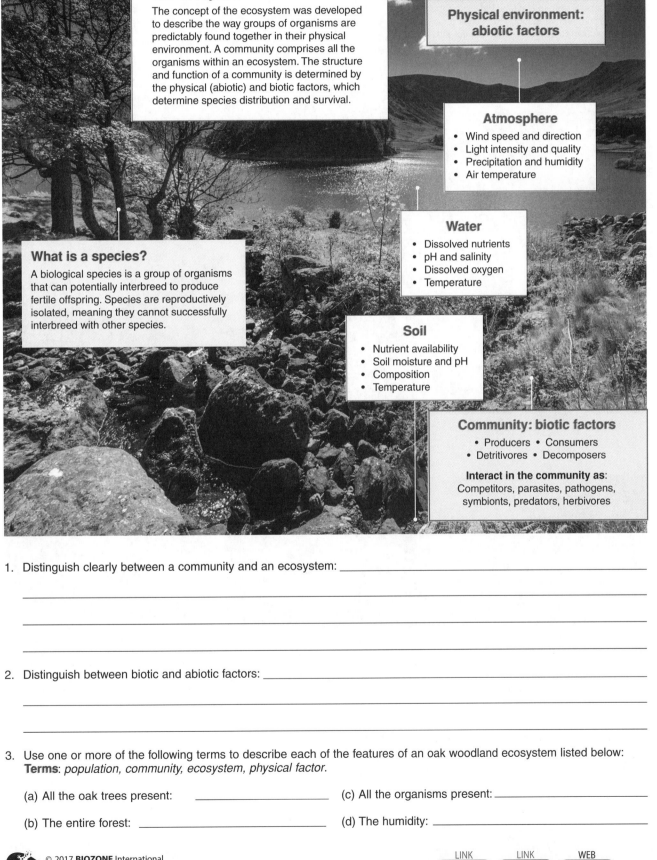

The ecosystem

The concept of the ecosystem was developed to describe the way groups of organisms are predictably found together in their physical environment. A community comprises all the organisms within an ecosystem. The structure and function of a community is determined by the physical (abiotic) and biotic factors, which determine species distribution and survival.

Physical environment: abiotic factors

Atmosphere
- Wind speed and direction
- Light intensity and quality
- Precipitation and humidity
- Air temperature

Water
- Dissolved nutrients
- pH and salinity
- Dissolved oxygen
- Temperature

What is a species?

A biological species is a group of organisms that can potentially interbreed to produce fertile offspring. Species are reproductively isolated, meaning they cannot successfully interbreed with other species.

Soil
- Nutrient availability
- Soil moisture and pH
- Composition
- Temperature

Community: biotic factors
- Producers • Consumers
- Detritivores • Decomposers

Interact in the community as:
Competitors, parasites, pathogens, symbionts, predators, herbivores

1. Distinguish clearly between a community and an ecosystem: _____

_____

_____

_____

2. Distinguish between biotic and abiotic factors: _____

_____

_____

3. Use one or more of the following terms to describe each of the features of an oak woodland ecosystem listed below:
   Terms: *population, community, ecosystem, physical factor.*

   (a) All the oak trees present: _____   (c) All the organisms present: _____

   (b) The entire forest: _____   (d) The humidity: _____

LINK **171**   LINK **149**   WEB **148**   KNOW

149 Types of Ecosystems

Key Idea: Ecosystems have no fixed boundaries and so can vary in size.

Ecosystems can be of any size. The only limit is the size determined by the human observer. For example, a tree can be thought of as an ecosystem, if we ignore the individual comings and goings of animals and look at the system as a whole. But the tree may be part of a larger ecosystem, a forest, which again is part of a larger biome, and so on until we encompass the entire biosphere, that narrow belt around the Earth containing all the Earth's living organisms.

Ecosystems can be on vastly different scales. Yosemite National Park in northern California covers 3000 km². Large parts of it are covered in mixed coniferous forests. The forest ecosystem comprises various tree species (e.g. Douglas fir, giant sequoia, and black oak). There are over 250 species of vertebrates including deer, bear, mountain lion, and a variety of bird life.

Tuxyso / Wikimedia Commons / CC-BY-SA-3.0

The ecosystem of a tree can be quite varied. The tree provides energy and materials for insects and other invertebrates that live on or in it. Bacteria and fungi decompose leaves and dead material on the tree or in the soil. The tree provides roosts for birds and fruit or seeds as a food source.

Within the forested areas there are clearings that consist of grasses and scrub with the occasional isolated tree. These areas provide good grazing for deer and open hunting areas for owls.

Tidal rock pools are micro-ecosystems. Each one will be slightly different to the next, with different species assemblages and abiotic factors. The ocean in the background is an ecosystem on a vastly larger scale.

The border of a garden or back yard can be used to define an ecosystem. Gardens can provide quite different ecosystems, ranging from tropical to dry depending on the type of plants and watering system.

Animals can be ecosystems in the same way as trees. All animals carry populations of microbes in their gut or on their bodies. Invertebrates, such as lice, may live in the fur and spend their entire life cycle there.

1. Describe the borders that would define each of the three Yosemite ecosystems described above:

   (a) _____

   (b) _____

   (c) _____

© 2017 **BIOZONE** International
ISBN: 978-1-927309-26-1
Photocopying Prohibited

150 Habitat

Key Idea: The environment in which an organism lives is its habitat. The habitat may not be homogeneous in its quality.

The environment in which an organism (or species) lives (including all the physical and biotic factors) is its **habitat**. Within any habitat, each species has a range of tolerance to variations in its environment. Within the population, individuals will have slightly different tolerance ranges based on small differences in genetic make-up, age, and health. The wider an organism's tolerance range for any one factor (e.g. temperature) the more likely it is that the organism will survive variations in that factor. For the same reasons, species with a wider tolerance range are likely to be more widely distributed. Organisms have a narrower **optimum range** within which they function best. This may vary seasonally or during development. Organisms are usually most abundant where the abiotic factors are closest to the optimum range.

Habitat occupation and tolerance range

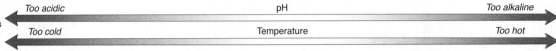

Examples of abiotic factors influencing niche size:

The law of tolerances states that *for each abiotic factor, a species population (or organism) has a tolerance range within which it can survive. Toward the extremes of this range, that abiotic factor tends to limit the organism's ability to survive.*

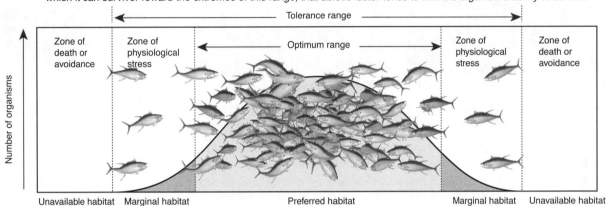

The scale of available habitats

A habitat may be vast and relatively homogeneous for the most part, as is the open ocean. Barracuda (above) occur around reefs and in the open ocean where they are aggressive predators.

For non-motile organisms, such as the fungus pictured above, a suitable habitat may be defined by the particular environment in a relatively small area, such as on this decaying log.

For microbial organisms, such as the bacteria and protozoans of the ruminant gut, the habitat is defined by the chemical environment within the rumen (R) of the host animal, in this case, a cow.

1. What is the relationship between an organism's tolerance range and the habitat it occupies? _____

_____

_____

2. (a) In the diagram above, in which range is most of the population found? Explain your answer: _____

_____

_____

   (b) What are the greatest constraints on an organism's growth and reproduction within this range?_____

_____

_____

3. Describe some probable stresses on an organism forced into a marginal habitat: _____

_____

_____

© 2017 **BIOZONE** International
ISBN: 978-1-927309-26-1
Photocopying Prohibited

LINK 149   LINK 148   WEB 150 **KNOW**

151 Food Chains

Key Idea: A food chain is a model to illustrate the feeding relationships between organisms.

Organisms in ecosystems interact by way of their feeding (trophic) relationships. These interactions can be shown in a **food chain**, which is a simple model to illustrate how energy or biomass, in the form of food, passes from one organism to the next. Each organism in the chain is a source of energy for the next. The levels of a food chain are called **trophic levels**. An

organism is assigned to a trophic level based on its position in the food chain. Organisms may occupy different trophic levels in different food chains or during different stages of their life. Arrows link the organisms in a food chain and their direction shows the flow of energy and biomass through the trophic levels. Most food chains begin with a producer, which is eaten by a primary consumer (**herbivore**). Higher level consumers (e.g. **carnivores**) eat other consumers.

Millipede

Producers (autotrophs) e.g. plants, algae, and autotrophic bacteria, make their own food from simple inorganic substances, often by photosynthesis using energy from the sun. Inorganic nutrients are obtained from the abiotic environment, such as the soil and atmosphere.

Consumers (heterotrophs) e.g. animals, get their energy by eating other organisms. Consumers are ranked according to the trophic level they occupy, i.e. 1st order, 2nd order, and classified according to diet (e.g. carnivores eat animal tissue, omnivores eat plant and animal tissue).

Detritivores and **saprotrophs** both gain nutrients from digesting detritus (dead organic matter). Detritivores ingest (eat) and digest detritus inside their bodies. Saprotrophs break it down using enzymes, which are secreted and work externally to their bodies. Nutrients are then absorbed by the organism.

1. (a) Draw arrows on the diagram below to show how the energy flows through the organisms in the food chain. Label each arrow with the process involved in the energy transfer. Draw arrows to show how energy is lost by respiration.

    (b) What is the original energy source for this food chain? _____

    (c) How is this energy source converted to biomass? _____

2. Energy flows through food chains. In what form is it transferred between trophic levels: _____

    _____

3. Describe how the following obtain energy, and give an example of each:

    (a) Producers: _____

    (b) Consumers: _____

    (c) Detritivores: _____

    (d) Saprotrophs: _____

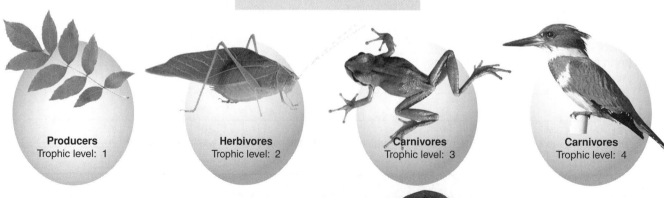

Respiration

Producers
Trophic level: 1

Herbivores
Trophic level: 2

Carnivores
Trophic level: 3

Carnivores
Trophic level: 4

Detritivores and saprotrophs

© 2017 **BIOZONE** International
ISBN: 978-1-927309-26-1
Photocopying Prohibited

152 Food Webs

Key Idea: A food web depicts all the interconnected food chains in an ecosystem. Sunlight is converted to biomass by plants and passed through subsequent trophic levels.

The different food chains in an ecosystem are interconnected to form a complex web of feeding interactions called a **food web.** Sunlight is the initial energy source for almost all ecosystems. Sunlight provides a continuous, but variable, energy supply, which is fixed in carbon compounds by photosynthesis, providing the building blocks and energy for biological materials. Energy stored in this biomass is passed through trophic levels. At each level, some of the energy is lost as heat to the environment so that progressively less is available at each level. This limits the number of links in most food chains to less than six.

▶ In any community, no species exists independently of others. All organisms, dead or alive, are potential sources of food for other organisms. Within a community, there are hundreds of feeding relationships, and most species participate in several food chains. The different food chains in an ecosystem tend to form food webs, a complex series of interactions showing the feeding relationships between organisms in an ecosystem.

▶ The complexity of feeding relationships in a community contributes to its structure and specific features. A simple community, like those that establish on bare soil after a landslide, will have a simpler web of feeding relationships than a mature forest. A food web model (below) can be used to show the trophic linkages between different organisms in a community and can be applied to any ecosystem.

Key to food web (below)

- - → Flow of nutrients from the living components to detritus or the nutrient pool.

──▶ Consumer–resource interactions.

▥▥▶ Losses of each food web component from the system and external input of limiting nutrients.

A simple food web

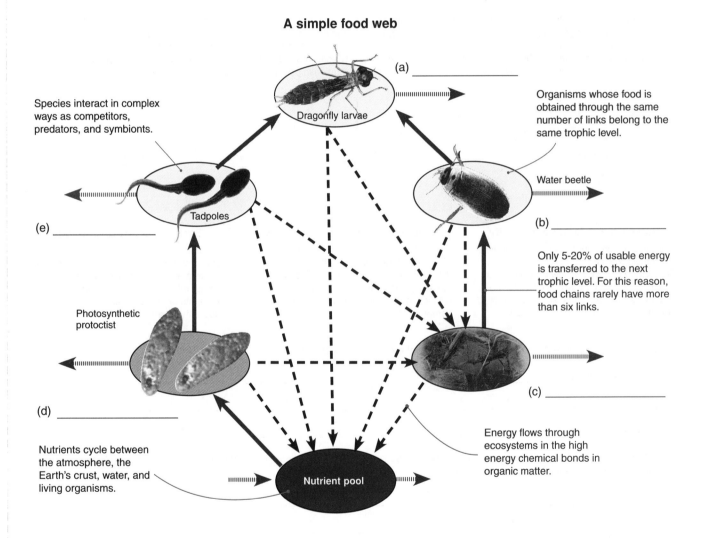

(a) _____

Organisms whose food is obtained through the same number of links belong to the same trophic level.

Dragonfly larvae

Species interact in complex ways as competitors, predators, and symbionts.

Tadpoles

Water beetle

(e) _____

(b) _____

Only 5-20% of usable energy is transferred to the next trophic level. For this reason, food chains rarely have more than six links.

Photosynthetic protoctist

(d) _____

(c) _____

Nutrients cycle between the atmosphere, the Earth's crust, water, and living organisms.

Nutrient pool

Energy flows through ecosystems in the high energy chemical bonds in organic matter.

1. (a) - (e) Complete the food web above by adding the following labels: carnivore, herbivore, autotroph, detritus, detritivore:

2. Why do most food chains have fewer than six links? _____

_____

_____

_____

153 Ecological Pyramids

Key Idea: Ecological pyramids are used to illustrate the number of organisms, amount of energy, or amount of biomass at each trophic level in an ecosystem.

The energy, biomass, or numbers of organisms at each trophic level in any ecosystem can be represented by an ecological pyramid. The first trophic level is placed at the bottom of the pyramid and subsequent trophic levels are stacked on top in their 'feeding sequence'. Ecological pyramids provide a convenient model to illustrate the relationship between different trophic levels in an ecosystem.

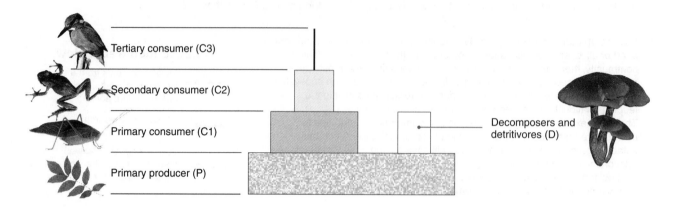

Tertiary consumer (C3)

Secondary consumer (C2)

Primary consumer (C1)

Primary producer (P)

Decomposers and detritivores (D)

The generalised ecological pyramid pictured above shows a conventional pyramid shape, with a large number (or biomass) of producers forming the base for an increasingly small number (or biomass) of consumers. Decomposers are placed at the level of the primary consumers and off to the side. They may obtain energy from many different trophic levels and so do not fit into the conventional pyramid structure. For any particular ecosystem at any one time (e.g. the forest ecosystem below), the shape of this typical pyramid can vary greatly depending on whether the trophic relationships are expressed as numbers, biomass or energy

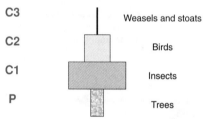

C3

C2

C1

P

Weasels and stoats

Birds

Insects

Trees

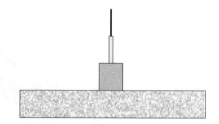

Numbers in a forest community

Pyramids of numbers display the number of individual organisms at each trophic level. The pyramid above has few producers, but they may be of a very large size (e.g. trees). This gives an 'inverted pyramid', although not all pyramids of numbers are like this.

Biomass in a forest community

Biomass pyramids measure the 'weight' of biological material at each trophic level. Water content of organisms varies, so 'dry weight' is often used. Organism size is taken into account, allowing meaningful comparisons of different trophic levels.

Energy in a forest community

Pyramids of energy are often very similar to biomass pyramids. The energy content at each trophic level is generally comparable to the biomass (i.e. similar amounts of dry biomass tend to have about the same energy content).

1. What do each of the following types of ecological pyramids measure?

   (a) Number pyramid: _____

   (b) Biomass pyramid: _____

   (c) Energy pyramid: _____

2. What is the advantage of using a biomass or energy pyramid rather than a pyramid of numbers to express the relationship between different trophic levels?

   _____

   _____

   _____

   _____

3. How can a forest community with relatively few producers (see next page) support a large number of consumers?

   _____

   _____

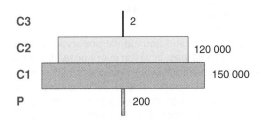

Pyramid of numbers: forest community

In a forest community, a few producers may support a large number of consumers. This is due to the large size of the producers; large trees can support many individual consumer organisms. The example above shows the numbers at each trophic level for an oak forest in England, in an area of 10 m².

Pyramid of numbers: grassland community

In a grassland community, a large number of (small) producers support a much smaller number of consumers. Grass plants can support only a few individual consumer organisms and take time to recover from grazing pressure. The example above shows the numbers at each trophic level for a derelict grassland area (10 m²) in Michigan, United States.

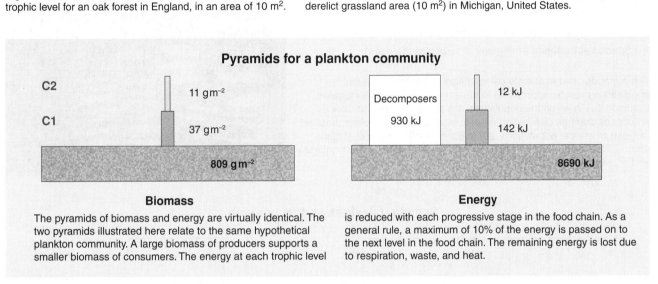

Pyramids for a plankton community

Biomass

The pyramids of biomass and energy are virtually identical. The two pyramids illustrated here relate to the same hypothetical plankton community. A large biomass of producers supports a smaller biomass of consumers. The energy at each trophic level

Energy

is reduced with each progressive stage in the food chain. As a general rule, a maximum of 10% of the energy is passed on to the next level in the food chain. The remaining energy is lost due to respiration, waste, and heat.

4. Determine the **energy transfer** between trophic levels in the plankton community example in the above diagram:

(a) Between producers and the primary consumers: _____

(b) Between the primary consumers and the secondary consumers: _____

(c) Why is the amount of energy transferred from the producer level to primary consumers considerably less than the expected 10% that occurs in many other communities?

_____

_____

(d) After the producers, which trophic group has the greatest energy content? _____

(e) Give a likely explanation why this is the case: _____

_____

_____

An unusual biomass pyramid

The biomass pyramids of some ecosystems appear rather unusual with an inverted shape. The first trophic level has a lower biomass than the second level. What this pyramid does not show is the rate at which the producers (algae) are reproducing in order to support the larger biomass of consumers.

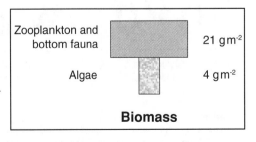

Biomass

5. Give a possible explanation of how a small biomass of producers (algae) can support a larger biomass of consumers (zooplankton):

_____

_____

_____

154 Measuring Distribution and Abundance

Key Idea: Random sampling using an appropriate technique provides unbiased information about the distribution and abundance of species in a community.

Most practical exercises in ecology involve collecting data about the distribution and abundance of one or more species in a community. Most studies also measure the physical factors in the environment as these may help to explain the

patterns of distribution and abundance observed. The use of random sampling methods, in which every possible sample of a given size the same chance of selection, provides unbiased data. As long as the sample size is large enough and the sampling technique is appropriate to the community being studied, sample data enables us to make inferences about aspects of the whole population.

Distribution and abundance

Ecological sampling collects data about where organisms are found and how they are distributed in the environment. This information can be used to determine the health and viability of a population and its ecosystem. When investigating populations it is useful to monitor:

▶ Species **distribution** (where the species are located)

▶ Species **abundance** (how many of a species there are)

The methods used to sample communities and their constituent populations must be appropriate to the ecosystem being investigated. Communities in which the populations are at low density and have a random or clumped distribution will require a different sampling strategy to those where the populations are uniformly distributed and at higher density. There are many sampling options (below), each with advantages and drawbacks for particular communities.

Sampling designs and techniques

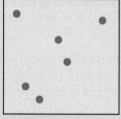
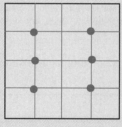

Random   Systematic (grid)

Point sampling
Individual points are chosen (using a grid reference or random numbers applied to a map grid) and the organisms are sampled at those points. Point sampling is most often used to collect data about vegetation distribution. It is time efficient and good for determining species abundance and community composition, but organisms in low abundance may be missed.

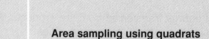

Area sampling using quadrats
A quadrat is a sampling tool that provides a known unit area of sample (e.g. 0.5 m²). Quadrats are placed randomly or in a grid pattern on the sample area. The presence and abundance of organisms in these squares is noted. Quadrat sampling is appropriate for plants and slow moving animals and can be used to evaluate community composition.

First sample: Second sample:
marked   proportion recapture

Mark and recapture sampling
Animals are captured, marked, and released. After a suitable time, the population is resampled. The number of marked animals recaptured in a second sample is recorded as a proportion of the total. Mark and recapture is useful for highly mobile species which are otherwise difficult to record. However, it is time consuming to do well.

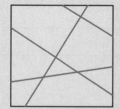
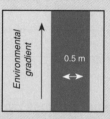

Line transects
A tape marks a line and species occurring at regular points along the line are recorded. Lines can be chosen randomly (above) or may follow an environmental gradient. Line transects have little impact on the environment and are good for assessing the presence/absence of plant species. However, rare species may be missed.

Belt transects
A measured strip is located across the study area and quadrats are used to sample the plants or animals at regular intervals along the belt. Belt transects provide information on abundance and distribution as well as presence/absence. Depending on the width of the belt and length of the transect, they can be time consuming.

© 2017 **BIOZONE** International
ISBN: 978-1-927309-26-1
Photocopying Prohibited

Sampling plants

Plants can be sampled by transects and quadrat in the same way as animals. However plants, especially ground cover plants, tend to spread and often overlap with other plants, making it difficult to count individuals. To overcome this, an estimate of percentage cover of the plant can be used. Because plant leaves overlap, it is possible that the summed estimates of percentage cover can add to more than 100%.

Estimating the percentage cover from a quadrat can be rather subjective (is it 45% or 50%?) and the larger the quadrat the more subjective it can be. To retain objectiveness, the quadrat can be divided into smaller squares and the number of squares covering a plant counted. Another way of estimating percentage cover is using a point quadrat.

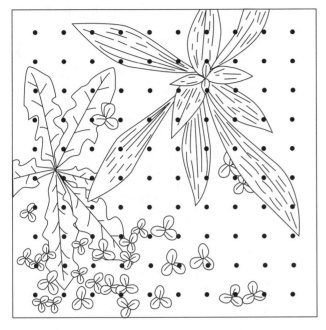

Point quadrat

When using a point quadrat a pin to placed vertically downward at each point and the plants it touches are recorded. The percentage cover is then calculated by the formula:

Percentage cover = (Hits (touches) ÷ total sampling points) x 100

Quadrat divided into smaller squares.

Dividing the quadrat into smaller squares helps to estimate percentage cover more accurately. For example, the large plant in the top right of the quadrat above fills approximately 21 squares out of 100 so covers 21% of the quadrat.

1. Distinguish between distribution and abundance: _____

_____

_____

2. Name a sampling technique that would be appropriate for determining:

   (a) Percentage cover of a plant species in pasture: _____

   _____

   (b) Change in community composition from low to high altitude on a mountain: _____

   _____

   (c) Association of plant species with particular soil types in a nature reserve: _____

   _____

3. Why is it common practice to also collect information about the physical environment when sampling populations?

_____

_____

4. Use the point quadrat to calculate the % cover of the large plant in the top right corner of the quadrat above:

_____

_____

155 Quadrat Sampling

Key Idea: Quadrat sampling involves a series of random placements of a frame of known size over an area of habitat to assess the abundance or diversity of organisms.

Quadrat sampling is a method by which organisms in a certain proportion (sample) of the habitat are counted directly. It is used when the organisms are too numerous to count in total. It can be used to estimate population abundance (number), density, frequency of occurrence, and distribution. Quadrats may be used without a transect when studying a relatively uniform habitat. In this case, the quadrat positions are chosen randomly using a random number table. The general procedure is to count all the individuals (or estimate their percentage cover) in a number of quadrats of known size and to use this information to work out the abundance or percentage cover value for the whole area.

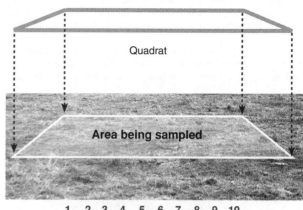

Quadrat

Area being sampled

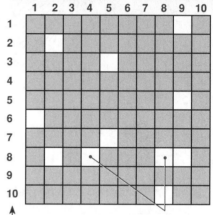

$$\text{Estimated average density} = \frac{\text{Total number of individuals counted}}{\text{Number of quadrats} \times \text{area of each quadrat}}$$

Guidelines for quadrat use:

1. The **area of each quadrat** must be known. Quadrats should be the same shape, but not necessarily square.

2. **Enough quadrat samples** must be taken to provide results that are representative of the total population.

3. The **population of each quadrat** must be known. Species must be distinguishable from each other, even if they have to be identified at a later date. It has to be decided beforehand what the count procedure will be and how organisms over the quadrat boundary will be counted.

4. The size of the quadrat should be appropriate to the organisms and habitat, e.g. a large size quadrat for trees.

5. The quadrats must be **representative of the whole area.** This is usually achieved by **random sampling** (right).

The area to be sampled is divided up into a grid pattern with indexed coordinates.

Quadrats are applied to the predetermined grid on a random basis. This can be achieved by using a random number table.

Sampling a centipede population

A researcher by the name of Lloyd (1967) sampled centipedes in Wytham Woods, near Oxford in England. A total of 37 hexagon–shaped quadrats were used, each with a diameter of 30 cm (see diagram on right). These were arranged in a pattern so that they were all touching each other. Use the data in the diagram to answer the following questions.

1. Determine the average number of centipedes captured per quadrat:

   _____

2. Calculate the estimated average density of centipedes per square metre (remember that each quadrat is 0.08 square metres in area):

   _____

3. Looking at the data for individual quadrats, describe in general terms the distribution of the centipedes in the sample area:

   _____

   _____

4. Describe one factor that might account for the distribution pattern:

   _____

   _____

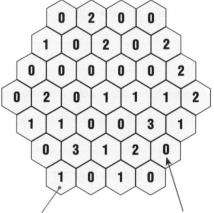

Each quadrat was a hexagon with a diameter of 30 cm and an area of 0.08 square meters.

The number in each hexagon indicates how many centipedes were caught in that quadrat.

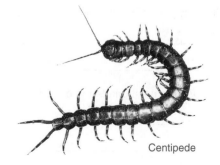

Centipede

© 2017 **BIOZONE** International
ISBN: 978-1-927309-26-1
Photocopying Prohibited

156 Quadrat-Based Estimates

Key Idea: The size and number of quadrats used to sample a community must be sufficient to be representative of that community without taking an excessively long time to use.

The simplest description of a community is a list of the species present. This does not provide information about the relative abundance of the species, although this can be estimated using abundance scales (e.g. ACFOR). Quadrats can provide quantitative information about a community. The size of the quadrat and the number of samples taken must represent the community as fairly as possible.

What size quadrat?

Quadrats are usually square, and cover 0.25 m² (0.5 m x 0.5 m) or 1 m², but they can be of any size or shape, even a single point. The quadrats used to sample plant communities are often 0.25 m². This size is ideal for low-growing vegetation, but quadrat size needs to be adjusted to habitat type. The quadrat must be large enough to be representative of the community, but not so large as to take a very long time to use.

A quadrat covering an area of 0.25 m² is suitable for most low growing plant communities, such as this alpine meadow, fields, and grasslands.

Larger quadrats (e.g.1m²) are needed for communities with shrubs and trees. Quadrats as large as 4 m x 4 m may be needed in woodlands.

Small quadrats (0.01 m² or 100 mm x 100 mm) are appropriate for lichens and mosses on rock faces and tree trunks.

How many quadrats?

As well as deciding on a suitable quadrat size, the other consideration is how many quadrats to take (the sample size). In species-poor or very homogeneous habitats, a small number of quadrats will be sufficient. In species-rich or heterogeneous habitats, more quadrats will be needed to ensure that all species are represented adequately.

Determining the number of quadrats needed

- Plot the cumulative number of species recorded (on the y axis) against the number of quadrats already taken (on the x axis).

- The point at which the curve levels off indicates the suitable number of quadrats required.

Fewer quadrats are needed in species-poor or very uniform habitats, such as this bluebell woodland.

Describing vegetation

Density (number of individuals per unit area) is a useful measure of abundance for animal populations, but can be problematic in plant communities where it can be difficult to determine where one plant ends and another begins. For this reason, plant abundance is often assessed using **percentage cover**. Here, the percentage of each quadrat covered by each species is recorded, either as a numerical value or using an abundance scale such as the ACFOR scale.

The ACFOR abundance scale

A = Abundant (30% +)
C = Common (20-29%)
F = Frequent (10-19%)
O = Occasional (5-9%)
R = Rare (1-4%)

The ACFOR scale could be used to assess the abundance of species in this wildflower meadow. Abundance scales are subjective, but it is not difficult to determine which abundance category each species falls into.

1. Describe one difference between the methods used to assess species abundance in plant and in animal communities:

_____

2. What is the main consideration when determining appropriate quadrat size? _____

3. What is the main consideration when determining number of quadrats? _____

4. Explain two main disadvantages of using the ACFOR abundance scale to record information about a plant community:

   (a) _____

   (b) _____

LINK
154

KNOW

157 Transect Sampling

Key Idea: Transect sampling is useful for providing information on species distribution along an environmental gradient.

A **transect** is a line placed across a community of organisms. Transects provide information on the distribution of species in the community. They are particularly valuable when the transect records community composition along an **environmental gradient** (e.g. up a mountain or across a seashore). The usual practice for small transects is to stretch a string between two markers. The string is marked off in measured distance intervals and the species at each marked point are noted. The sampling points along the transect may also be used for the siting of quadrats, so that changes in density and community composition can be recorded. Belt transects are essentially a form of continuous quadrat sampling. They provide more information on community composition but can be difficult to carry out. Some transects provide information on the vertical, as well as horizontal, distribution of species (e.g. tree canopies in a forest).

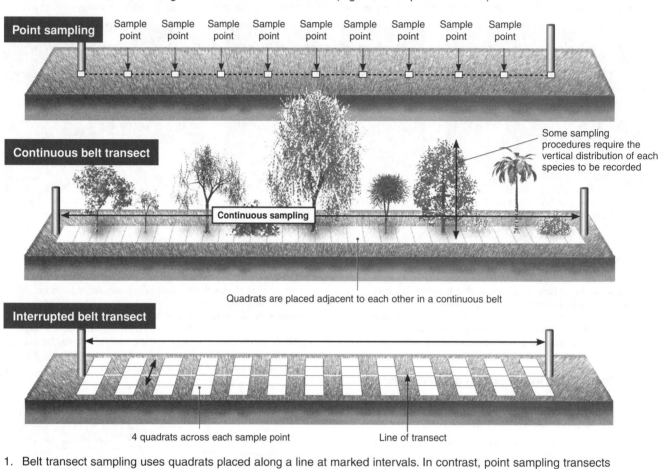

1. Belt transect sampling uses quadrats placed along a line at marked intervals. In contrast, point sampling transects record only the species that are touched or covered by the line at the marked points.

   (a) Describe one disadvantage of belt transects: _____

   _____

   (b) Why might line transects give an unrealistic sample of the community in question? _____

   _____

   _____

   (c) How do belt transects overcome this problem? _____

   _____

   (d) When would it not be appropriate to use transects to sample a community? _____

   _____

2. How could you test whether or not a transect sampling interval was sufficient to accurately sample a community?

   _____

   _____

   _____

© 2017 **BIOZONE** International
ISBN: 978-1-927309-26-1
Photocopying Prohibited

A **kite graph** is a good way to show the distribution of organisms sampled using a belt transect. Data may be expressed as abundance or percentage cover along an environmental gradient. Several species can be shown together on the same plot so that the distributions can be easily compared.

3. The data on the right were collected from a rocky shore field trip. Four common species of barnacle were sampled in a continuous belt transect from the low water mark, to a height of 10 m above that level. The number of each of the four species in a 1 m^2 quadrat was recorded.

Plot a **kite graph** of the data for all four species on the grid below. Be sure to choose a scale that takes account of the maximum number found at any one point and allows you to include all the species on the one plot. Include the scale on the diagram so that the number at each point on the kite can be calculated.

An example of a kite graph

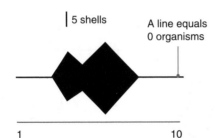

| 5 shells

A line equals
0 organisms

1   10
Distance above water line (m)

Field data notebook

Numbers of barnacles (4 common species) showing distribution on a rocky shore

Height above low water (m)	Plicate barnacle	Columnar barnacle	Brown barnacle	Sheet barnacle
0	0	0	0	65
1	10	0	0	12
2	32	0	0	0
3	55	0	0	0
4	100	18	0	0
5	50	124	0	0
6	30	69	2	0
7	0	40	11	0
8	0	0	47	0
9	0	0	59	0
10	0	0	65	0

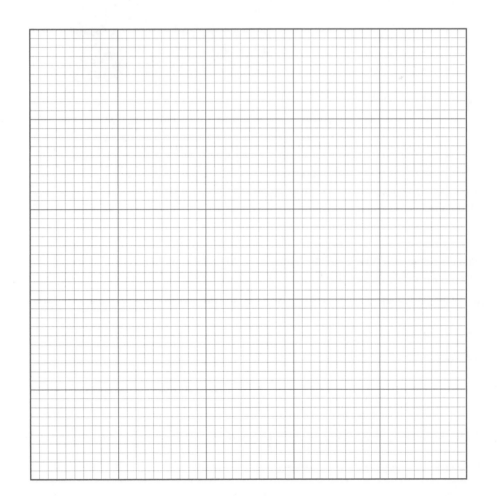

158 Qualitative Practical Work: Seaweed Zonation

Key Idea: Qualitative and quantitative data can be used to explain patterns of zonation in seashore communities.

Three species of brown algae (genus *Fucus*), together with the brown alga *Ascophyllum nodosum*, form the dominant seaweeds on rocky shores in Britain, where they form distinct zones along the shore. Zonation is a characteristic feature of many seashore communities where species' distribution is governed by tolerances to particular physical conditions (e.g. time of exposure to air). When collecting data on the distribution and abundance of *Fucus* species, it is useful to also make qualitative observations about the size, vigour, and degree of desiccation of specimens at different points on the shore. These observations provide biological information which can help to explain the observed patterns.

Spiral wrack (*Fucus spiralis*)

Andreas Trepte

Fucus is a genus of marine brown algae, commonly called wracks, which are found in the midlittoral zone of rocky seashores (i.e. the zone between the low and high levels). A group of students made a study of a rocky shore dominated by three species of *Fucus*: spiral wrack, bladder wrack, and serrated wrack. Their aim was to investigate the distribution of three *Fucus* species in the midlittoral zone and relate this to the size and vigour (V) of the seaweeds and the degree of desiccation (D) evident.

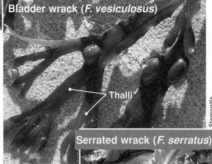
Bladder wrack (*F. vesiculosus*)
Thalli
Stemonitis

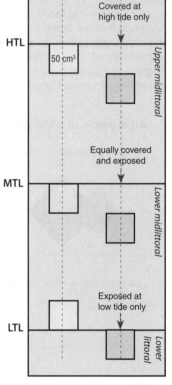

Procedure

Three 50 cm³ quadrats were positioned from the LTL to the HTL at two sites on the shore as shown in the diagram (far right). An estimate of **percentage cover (C)** of each species of *Fucus* was made for each sample. Information on vigour and degree of desiccation was collected at the same time.

Serrated wrack (*F. serratus*)
Stemonitis

Qualitative data were collected as simple scores:
+ = vigorous with large thalli
    no evidence of dessication
0 = less vigorous with smaller thalli
    some evidence of dessication
– = small, poorly grown thalli
    obvious signs of desiccation

1. (a) Describe the quantitative component of this study:

_____

_____

(b) Describe the qualitative component of this study:

Species	SITE 1									SITE 2								
	HTL			MTL			LTL			HTL			MTL			LTL		
	C	D	V	C	D	V	C	D	V	C	D	V	C	D	V	C	D	V
Spiral wrack	50	0	+	0	na	na	0	na	na	30	+	0	0	na	na	0	na	na
Bladder wrack	15	–	–	80	+	+	20	+	0	50	0	–	70	+	+	0	na	na
Serrated wrack	0	na	na	0	na	na	75	+	+	0	na	na	10	–	–	80	+	+

_____

2. The results of the quadrat survey are tabulated above. On a separate sheet, plot a column graph of the percentage coverage of each species at each position on the shore and at sites 1 and 2. Staple it to this page.

3. Relate the distribution pattern to the changes in degree of desiccation and in size and vigour of the seaweed thalli:

_____

_____

_____

_____

4. Suggest why the position of the quadrats was staggered for the two sites and describe a disadvantage of this design:

_____

_____

_____

LINK 154   LINK 157

KNOW

© 2017 **BIOZONE** International
ISBN: 978-1-927309-26-1
Photocopying Prohibited

159 Sampling Techniques and Population Estimates

Key Idea: Population estimates made from samples may vary depending on the sampling technique, the number of samples, and where the data was collected.

The diagram (following page) represents an area of wasteland that has been invaded by various weeds. The distribution of five weed species is shown (simply noted as plants 1 to 5). This exercise is designed to show you how different sampling techniques and the way those techniques are applied can give different pictures of the make up of the community being studied. This exercise can be done in groups.

Setting up the sampling grid

1. Mark out a grid pattern
Use a ruler to mark out 3 cm intervals along each side of the sampling area (area of quadrat = 0.03 x 0.03 m). **Draw lines** between these marks to create a 6 x 6 grid pattern (total area = 0.18 x 0.18 m). This will provide a total of 36 quadrats that can be investigated.

2. Number the axes of the grid
Only a small proportion of the possible quadrat positions will be sampled. It is necessary to select the quadrats in a random manner. It is not sufficient to simply guess or choose your own on a 'gut feeling'. The best way to choose the quadrats randomly is to create a numbering system for the grid pattern and then select the quadrats from a random number table. Starting at the top left hand corner, **number the columns and rows from 1 to 6 on each axis**.

Quadrat sampling (counts and % cover)

3. Choose quadrats randomly
To select the required number of quadrats randomly, use random numbers from a random number table. The random numbers are used as an index to the grid coordinates. Choose 6 quadrats from the total of 36 using table of random numbers provided at the bottom of the next page. Make a note of which column of random numbers you choose. Each member of your group should choose a different set of random numbers (i.e. different column: A–D) so that you can compare the effectiveness of the sampling method.

Column of random numbers chosen: _____

NOTE: Highlight the boundary of each selected quadrat with coloured pen/highlighter.

4a. Decide on the counting criteria
Before you count the individuals of each species, the criteria for counting need to be established. You must decide before

sampling begins as to what to do about individuals that are only partly inside the quadrat. Possible answers include:

(a) Only counting individuals that are completely inside the quadrat.
(b) Only counting individuals with a certain part of the body (e.g. the main stem and root mass) inside the quadrat.
(c) Allowing for 'half individuals' (e.g. 3.5 plants).
(d) Counting an individual that is inside the quadrat by half or more as one complete individual.

Discuss the merits and problems of the suggestions above with other members of the class (or group). You may even have counting criteria of your own. Think about other factors that could cause problems with your counting.

4b. Carry out the sampling
Examine each selected quadrat and **count the number of individuals** of each species present. Record your data in the spaces provided in the quadrat count table (Table 1).

5. Percentage cover
Carefully examine each selected quadrat again and **estimate the percentage cover** of each species present. Record your data in the spaces provided in the percentage cover table (Table 2) (to help you, the area of each plant type is given in the table. The quadrat area in 9 cm²).

Transect sampling

6. Line transect
Draw **6 transect lines** across the sampling area from side to side or top to bottom. Use the random number table to work out where the transect line should go. For example using the numbers in column A (2,2) the first line should start in the middle of column 2 in the top row and go across the grid to the middle of column 2 in the bottom row.

Mark the line every 1 cm. **Count** and record every plant the line touches at every 1 cm mark. Record the results in the line transect table (Table 3).

Table 1: Quadrat count

Coordinates for each quadrat	Plant 1	Plant 2	Plant 3	Plant 4	Plant 5
1:					
2:					
3:					
4:					
5:					
6:					
TOTAL					

Table 2: Percentage cover

Coordinates for each quadrat	2.59 cm² Plant 1	2.27 cm² Plant 2	0.79 cm² Plant 3	0.13 cm² Plant 4	0.5 cm² Plant 5
1:					
2:					
3:					
4:					
5:					
6:					
MEAN %					

LINK 154

KNOW

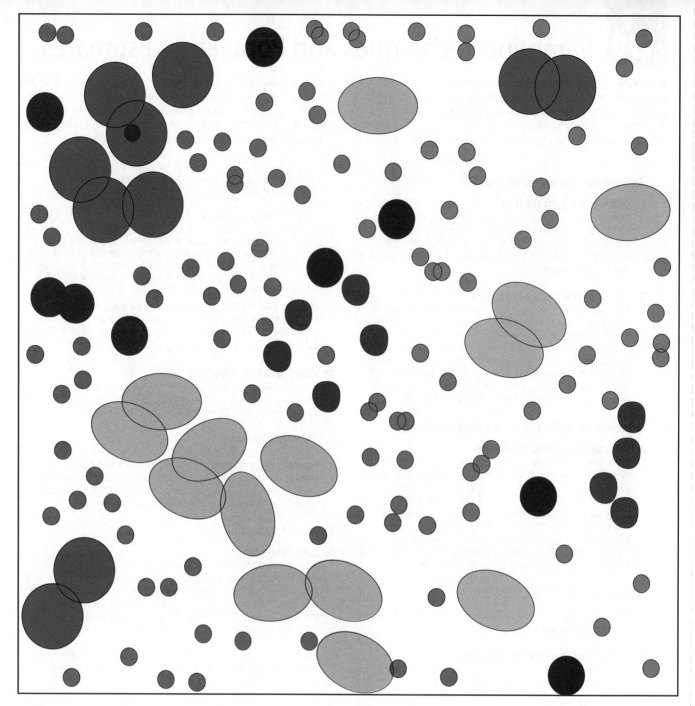

Table 3: Line transect

	Tally plant species	Total number	Relative abundance / % (plant X ÷ total plants x 100)
Plant 1			
Plant 2			
Plant 3			
Plant 4			
Plant 5			

Table of random numbers

A	B	C	D
2 2	3 1	6 2	2 2
3 2	1 5	6 3	4 3
3 1	5 6	3 6	6 4
4 6	3 6	1 3	4 5
4 3	4 2	4 5	3 5
5 6	1 4	3 1	1 4

The table above has been adapted from a table of random numbers from a statistics book. Use this table to select quadrats randomly from the grid above. Choose one of the columns (A to D) and use the numbers in that column as an index to the grid. The first digit refers to the row number and the second digit refers to the column number. To locate each of the 6 quadrats, find where the row and column intersect, as shown below:

Example: | 5 2 | refers to the 5th row and the 2nd column

© 2017 **BIOZONE** International
ISBN: 978-1-927309-26-1
Photocopying Prohibited

1. (a) Use the combined data TOTALS (Table 1) for the sampled quadrats to estimate the average density for each species by using the formula:

$$\text{Density} = \frac{\text{Total number in all quadrats sampled}}{\text{Number of quadrats sampled} \times \text{area of a quadrat}}$$

Remember that a total of 6 quadrats are sampled and each has an area of 0.0009 m². The density should be expressed as the number of individuals per square metre (no. m⁻²).

Plant 1: _____ Plant 2: _____ Plant 3: _____ Plant 4: _____ Plant 5: _____

(b) Use the direct count data from your quadrats (Table 1) to calculate a relative abundance of the plants (abundance as a percentage of the community). Use the formula:

$$\text{Relative abundance} = \frac{\text{Number of plant } X \text{ in all quadrats sampled}}{\text{Total number of all plants counted}} \times 100$$

Plant 1: _____ Plant 2: _____ Plant 3: _____ Plant 4: _____ Plant 5: _____

2. Use the percentage cover data (Table 2) to calculate the average percentage cover for each plant over the 6 quadrats:

Plant 1: _____ Plant 2: _____ Plant 3: _____ Plant 4: _____ Plant 5: _____

3. Use the line transect data (Table 3) to calculate relative abundance as in question 1 (b). Transfer your result here:

Plant 1: _____ Plant 2: _____ Plant 3: _____ Plant 4: _____ Plant 5: _____

4. (a) Carry out a direct count of all 5 plant species for the whole sample area (all 36 quadrats). Apply the data from your direct count to the equation given in (1) above to calculate the actual population density (remember that the number of quadrats in this case = 36):

Plant 1: _____ Plant 2: _____ Plant 3: _____ Plant 4: _____ Plant 5: _____

(b) Compare your estimated population density to the actual population density for each species:

_____

_____

_____

(c) Now calculate the actual relative abundance of the plants as in question 1(b):

Plant 1: _____ Plant 2: _____ Plant 3: _____ Plant 4: _____ Plant 5: _____

(d) Compare your estimated population abundance calculations to the actual population density for each species:

_____

_____

_____

5. Comment on how the picture of the community provided by the different sampling methods compare. Compare your results with people in your class who have used different coordinates for their quadrats. What picture of the community was provided by their results?

_____

_____

_____

_____

_____

_____

© 2017 **BIOZONE** International
ISBN: 978-1-927309-26-1
Photocopying Prohibited

160 Quantifying Variation Using Student's *t* Test

Key Idea: Differences between two populations can be tested for significance using the Student's *t* test.

The Student's *t* test is commonly used to compare two sample means, e.g. means for a treatment and a control in an experiment, or the means of some measured characteristic between two animal or two plant populations. It is a simple test and useful for distinguishing real but marginal differences between samples. Usefully, the test remains robust even when sample sizes are small. A simple example outlining the steps in the Student's *t* test is provided below. It compares data for a treatment and a control from a hypothetical experiment (the units are not relevant in this case, only the values).

Steps in performing a Student's *t* test

1 Calculate summary statistics for the two data sets

Control (A)	Treatment (B)
6.6	6.3
5.5	7.2
6.8	6.5
5.8	7.1
6.1	7.5
5.9	7.3

$n_A = 6$, $\bar{x}_A = 6.12$, $s_A = 0.496$

$n_B = 6$, $\bar{x}_B = 6.98$, $s_B = 0.475$

n_A and n_B are the number of values in the first and second data sets respectively (these do not need to be the same).

$\bar{x}$ is the mean.

s is the standard deviation (a measure of scatter in the data).

2 Set up and state your null hypothesis (H_0)

H_0: there is no treatment effect. The differences in the data sets are the result of chance and they are not really different. The alternative hypothesis is that there is a treatment effect and the two sets of data are truly different.

3 Decide if your test is one or two tailed

A one-tailed test looks for a difference only in one particular direction. A two-tailed test looks for any difference (+ or –). This tells you what section of the t table to consult. Most biological tests are two-tailed. Very few are one-tailed.

4 Calculate the *t* statistic

For our sample data above the calculated value of *t* is –3.09. The degrees of freedom (df) are $n_1 + n_2 - 2 = 10$.

Calculation of the *t* value uses the variance which is simply the square of the standard deviation (s^2). You may compute *t* using a spreadsheet but manual computation is not difficult (see opposite). It does not matter if the calculated *t* value is a positive or negative (the sign is irrelevant).

The absolute value of the *t* statistic (3.09) well exceeds the critical value for $P = 0.05$ at 10 degrees of freedom.

We can reject H_0 and conclude that the means are different at the 5% level of significance.

If the calculated absolute value of *t* had been less than 2.23, we could not have rejected H_0.

1. (a) In an experiment, data values were obtained from four plants in experimental conditions and three plants in control conditions. The mean values for each data set (control and experimental conditions) were calculated. The *t* value was calculated to be 2.16. The null hypothesis was: "The plants in the control and experimental conditions are not different". State whether the calculated *t* value supports the null hypothesis or its alternative (consult *t* table below):

_____

_____

   (b) The experiment was repeated, but this time using 6 control and 6 "experimental" plants. The new *t* value was 2.54. State whether the calculated *t* value supports the null hypothesis or its alternative now:

_____

_____

2. Explain what you understand by statistical significance:

_____

_____

_____

_____

_____

Table of critical values of *t* at different levels of *P*.

Degrees of freedom	Level of Probability		
	0.05	0.01	0.001
1	12.71	63.66	636.6
2	4.303	9.925	31.60
3	3.182	5.841	12.92
4	2.776	4.604	8.610
5	2.571	4.032	6.869
6	2.447	3.707	5.959
7	2.365	3.499	5.408
8	2.306	3.355	5.041
9	2.262	3.250	4.781
10	2.228	3.169	4.587
15	2.131	2.947	4.073
16	2.120	2.921	4.015
17	2.110	2.898	3.965
18	2.101	2.878	3.922
19	2.093	2.861	3.883
20	2.086	2.845	3.850
25	2.060	2.787	3.725
30	2.042	2.750	3.646
40	2.021	2.704	3.551
50	2.009	2.678	3.496
60	2.000	2.660	3.460
100	1.984	2.626	3.390

WEB   LINK

DATA   160   161

3. The table below presents data for heart rate (beats per minute) in samples of ten males and females from a population.
   (a) Complete the calculations to perform the t test for these two samples. The steps are outlined in the right hand column.

x (bpm) Male	x (bpm) Female	x − x̄ (deviation from the mean) Male	x − x̄ (deviation from the mean) Female	$(x − \bar{x})^2$ (deviation from mean)² Male	$(x − \bar{x})^2$ (deviation from mean)² Female
70	69	-2.3	1	5.29	1
74	62	1.7	-6	2.89	36
80	75				
73	66				
75	68				
82	57				
62	61				
69	84				
70	61				
68	77				

$n_A = 10$ $n_B = 10$

The number of samples in each data set

The sum of each column is called the sum of squares

$\Sigma (x − \bar{x})^2$ $\Sigma (x − \bar{x})^2$

(b) The variance for males: $s^2_A =$

   The variance for females: $s^2_B =$

(c) The difference between the means for males and females

   $(\bar{x}_A − \bar{x}_B) =$

(d) $t_{(calculated)} =$

(e) Determine the degrees of freedom (d.f.)

   d.f. $(n_A + n_B − 2) =$

(f) $P =$

   $t_{(critical\ value)} =$

(g) Your decision is: _____

   _____

   _____

   _____

   _____

   _____

Step 1: Summary statistics

Tabulate the data as shown in the first 2 columns of the table (left). Calculate the mean and give the n value for each data set. Compute the standard deviation if you wish.

Males $\bar{x}_A = 72.3$ Females $\bar{x}_B = 68.0$
   $n_A = 10$ $n_B = 10$
   $s_A = 5.87$ $s_B = 8.47$

Step 2: State your null hypothesis

Step 3: Test is one tailed / two tailed (delete one)

Step 4: Calculating t

4a: Calculate sums of squares

Complete the computations outlined in the table left. The sum of each of the final two columns (left) is called the sum of squares.

4b: Calculate the variances

Calculate the variance (s^2) for each data set. This is the sum of squares ÷ by $n − 1$ (number of samples in each data set − 1). In this case the n values are the same, but they need not be.

$$s^2_A = \frac{\Sigma(x − \bar{x})^2}{n_A − 1}(A) \qquad s^2_B = \frac{\Sigma(x − \bar{x})^2}{n_B − 1}(B)$$

4c: Differences between the means

Calculate the difference between the means

$$(\bar{x}_A − \bar{x}_B)$$

4d: Calculate t

$$t = \frac{(\bar{x}_A − \bar{x}_B)}{\sqrt{\dfrac{s^2_A}{n_A} + \dfrac{s^2_B}{n_B}}}$$

4e: Determine the degrees of freedom

Degrees of freedom (d.f.) $= n_A + n_B − 2$ where n_A and n_B are the number of counts in each of populations A and B.

Step 5: Consult the t table

Consult the t-tables (opposite) for the critical t value at the appropriate degrees of freedom and the acceptable probability level (e.g. P = 0.05).

5a: Make your decision

Make your decision whether or not to reject H_0. If t_{calc} is large enough you may be able to reject H_0 at a lower P value (e.g. 0.001), increasing confidence in the alternative hypothesis.

161 Quantitative Investigation of Variation

Key Idea: The Student's *t* test can be used to test the significance of differences between populations for a variable phenotypic character.

White clover (*Trifolium repens*) is a common pasture plant.

It has white flowers and distinctive leaves with three (or occasionally four) leaflets. The leaves are held on petioles that can be 150 mm or more long if left undisturbed. In pasture that is regularly grazed petiole length can be shorter.

Two paddocks containing white clover were grazed by cattle under different regimes during the peak growing season (late winter to early summer). Paddock A was grazed for one day every week whereas paddock B was grazed for one day every four weeks. At the end of the trial, quadrats were used to select random samples of clover and the lengths of the petioles were measured to evaluate the effect of grazing on morphology (in this case petiole length). The results are shown below. Use the Student's *t* test to determine the significance of the differences between the two populations (grazing regimes). The calculation steps are given in the blue boxes. Steps for calculating the summary statistics with a calculator are in the grey boxes.

Leaflets

Petiole ——

Clover leaf

x (length / mm)		$x - \bar{x}$ (deviation from the mean)		$(x - \bar{x})^2$ (deviation from mean)^2	
Paddock A	Paddock B	Paddock A	Paddock B	Paddock A	Paddock B
83	30	40.2	-77.5	1616.04	6006.25
70	87	27.2	-20.5	739.84	420.25
32	48				
61	92				
70	54				
45	33				
28	135				
34	60				
37	81				
20	139				
25	90				
30	78				
31	125				
35	174				
80	167				
22	184				
62	80				
35	125				
25	163				
44	197				
30	116				

The sum of each column is called the sum of squares

$\Sigma (x - \bar{x})^2$ $\Sigma (x - \bar{x})^2$

Step 1: Summary statistics

Tabulate the data as shown in the first 2 columns of the table (left). Calculate the mean and give the n value for each data set. Compute the standard deviation if you wish.

Popn A $\bar{x}_A$ = [ ]   Popn B $\bar{x}_B$ = [ ]

n_A = [ ] n_B = [ ]

s_A^* = [ ] s_B^* = [ ]

* These can be calculated using the variance equation or a standard scientific calculator (see below).

Step 2: State your null hypothesis

Step 3: Test is one tailed / two tailed (delete one)

Summary statistics on a calculator

Most standard scientific calculators will be able to provide you with the number of sample entrants (n), the mean ($\bar{x}$) and the standard deviation (s) once you have entered the data. The procedure shown below is for a Casio fx-82 calculator, a standard classroom calculator. In most Casio models the procedure is similar. Consult the calculator's manual if necessary.

Input the data on a calculator

Step 1 Set the calculator to SD mode:

`MODE` `2`

Step 2 Clear the memory:

`SHIFT` `CLR` `1` `=`

Step 3 Enter the data for paddock A

83 `DT` 70 `DT` 32 `DT`

Repeat this procedure for paddock B after you have retrieved all the summary statistics and calculated the variance for paddock A (see next page).

© 2017 **BIOZONE** International
ISBN: 978-1-927309-26-1
Photocopying Prohibited

Step 4: Calculating t

4a: Calculate sums of squares

Complete the computations outlined in the table left. The sum of each of the final two columns (left) is called the sum of squares.

4b: Calculate the variances

Calculate the variance (s^2) for each data set. This is the sum of squares ÷ by $n - 1$ (number of samples in each data set $- 1$). In this case the n values are the same, but they need not be.

$$s^2_A = \frac{\sum(x - \bar{x})^2}{n_A - 1} \text{(A)} \qquad s^2_B = \frac{\sum(x - \bar{x})^2}{n_B - 1} \text{(B)}$$

4c: Differences between the means

Calculate the difference between the means

$$(\bar{x}_A - \bar{x}_B)$$

4d: Calculate t

$$t = \frac{(\bar{x}_A - \bar{x}_B)}{\sqrt{\dfrac{s^2_A}{n_A} + \dfrac{s^2_B}{n_B}}}$$

4e: Determine the degrees of freedom

Degrees of freedom (d.f.) $= n_A + n_B - 2$
where n_A and n_B are the number of counts in each of populations A and B.

Step 5: Consult the t table

Consult the t-tables in the previous activity for the critical t value at the appropriate degrees of freedom and probability level (e.g. P = 0.05).

5a: Make your decision

Make your decision whether or not to reject H_0. If t_{calc} is large enough you may be able to reject H_0 at a lower P value (e.g. 0.001), increasing confidence in the alternative hypothesis.

Retrieving the summary statistics

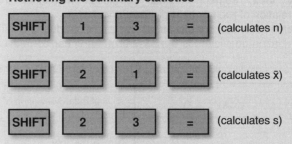

SHIFT	1	3	=	(calculates n)
SHIFT	2	1	=	(calculates x̄)
SHIFT	2	3	=	(calculates s)

Calculate the variance

| SHIFT | 2 | 3 | x^2 | = |

1. The variance for population A: $s^2_A =$ _____

   The variance for population B: $s^2_B =$ _____

2. The difference between the population means:

   $(\bar{x}_A - \bar{x}_B) =$ _____

3. (a) Calculate t:

   (b) $t_{(calculated)} =$ _____

4. Determine the degrees of freedom (d.f.)

   d.f. $(n_A + n_B - 2) =$ _____

   _____

5. $P =$ _____

   $t_{(critical value)} =$ _____

6. Your decision is: _____

7. Write a conclusion for the investigation: _____

   _____

   _____

8. To further the investigation, it was decided to find out if the regular grazing affected the rate of dry matter increase in the clover. Suggest a way in which this could done:

   _____

   _____

   _____

162 Pearson's Linear Correlation

Key Idea: Pearson's linear correlation measures the correlation of two normally distributed variables.
Pearson's linear correlation or Pearson's product-moment correlation coefficient is a measure of the linear correlation between two variables, each of which has a normal distribution. It ranges from +1 to -1 inclusive. +1 represents the strongest positive correlation, while -1 represents the strongest negative correlation. 0 indicates no correlation.

Pearson's product-moment correlation can be calculated using the formula:

$$r = \frac{\Sigma xy - n\bar{x}\bar{y}}{n s_x s_y}$$

s_x = standard deviation of x
s_y = standard deviation of y

To find s_x and s_y use the population standard deviation:

$$s = \sqrt{\frac{\Sigma(x - \bar{x})^2}{n-1}}$$

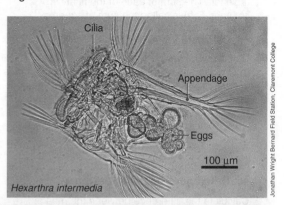
Cilia
Appendage
Eggs
100 µm
Hexarthra intermedia
Jonathan Wright Bernard Field Station, Claremont College

Hexarthra intermedia (right) is a species of rotifer. Rotifers are small ciliated animals found in fresh water ponds. Most feed on small algae. A study was carried out in order to understand how changes in their abundance might be related to seasonal changes in environmental factors. The data below records abundance per litre of pond water against pond temperature at the time that sample was taken. Note that the *Hexarthra* counts are not in whole numbers because number per litre was calculated from a larger, filtered sample volume.

Hexarthra no. (x) / L	Temperature (y) / °C	$(x - \bar{x})^2$	$(y - \bar{y})^2$	xy
36.21	19.75			
33.76	17.53			
10.83	15.05			
1.88	14.40			
0.33	11.73			
2.40	11.05			
0.35	9.23			
0.08	8.75			
0.00	12.35			
0.04	13.13			
0.00	14.15			
0.21	14.63			
0.29	15.98			
5.72	19.63			
4.39	18.00			
7.42	19.80			
72.87	23.33			
443.38	23.30			
34.38	22.30			
147.58	25.88			
947.64	24.58			
573.47	22.90			
444.63	20.95			
338.25	21.10			
34.33	18.90			
$\bar{x}$=	$\bar{y}$=	$\Sigma(x - \bar{x})^2$ =	$\Sigma(y - \bar{y})^2$ =	Σxy =
Standard deviation x =		Standard deviation y =	r =	

Data kindly supplied by Dr Ian Duggan, University of Waikato

1. Complete the table above to calculate r.

2. What does r tell you about the relationship between *Hexarthra* numbers and temperature? _____

_____

_____

DATA

163 Spearman Rank Correlation

Key Idea: The Spearman rank correlation is a test used to determine if there is a statistical dependence (correlation) between two variables.

The Spearman rank correlation is appropriate for data that have a non-normal distribution (or where the distribution is not known) and assesses the degree of association between the X and Y variables (if they are correlated). For the test to work, the values used must be monotonic i.e. the values must increase or decrease together or one increases while the other decreases. A value of 1 indicates a perfect correlation; a value of 0 indicates no correlation between the variables. The example below examines the relationship between precipitation and the number of plant species in southern Africa.

Spearman's rank data for number of plant species and precipitation

Site	No. plant species	Rank (R_1)	Annual precipitation / mm	Rank (R_2)	Difference (D) (R_1-R_2)	D^2	Working space
1	60		60				
2	30		150				
3	40		240				
4	70		330				
5	120		410				
6	50		450				
7	160		550				
8	280		500				
9	150		610				
10	320		520				
11	340		750				
12	140		910				
13	400		400				
14	550		550				
15	570	1	500	7.5			r_s value
					$\Sigma D^2=$		

Analysing the data

Step one: Rank the data for each variable. For each variable, the numbers are ranked in descending order, e.g. for the variable, volume, the highest value 570 species is given the rank of 1 while its corresponding frequency value is given the rank of 7.5. Fill in the rank columns in the table above in the same way. If two numbers have the same rank value, then use the mean rank of the two values (e.g. 1+2 = 3. 3/2= 1.5).

Step two: Calculate the difference (D) between each pair of ranks (R_1-R_2) and enter the value in the table (as a check, the sum of all differences should be 0).

Step three: Square the differences and enter them into the table above (this removes any negative values).

Step four: Sum all the D^2 values and enter the total into the table.

Step five: Use the formula below to calculate the Spearman Rank Correlation Coefficient (r_s). Enter the r_s value in the box above.

$$r_s = 1 - \left(\frac{6 \Sigma D^2}{n^3-n} \right)$$

Spearman rank correlation coefficient

Step six: Compare the r_s value to the table of critical values (right) for the appropriate number of pairs. If the r_s value (ignoring sign) is greater than or equal to the critical value then there is a significant correlation. If r_s is positive then there is a positive correlation. If r_s is negative then there is a negative correlation.

Number of pairs of measurements	Critical value
5	1.00
6	0.89
7	0.79
8	0.74
9	0.68
10	0.65
12	0.59
15	0.521
20	0.45
25	0.398
30	0.362

1. State the null hypothesis (H_0) for the data set: _____

_____

2 (a) Identify the critical value for the plant-precipitation data: _____

(b) State if the correlation is positive or negative: _____

(c) State whether the correlation is significant: _____

DATA

164 What is Primary Productivity?

Key Idea: Measuring the amount of photosynthesis and the amount of respiration per unit volume per unit time enables us to determine the gross primary productivity of a system.
The energy entering an ecosystem is determined by the rate at which producers can convert sunlight energy or inorganic compounds into chemical energy. Photosynthesis accounts for most of the energy entering most of Earth's ecosystems.

The total energy fixed by photosynthesis per unit area or volume per unit time is the **gross primary productivity** (GPP) and it is usually expressed as $J\ m^{-2}$ (or $kJ\ m^{-2}$), or as $g\ m^{-2}$. However, some of this energy is required for respiration. Subtracting respiration from GPP gives the **net primary productivity** (NPP). This represents the energy or biomass (mass of biological material) available to consumers.

The productivity of ecosystems

The **gross primary productivity** of an ecosystem will depend on the capacity of the producers to capture and fix carbon in organic compounds. In most ecosystems, this is limited by constraints on photosynthesis (availability of light, nutrients, or water for example). The **net primary productivity** (NPP) is then determined by how much of this goes into plant biomass per unit time, after respiratory needs are met. This will be the amount available to the next trophic level.

Production vs productivity: What's the difference?

Strictly speaking, the primary production of an ecosystem is distinct from its productivity, which is a rate. However because values for production (accumulated biomass) are usually given for a certain period of time in order to be meaningful, the two terms are often used interchangeably.

Estuaries	
Swamps and marshes	
Tropical rainforest	
Temperate forest	
Boreal forest	
Savanna	
Agricultural land	
Woodland and shrubland	
Temperate grassland	
Lakes and streams	
Continental shelf	
Tundra	
Open ocean	
Desert scrub	
Extreme desert	

Globally, the least productive ecosystems are those that are limited by heat energy and water. The most productive are those with high temperatures, plenty of water, and non-limiting supplies of soil nitrogen. The primary productivity of oceans is lower overall than that of terrestrial ecosystems because the water reflects (or absorbs) much of the light energy before it reaches and is utilised by producers.

5   10   15   20   25   30   35   40   45   50
Average net primary productivity / x 1000 $kJ\ m^{-2}y^{-1}$

Measuring productivity

Measuring gross primary productivity (GPP) can be difficult due to the effect of on-going respiration, which uses up some of the organic material produced (glucose). One method for measuring GPP is to measure the difference in production between plants kept in the dark and those in the light. A simple method for measuring GPP in phytoplankton is illustrated below:

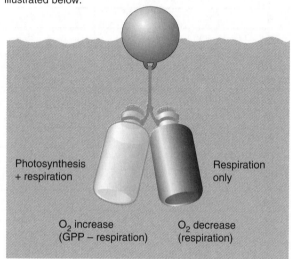

Photosynthesis + respiration

Respiration only

O_2 increase (GPP – respiration)

O_2 decrease (respiration)

Two bottles are lowered into the ocean or lake to a specified depth, filled with water, and then stoppered. One bottle is transparent, the other is opaque. The O_2 concentration of the water surrounding the bottles is measured and the bottles are left for a specified amount of time. The phytoplankton in the transparent bottle will photosynthesise, increasing the O_2 concentration, and respire, using some of that O_2. The phytoplankton in the opaque bottle will only respire. The final measured difference in O_2 between the bottles gives the amount of O_2 produced by the phytoplankton in the specified time (including that used for respiration). The amount of O_2 used allows us to determine the amount of glucose produced and therefore the GPP of the phytoplankton.

1. Suggest possible reasons for the high net productivity of estuaries, swamps, and tropical rainforests:

_____

_____

2. An experiment was carried out to measure the gross primary production of a lake system. The lake was initially measured to have 8 mg O_2 L^{-1}. A clear flask and an opaque flask were lowered into the lake filled and stoppered. When the flasks were retrieved it was found the clear flask contained 10 mg O_2 L^{-1} while the opaque contained 5 mg O_2 L^{-1}.

(a) How much O_2 was used (respired) in the opaque flask? _____

(b) Was is the net O_2 production in the clear flask? _____

(c) What is the gross O_2 production in the system? _____

(d) For every 10 g of O_2 formed during photosynthesis, 9.4 grams of glucose is formed. How much glucose formed during the experiment?

_____

165 Productivity and Trophic Efficiency

Key Idea: The net primary productivity of an ecosystem determines the amount of biomass available to primary consumers. It varies widely between different ecosystems.

The energy entering ecosystems is fixed by producers at a rate that depends on limiting factors such as temperature and the availability of light and water. This energy is converted to biomass by anabolic reactions. The rate of biomass production (net primary productivity), is the biomass produced per area per unit time. Trophic (or ecological) efficiency refers to the efficiency of energy transfer from one trophic level to the next. The trophic efficiencies of herbivores vary widely, depending on how much of the producer biomass is consumed and assimilated (incorporated into new biomass). In some natural ecosystems this can be surprisingly high. Humans intervene in natural energy flows by simplifying systems and reducing the number of transfers occurring between trophic levels.

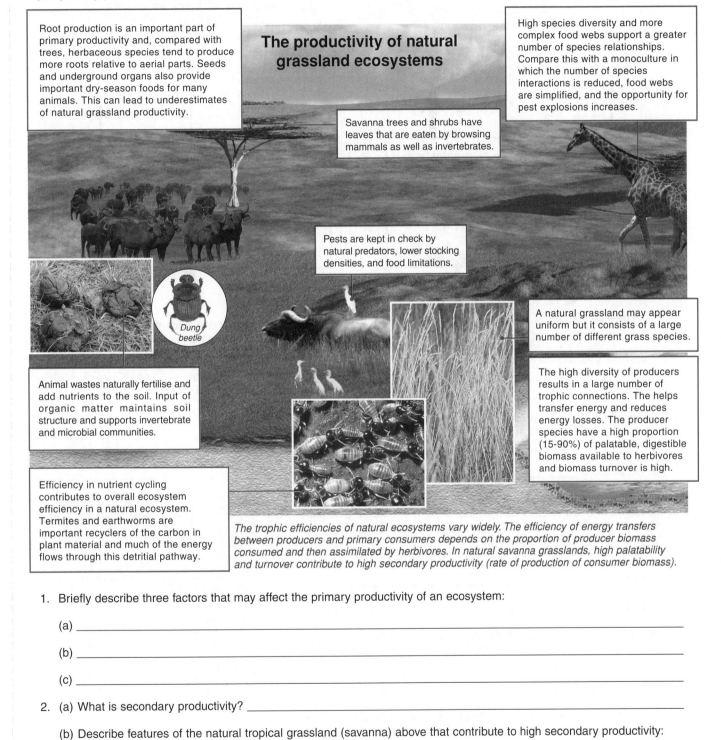

The productivity of natural grassland ecosystems

Root production is an important part of primary productivity and, compared with trees, herbaceous species tend to produce more roots relative to aerial parts. Seeds and underground organs also provide important dry-season foods for many animals. This can lead to underestimates of natural grassland productivity.

High species diversity and more complex food webs support a greater number of species relationships. Compare this with a monoculture in which the number of species interactions is reduced, food webs are simplified, and the opportunity for pest explosions increases.

Savanna trees and shrubs have leaves that are eaten by browsing mammals as well as invertebrates.

Pests are kept in check by natural predators, lower stocking densities, and food limitations.

A natural grassland may appear uniform but it consists of a large number of different grass species.

Animal wastes naturally fertilise and add nutrients to the soil. Input of organic matter maintains soil structure and supports invertebrate and microbial communities.

The high diversity of producers results in a large number of trophic connections. The helps transfer energy and reduces energy losses. The producer species have a high proportion (15-90%) of palatable, digestible biomass available to herbivores and biomass turnover is high.

Efficiency in nutrient cycling contributes to overall ecosystem efficiency in a natural ecosystem. Termites and earthworms are important recyclers of the carbon in plant material and much of the energy flows through this detritial pathway.

Dung beetle

The trophic efficiencies of natural ecosystems vary widely. The efficiency of energy transfers between producers and primary consumers depends on the proportion of producer biomass consumed and then assimilated by herbivores. In natural savanna grasslands, high palatability and turnover contribute to high secondary productivity (rate of production of consumer biomass).

1. Briefly describe three factors that may affect the primary productivity of an ecosystem:

    (a) _____

    (b) _____

    (c) _____

2. (a) What is secondary productivity? _____

    (b) Describe features of the natural tropical grassland (savanna) above that contribute to high secondary productivity:

    _____

    _____

    _____

    _____

LINK
164
WEB
165
KNOW

166 Energy Inputs and Outputs

Key Idea: The efficiency of energy transfers in ecosystems can be quantified if we know the amount of energy entering and leaving the different trophic levels.

The GPP of any ecosystem will be determined by the efficiency with which solar energy is captured by photosynthesis. The efficiency of subsequent energy transfers will determine the amount of energy available to consumers. These energy transfers can be quantified using dry mass or calorimetry.

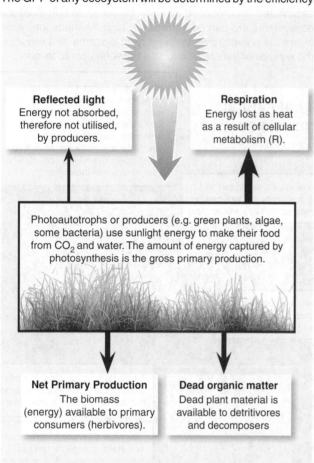

Reflected light
Energy not absorbed, therefore not utilised, by producers.

Respiration
Energy lost as heat as a result of cellular metabolism (R).

Photoautotrophs or producers (e.g. green plants, algae, some bacteria) use sunlight energy to make their food from CO_2 and water. The amount of energy captured by photosynthesis is the gross primary production.

Net Primary Production
The biomass (energy) available to primary consumers (herbivores).

Dead organic matter
Dead plant material is available to detritivores and decomposers

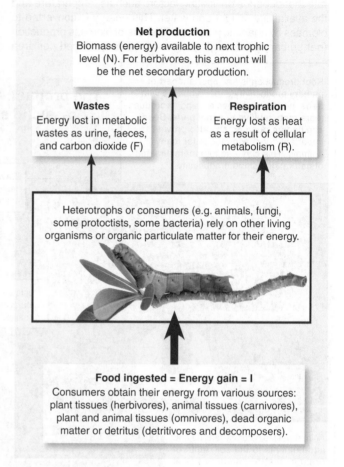

Net production
Biomass (energy) available to next trophic level (N). For herbivores, this amount will be the net secondary production.

Wastes
Energy lost in metabolic wastes as urine, faeces, and carbon dioxide (F)

Respiration
Energy lost as heat as a result of cellular metabolism (R).

Heterotrophs or consumers (e.g. animals, fungi, some protoctists, some bacteria) rely on other living organisms or organic particulate matter for their energy.

Food ingested = Energy gain = I
Consumers obtain their energy from various sources: plant tissues (herbivores), animal tissues (carnivores), plant and animal tissues (omnivores), dead organic matter or detritus (detritivores and decomposers).

1. Describe how energy may be lost from organisms in the form of:

   (a) Wastes: _____

   (b) Respiration: _____

2. The energy budgets of two agricultural systems (4000 m^2 area) were measured over a growing season of 100 days. The results are tabulated right.

   (a) For each system, calculate the percentage efficiency of energy utilisation (how much incident solar radiation is captured by photosynthesis):

   Corn: _____

   Mature pasture: _____

   (b) For each system, calculate the percentage losses to respiration:

   Corn: _____

   Mature pasture: _____

	Corn field	Mature pasture
	kJ x 10^6	kJ x 10^6
Incident solar radiation	8548	1971
Plant utilisation		
Net primary production (NPP)	105.8	20.7
Respiration (R)	32.2	3.7
Gross primary production (GPP)	138.0	24.4

   (c) For each system, calculate the percentage efficiency of net primary production:

   Corn: _____ Mature pasture: _____

   (d) Which system has the greatest efficiency of energy transfer to biomass? _____

3. Net production in consumers (N), or secondary production, can be expressed as N = I - (F+R). Red meat contains approximately 700 kJ per 100 grams. If N = 20% of the energy gain (I), how much energy is lost as F and R?

   _____

© 2017 **BIOZONE** International
ISBN: 978-1-927309-26-1
Photocopying Prohibited

Estimating NPP in *Brassica rapa*

Background

Brassica rapa (right) is a fast growing brassica species, which can complete its life cycle in as little as 40 days if growth conditions are favourable. A class of students wished to estimate the gross and net primary productivity of a crop of these plants using wet and dry mass measurements made at three intervals over 21 days.

The method

▶ Seven groups of three students each grew 60 *B. rapa* plants in plant trays under controlled conditions. On day 7, each group made a random selection of 10 plants and removed them, with roots intact. The 10 plants were washed, blotted dry, and then weighed collectively (giving wet mass).

▶ The 10 plants were placed in a ceramic drying bowl and placed in a drying oven at 200°C for 24 hours, then weighed (giving dry mass).

▶ On day 14 and again on day 21, the procedure was repeated with a further 10 plants (randomly selected).

▶ The full results for group 1 are presented in Table 1. You will complete the calculation columns.

Table 1: Group 1's results for growth of 10 *B. rapa* plants over 21 days

Age in days	Wet mass of 10 plants /g	Dry mass of 10 plants /g	Percent biomass	Energy in 10 plants / kJ	Energy per plant / kJ	NPP / kJ plant^{-1} d^{-1}
7	19.6	4.2				
14	38.4	9.3				
21	55.2	15.5				

4. Calculate percent biomass using the equation: % biomass = dry mass ÷ wet mass x 100. Enter the values in Table 1.

5. Each gram of dry biomass is equivalent to 18.2 kJ of energy. Calculate the amount of energy per 10 plants and per plant for plants at 7, 14, and 21 days. Enter the values in Table 1.

6. Calculate the Net Primary Productivity per plant, i.e. the amount of energy stored as biomass per day (kJ plant^{-1} d^{-1}). Enter the values in Table 1. We are using per plant in this exercise as we do not have a unit area of harvest.

7. The other 6 groups of students completed the same procedure and, at the end of the 21 days, the groups compared their results for NPP. The results are presented in Table 2, right.

   Transfer group 1's NPP results from Table 1 to complete the table of results and calculate the mean NPP for *B. rapa*.

Table 2: Class results for NPP of *B. rapa* over 21 days

Time in days / d	Group NPP / kJ plant^{-1} d^{-1}							
	1	2	3	4	5	6	7	Mean NPP
7		1.05	1.05	1.13	1.09	1.13	1.09	
14		1.17	1.21	1.25	1.21	1.25	1.17	
21		1.30	1.34	1.30	1.34	1.38	1.34	

8. On the grid, plot the class mean NPP vs time.

9. (a) What is happening to the NPP over time?

   _____

   (b) Explain why this is happening: _____

   _____

   _____

   _____

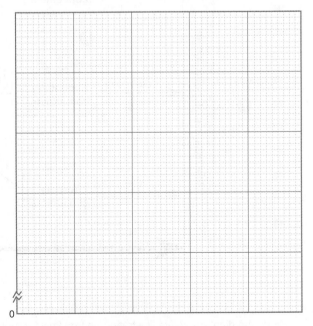

10. What would you need to know to determine the gross primary productivity of *B. rapa*?

   _____

11. As a group, devise a methodology to determine the net secondary production and respiratory losses of 10, 12 day old cabbage white caterpillars feeding on 30 g of brussels sprouts for 3 days. How would you calculate the efficiency of energy transfer from producers to consumers?
   Staple your methodology to this page. You will need to know:

   Energy value of plant material: dry mass x 18.2 kJ.
   Energy value of animal material: dry mass x 23.0 kJ
   Energy value of egested waste (frass): mass x 19.87 kJ

167 Energy Budget in an Ecosystem

Key Idea: Chemical energy in the bonds of molecules flows through an ecosystem between trophic levels. Only 5-20% of energy is transferred from one trophic level to the next.

Energy cannot be created or destroyed, only transformed from one form (e.g. light energy) to another (e.g. chemical energy in the bonds of molecules). This means that the flow of energy through an ecosystem can be measured. Each time energy is transferred from one trophic level to the next (by eating, defaecation, etc.), some energy is given out as heat to the environment, usually during cellular respiration. Living organisms cannot convert heat to other forms of energy, so the amount of energy available to one trophic level is always less than the amount at the previous level. Potentially, we can account for the transfer of energy from its input (as solar radiation) to its release as heat from organisms, because energy is conserved. Recall that the percentage of energy transferred from one trophic level to the next is the **trophic efficiency**. It varies between 5% and 20% and measures the efficiency of energy transfer. An average figure of 10% trophic efficiency is often used. This is called the **ten percent rule**.

Energy flow through an ecosystem

NOTE

Numbers represent **kilojoules** of energy per square metre per year ($kJ\ m^{-2}\ yr^{-1}$)

Sunlight falling on plant surfaces
7 000 000

Light absorbed by plants
1 700 000

Ⓐ

Producers
87 400

50 450

(a)

7800

Primary consumers

Ⓑ

1600

1330

(b)

Secondary consumers

90

55

Tertiary consumers

(c)

Ⓕ

Heat loss in metabolic activity

4600

Ⓖ

22 950

Detritus

2000

10 465

Ⓓ

19 300

(d)

Ⓒ

Decomposers and detritivores

19 200

Ⓔ

Energy absorbed from the previous trophic level

100

Energy lost as heat 65 **Trophic level** 15 Energy lost to detritus

20

Energy passed on to the next trophic level

The energy available to each trophic level will always equal the amount entering that trophic level, minus total losses to that level (due to metabolic activity, death, excretion etc). Energy lost as heat will be lost from the ecosystem. Other losses become part of the detritus and may be utilised by other organisms in the ecosystem.

1. Study the diagram above illustrating energy flow through a hypothetical ecosystem. Use the example at the top of the page as a guide to calculate the missing values (a)–(d) in the diagram. Note that the sum of the energy inputs always equals the sum of the energy outputs. Place your answers in the spaces provided on the diagram.

© 2017 **BIOZONE** International
ISBN: 978-1-927309-26-1
Photocopying Prohibited

2. What is the original source of energy for this ecosystem? _____

3. Identify the processes occurring at the points labelled **A – G** on the diagram:

   A. _____   E. _____

   B. _____   F. _____

   C. _____   G. _____

   D. _____

4. (a) Calculate the percentage of light energy falling on the plants that is absorbed at point **A**:

   Light absorbed by plants ÷ sunlight falling on plant surfaces x 100 = _____

   (b) What happens to the light energy that is not absorbed? _____

   _____

5. (a) Calculate the percentage of light energy absorbed that is actually converted (fixed) into producer energy:

   Producers ÷ light absorbed by plants x 100 = _____

   (b) How much light energy is absorbed but not fixed: _____

   (c) Account for the difference between the amount of energy absorbed and the amount actually fixed by producers:

   _____

   _____

6. Of the total amount of energy **fixed** by producers in this ecosystem (at point **A**) calculate:

   (a) The total amount that ended up as metabolic waste heat (in kJ): _____

   (b) The percentage of the energy fixed that ended up as waste heat: _____

7. (a) State the groups for which detritus is an energy source: _____

   (b) How could detritus be removed or added to an ecosystem? _____

   _____

8. Under certain conditions, decomposition rates can be very low or even zero, allowing detritus to accumulate:

   (a) From your knowledge of biological processes, what conditions might slow decomposition rates?

   _____

   (b) What are the consequences of this lack of decomposer activity to the energy flow? _____

   _____

   (c) Add an additional arrow to the diagram on the previous page to illustrate your answer.

   (d) Describe three examples of materials that have resulted from a lack of decomposer activity on detrital material:

   _____

   _____

9. The **ten percent rule** states that the total energy content of a trophic level in an ecosystem is only about one-tenth (or 10%) that of the preceding level. For each of the trophic levels in the diagram on the preceding page, determine the amount of energy passed on to the next trophic level as a percentage:

   (a) Producer to primary consumer: _____

   (b) Primary consumer to secondary consumer: _____

   (c) Secondary consumer to tertiary consumer: _____

   (d) Which of these transfers is the most efficient? _____

168 Nutrient Cycles

Key Idea: Matter cycles through the biotic and abiotic compartments of Earth's ecosystems in nutrient cycles.
Nutrient cycles move and transfer chemical elements (e.g. carbon, hydrogen, nitrogen, and oxygen) through the abiotic and biotic components of an ecosystem. Commonly, nutrients must be in an ionic (rather than elemental) form in order for plants and animals to have access to them. The supply of nutrients in an ecosystem is finite and limited. Macronutrients are required in large amounts by an organism, whereas micronutrients are needed in much smaller quantities.

Essential nutrients

Macronutrient	Common form	Function
Carbon (C)	CO_2	Organic molecules
Oxygen (O)	O_2	Respiration
Hydrogen (H)	H_2O	Cellular hydration
Nitrogen (N)	N_2, NO_3^-, NH_4^+	Proteins, nucleic acids
Potassium (K)	K^+	Principal ion in cells
Phosphorus (P)	$H_2PO_4^-$, HPO_4^{2-}	Nucleic acids, lipids
Calcium (Ca)	Ca^{2+}	Membrane permeability
Magnesium (Mg)	Mg^{2+}	Chlorophyll
Sulfur (S)	SO_4^{2-}	Proteins

Micronutrient	Common form	Function
Iron (Fe)	Fe^{2+}, Fe^{3+}	Chlorophyll, blood
Manganese (Mn)	Mn^{2+}	Enzyme activation
Molybdenum (Mo)	MoO_4^-	Nitrogen metabolism
Copper (Cu)	Cu^{2+}	Enzyme activation
Sodium (Na)	Na^+	Ion in cells
Silicon (Si)	$Si(OH)_4$	Support tissues

Tropical rainforest

Nutrients in plants and animals

High speed return of nutrients to plants and animals leaving soil nutrient deficient

Nutrients in soil

Temperate woodland

Nutrients in plants and animals

Slow return of nutrients allowing greater build up of nutrients in the soil

Nutrients in soil

The speed of nutrient cycling can vary markedly. Some nutrients are cycled slowly, others quickly. The environment and diversity of an ecosystem can also have a large effect on the speed at which nutrients are recycled.

The role of organisms in nutrient cycling

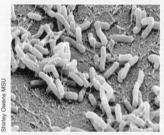

Bacteria
Bacteria play an essential role in nutrient cycles. They act as decomposers, but can also convert nutrients into forms accessible to plants and animals.

Fungi
Fungi are saprophytes and are important decomposers, returning nutrients to the soil or converting them into forms accessible to plants and animals.

Plants
Plants have a role in absorbing nutrients from the soil and making them directly available to browsing animals. They also add their own decaying matter to soils.

Animals
Animals utilise and break down materials from bacteria, plants and fungi and return the nutrients to soils and water via their wastes and when they die.

1. Describe the role of each of the following in nutrient cycling:

   (a) Bacteria: _____

   (b) Fungi: _____

   (c) Plants: _____

   (d) Animals: _____

2. Why are soils in tropical rainforests nutrient deficient relative to soils in temperate woodlands? _____
   _____
   _____

3. Distinguish between macronutrients and micronutrients: _____
   _____
   _____

169 The Nitrogen Cycle

Key Idea: The nitrogen cycle describes how nitrogen is converted between its various chemical forms. Nitrogen gas is converted to nitrates which are taken up by plants. Heterotrophs obtain their nitrogen by eating other organisms. Nitrogen is an essential component of proteins and nucleic acids and required by all living things. The Earth's atmosphere is about 80% nitrogen gas (N_2), but molecular nitrogen is so stable that it is only rarely available directly to organisms and is often in short supply in biological systems. Bacteria transfer nitrogen between the biotic and abiotic environments. Some can fix atmospheric nitrogen, while others convert ammonia to nitrate, making it available to plants. Lightning discharges also cause the oxidation of nitrogen gas to nitrate. Nitrogen-fixing bacteria are found free in the soil (*Azotobacter*) and in symbioses with some plants in root nodules (*Rhizobium*). Denitrifying bacteria reverse this activity and return fixed nitrogen to the atmosphere. Humans intervene in the nitrogen cycle by applying nitrogen fertilisers to the land.

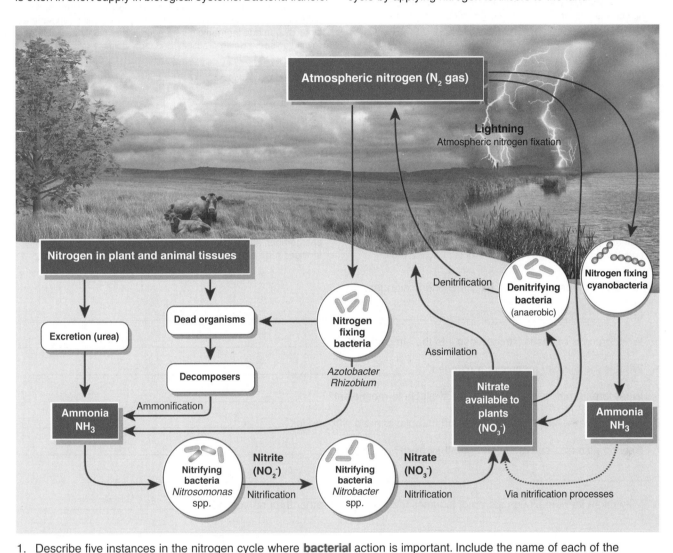

1. Describe five instances in the nitrogen cycle where **bacterial** action is important. Include the name of each of the processes and the changes to the form of nitrogen involved:

(a) _____

_____

(b) _____

_____

(c) _____

_____

(d) _____

_____

(e) _____

_____

Nitrogen fixation in root nodules

Root nodules are a root **symbiosis** between a higher plant and a bacterium. The bacteria fix atmospheric nitrogen and are extremely important to the nutrition of many plants, including the economically important legume family. Root nodules are extensions of the root tissue caused by entry of a bacterium. In legumes, this bacterium is *Rhizobium*. Other bacterial genera are involved in the root nodule symbioses in non-legumes.

The bacteria in these symbioses live in the nodule where they fix atmospheric nitrogen and provide the plant with most, or all, of its nitrogen requirements. In return, they have access to a rich supply of carbohydrate. The fixation of atmospheric nitrogen to ammonia occurs within the nodule, using the enzyme **nitrogenase**. Nitrogenase is inhibited by oxygen and the nodule provides a low O_2 environment in which fixation can occur.

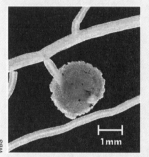 

Two examples of legume nodules caused by *Rhizobium*. The images above show the size of a single nodule (left), and the nodules forming clusters around the roots of *Acacia* (right).

Human intervention in the nitrogen cycle

The largest interventions in the nitrogen cycle by humans occur through farming and effluent discharges. Other interventions include burning, which releases nitrogen oxides into the atmosphere, and irrigation and land clearance, which leach nitrate ions from the soil.

Farmers apply organic nitrogen fertilisers to their land in the form of green crops and manures, replacing the nitrogen lost through cropping and harvest. Until the 1950s, atmospheric nitrogen could not be made available to plants except through microbial nitrogen fixation (left). However, during WW II, Fritz Haber developed the Haber process, combining nitrogen and hydrogen gas to form gaseous ammonia. The ammonia is converted into ammonium salts and sold as inorganic fertiliser. This process, although energy expensive, made inorganic nitrogen fertilisers readily available and revolutionised farming practices and crop yields.

Two examples of human intervention in the nitrogen cycle. The photographs above show the aerial application of a commercial fertiliser (left), and the harvesting of an agricultural crop (right).

2. Identify three processes that **fix** atmospheric nitrogen:

(a) _____ (b) _____ (c) _____

3. What process releases nitrogen gas into the atmosphere? _____

4. What is the primary reservoir for nitrogen? _____

5. What form of nitrogen is most readily available to most plants? _____

6. Name one essential organic compound that plants need nitrogen for: _____

7. How do animals acquire the nitrogen they need? _____

_____

8. Why might farmers plough a crop of legumes into the ground rather than harvest it? _____

_____

9. Describe five ways in which humans may intervene in the nitrogen cycle and the effects of these interventions:

(a) _____

_____

(b) _____

_____

(c) _____

_____

(d) _____

_____

(e) _____

_____

© 2017 **BIOZONE** International
ISBN: 978-1-927309-26-1
Photocopying Prohibited

170 The Carbon Cycle

Key Idea: The continued availability of carbon in ecosystems depends on carbon cycling through the abiotic and biotic components of an ecosystem.

Carbon is an essential element of life and is incorporated into the organic molecules that make up living organisms. Large quantities of carbon are stored in **sinks**, which include the atmosphere as carbon dioxide gas (CO_2), the ocean

as carbonate and bicarbonate, and rocks such as coal and limestone. Carbon moves between the biotic and abiotic environment. Autotrophs convert CO_2 into carbohydrates via photosynthesis and CO_2 is returned to the atmosphere through respiration. Some of the sinks and processes involved in the carbon cycle, together with the movement of carbon (carbon fluxes), are shown below.

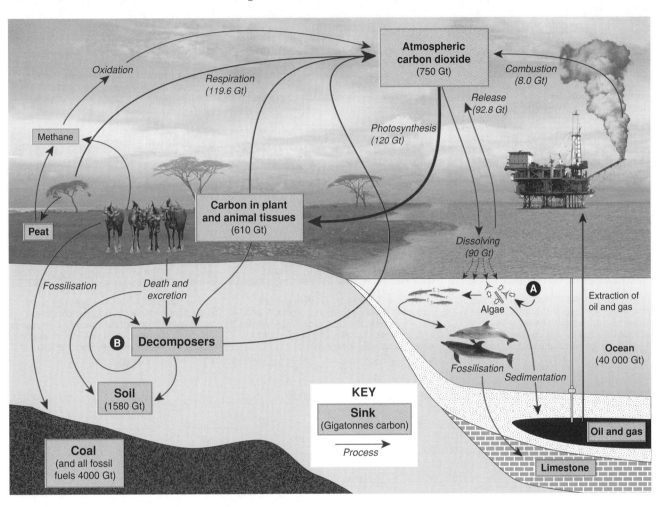

1. Add **arrows** and **labels** to the diagram above to show:

   (a) Dissolving of limestone by acid rain   (c) Mining and burning of coal
   (b) Release of carbon from the marine food chain   (d) Burning of plant material.

2. (a) Name the processes that release carbon into the atmosphere: _____

   _____

   (b) In what form is the carbon released? _____

3. Name the four geological reservoirs (sinks), in the diagram above, that can act as a source of carbon:

   (a) _____   (c) _____

   (b) _____   (d) _____

4. (a) Identify the process carried out by algae at point [**A**]: _____

   (b) Identify the process carried out by decomposers at [**B**]: _____

5. What would be the effect on carbon cycling if there were no decomposers present in an ecosystem? _____

   _____

   _____

© 2017 **BIOZONE** International
ISBN: 978-1-927309-26-1
Photocopying Prohibited

Bracket fungus on tree trunk

Coal mine in Wyoming

Carbon may be locked up in biotic or abiotic systems for long periods of time, e.g. in the wood of trees or in fossil fuels such as coal or oil. Human activity, e.g. extraction and combustion of fossil fuels, has disturbed the balance of the carbon cycle.

Organisms break down organic material to release carbon. Fungi and decomposing bacteria break down dead plant matter in the leaf litter of forests. Termites, with the aid of symbiotic protozoans and bacteria in their guts, digest the cellulose of woody tree tissue.

Coal is formed from the remains of terrestrial plant material buried in shallow swamps and subsequently compacted under sediments to form a hard black material. Coal is composed primarily of carbon and is a widely used fuel source.

Oil and **natural gas** formed in the past when dead algae and zooplankton settled to the bottom of shallow seas and lakes. These remains were buried and compressed under layers of non-porous sediment.

Limestone is a type of sedimentary rock composed mostly of calcium carbonate. It forms when the shells of molluscs and other marine organisms with calcium carbonate ($CaCO_3$) skeletons become fossilised.

Peat (partly decayed organic material) forms when plant material is not fully decomposed due to acidic or anaerobic conditions. Peatlands are a very efficient carbon sink but are easily lost through oxidation when land is drained.

6. Describe the **biological origin** of the following geological deposits:

   (a) Coal: _____

   _____

   (b) Oil: _____

   _____

   (c) Limestone: _____

   _____

   (d) Peat: _____

   _____

7. Describe the role of living organisms in the carbon cycle: _____

   _____

   _____

8. In natural circumstances, accumulated reserves of carbon such as peat, coal and oil represent a sink or natural diversion from the cycle. Eventually, the carbon in these sinks returns to the cycle through the action of geological processes which return deposits to the surface for oxidation.

   (a) What is the effect of human activity on the amount of carbon stored in sinks? _____

   _____

   (b) Describe the effect of human activity on atmospheric CO_2 levels: _____

   _____

© 2017 **BIOZONE** International
ISBN: 978-1-927309-26-1
Photocopying Prohibited

171 Ecosystems Are Dynamic

Key Idea: Natural ecosystems are dynamic systems, responding to short-term and cyclical changes, but remaining relatively stable in the long term.

Ecosystems experience constant changes, from the daily light-dark cycle and seasonal changes, to the loss and gain of organisms. However, over the long term, a mature (or climax) ecosystem remains much the same, a situation known as a **dynamic equilibrium**.

The dynamic ecosystem

▶ Ecosystems are dynamic in that they are constantly changing. Temperature changes over the day, water enters as rain and leaves as water vapour, animals enter and leave. Many ecosystem changes are cyclical. Some cycles may be short term e.g. the seasons, others long term, e.g climatic cycles such as El Niño.

▶ Although ecosystems may change constantly over the short term, they may be relatively static over the middle to long term. For example, some tropical areas have wet and dry seasons, but over hundreds of years the ecosystem as a whole remains unchanged.

▶ However, over the long to very long term ecosystems change as the position of the continents and tilt of the Earth change, and as animals and plants evolve.

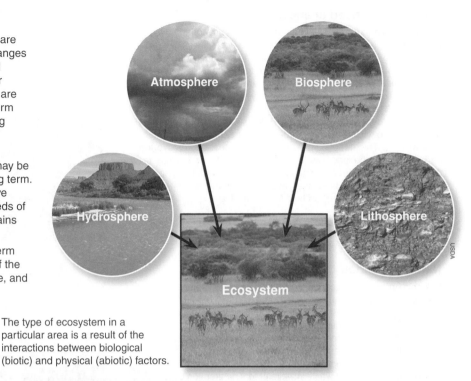

The type of ecosystem in a particular area is a result of the interactions between biological (biotic) and physical (abiotic) factors.

An ecosystem may remain stable for many hundreds or thousands of years provided that the components interacting within it remain stable.

Small scale changes usually have little effect on an ecosystem. Fire or flood may destroy some parts, but enough is left for the ecosystem to return to is original state relatively quickly.

Large scale disturbances such as volcanic eruptions, sea level rise, or large scale open cast mining remove all components of the ecosystem, changing it forever.

1. What is meant by the term dynamic ecosystem? _____

_____

2. (a) Describe two small scale events that an ecosystem may recover from: _____

_____

(b) Describe two large scale events that an ecosystem may not recover from: _____

_____

3. "Climax communities are ones that have reached an equilibrium." Explain what this means: _____

_____

_____

_____

© 2017 **BIOZONE** International
ISBN: 978-1-927309-26-1
Photocopying Prohibited

LINK LINK WEB
172 148 171

KNOW

172 Ecosystem Changes

Key Idea: Sometimes disturbances to an ecosystem are so extreme that the ecosystem never returns to its original state. Ecosystems are dynamic, constantly fluctuating between different states, as occurs during seasonal changes. However, large scale changes to the characteristics of an ecosystem can occur as a result of climate change, volcanic eruptions, or large scale fires. These drivers for change can alter an ecosystem so much that it never returns to its previous state.

Human influenced changes

Peat bogs take thousands of years to develop. They form in wet areas where plant material is prevented from decay by acidic and anaerobic conditions. When dry, peat is used as a fuel source. Mining of peat on a large scale began in Europe in the first millennium. The mining of peat destroys the peat ecosystem. Peat forms very slowly, so it may take hundreds or thousands of years for a mined peat bog to recover (if ever).

Advances in peat mining during the 1500s allowed peat bogs to be mined far below the water table. The mined areas filled with water to form lakes. This removed any chance of the peat bog recovering and also meant the land was no longer available for agriculture. In the Netherlands, 115-230 hectares of land a year was being lost to the formation of these peat lakes. In total, the Netherlands has lost 60 000 hectares (600 km^2) of land to peat mining.

Photograph, right: Abandoned peat workings. The mining of peat below the water table has resulted in flooded man-made lakes.

Natural changes

Volcanic eruptions can cause extreme and sudden changes to the local (or even global) ecosystem. The eruption of Mount St. Helens in 1980 provides a good example of how the natural event of a volcanic eruption can cause extreme and long lasting changes to an ecosystem. Before the 1980 eruption, Mount St. Helens had an almost perfect and classical conical structure. The forests surrounding it were predominantly conifer, including Douglas-fir, western red cedar, and western white pine. The eruption covered about 600 km^2 (dark blue below) in ash (up to 180 m deep in some areas) and blasted flat 370 km^2 of forest.

Mount St. Helens, one day before the eruption.

Schematic of eruption and recovery

The schematic shows the general area of bare land per decade since the eruption

Coldwater Lake was formed when Coldwater Creek was blocked by eruption debris.

Spirit Lake was completely emptied in the initial eruption. All life except bacteria was extinguished. The lake has since begun to recover, but stall has a floating raft of logs that covers half the lake surface.

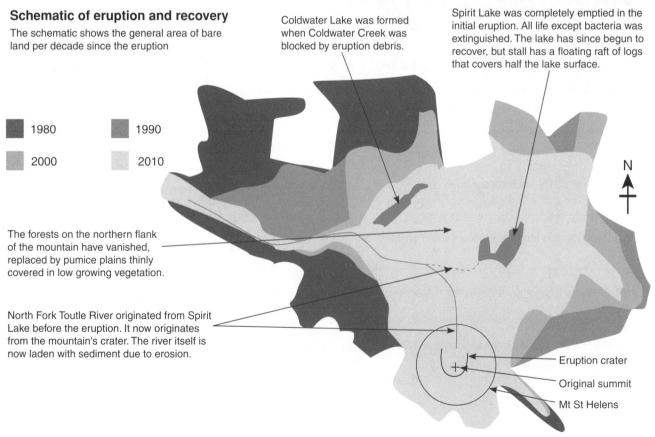

	1980		1990
	2000		2010

N

The forests on the northern flank of the mountain have vanished, replaced by pumice plains thinly covered in low growing vegetation.

North Fork Toutle River originated from Spirit Lake before the eruption. It now originates from the mountain's crater. The river itself is now laden with sediment due to erosion.

Eruption crater

Original summit

Mt St Helens

© 2017 **BIOZONE** International
ISBN: 978-1-927309-26-1
Photocopying Prohibited

1. (a) Explain why peat is cut from peat bogs: _____

    _____

    (b) Why does large scale cutting of peat from peat bogs destroy the bog ecosystem? _____

    _____

    _____

    (c) Explain why mining peat from below the water table causes very large scale ecosystem change: _____

    _____

    _____

    _____

    _____

2. Describe the major change in the ecosystem on Mount St Helens' northern flank after the eruption: _____

    _____

    _____

    _____

3. Study the eruption schematic on the previous page. Why has the recovery of the ecosystem area shown in light blue (2010) been so much slower than elsewhere?

    _____

    _____

    _____

    _____

4. Describe the large scale change that occurred at Coldwater Creek after the eruption. What effect would this have had on the local ecosystem?

    _____

    _____

    _____

    _____

5. Describe the large scale change that occurred at Spirit Lake. Explain why this would cause an almost complete change in the lake ecosystem:

    _____

    _____

    _____

6. (a) What two major changes have occurred in the North Fork Toutle River? _____

    _____

    _____

    _____

    (b) How might this affect this riverine ecosystem? _____

    _____

    _____

    _____

173 Primary Succession

Key Idea: Primary succession is a type of ecological succession occurring in a region where there is no pre-existing vegetation or soil.

Ecological succession is the process by which communities change over time. Succession occurs as a result of the interactions between biotic and abiotic factors. Earlier communities modify the physical environment, making it more favourable for species that make up the later communities. Over time, a succession results in a stable climax community. **Primary succession** is a type of ecological succession describing the colonisation of a region where there is no pre-existing vegetation or soil.

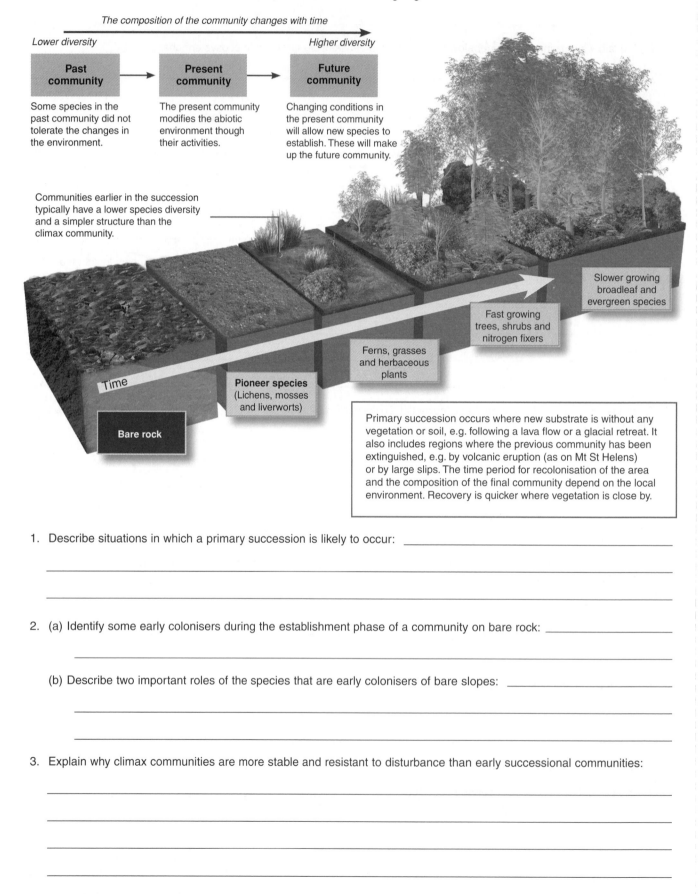

The composition of the community changes with time

Lower diversity → Higher diversity

Past community → **Present community** → **Future community**

Some species in the past community did not tolerate the changes in the environment.

The present community modifies the abiotic environment though their activities.

Changing conditions in the present community will allow new species to establish. These will make up the future community.

Communities earlier in the succession typically have a lower species diversity and a simpler structure than the climax community.

Time

Bare rock

Pioneer species (Lichens, mosses and liverworts)

Ferns, grasses and herbaceous plants

Fast growing trees, shrubs and nitrogen fixers

Slower growing broadleaf and evergreen species

Primary succession occurs where new substrate is without any vegetation or soil, e.g. following a lava flow or a glacial retreat. It also includes regions where the previous community has been extinguished, e.g. by volcanic eruption (as on Mt St Helens) or by large slips. The time period for recolonisation of the area and the composition of the final community depend on the local environment. Recovery is quicker where vegetation is close by.

1. Describe situations in which a primary succession is likely to occur: _____

_____

_____

2. (a) Identify some early colonisers during the establishment phase of a community on bare rock: _____

_____

(b) Describe two important roles of the species that are early colonisers of bare slopes: _____

_____

_____

3. Explain why climax communities are more stable and resistant to disturbance than early successional communities:

_____

_____

_____

_____

174 Succession on Surtsey Island

Key Idea: The successional events occurring on the island of Surtsey confirm that primary succession occurs in stages. Surtsey Island is a volcanic island, 33 km off Iceland. The island was formed over four years from 1963 to 1967 when a submerged volcano built up an island. The island is 150 m above sea level and 1.4 km². As an entirely new island,

Surtsey provided researchers with an ideal environment to study primary succession. Its colonisation by plants and animals has been recorded since its formation. The first vascular plant was discovered in 1965, two years before the eruptions ended. Since then, 69 plant species have colonised the island and there are several established seabird colonies.

Sea rocket

H. peploides

The first stage of colonisation of Surtsey (1965-1974) was dominated by shore plants colonising the northern shores of the island. The most successful coloniser was *Honckenya peploides* which established on tephra sand and gravel flats. It first set seed in 1971 and then spread across the island. Carbon and nitrogen levels in the soil were very low during this time. This initial colonisation by shore plants was followed by a lag phase (from 1975-1984). There was further establishment of shore plants but few new colonisers, which slowed the rate of succession.

P. annua

S. phylicifolia

After the establishment of a gull colony on the southern end of the island a number of new plant species arrived (1985 -1994). Populations of plants inside or near the gull colony expanded rapidly covering about 3 ha, while populations outside the colony remained low but stable. Grasses such as *Poa annua* formed extensive patches of vegetation. After this rapid increase in plant species, the arrival of new colonisers again slowed (1995-2008). A second wave of colonisers began to establish following this slower phase and soil organic matter increased markedly. The first bushy plants established in 1998, with the arrival of the willow *Salix phylicifolia*. The area of vegetation cover near the gull colony expanded to about 10 ha.

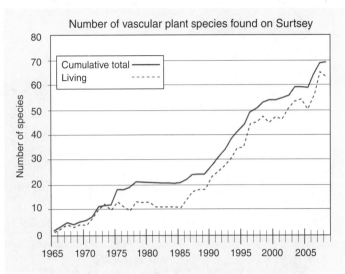

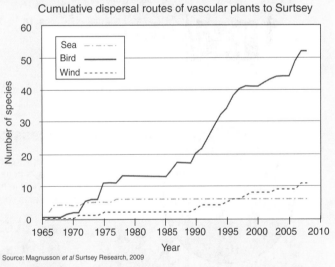
Source: Magnusson *et al* Surtsey Research, 2009

1. Explain why Surtsey provided ideal conditions for studying primary succession: _____

_____

2. Explain why the first colonising plants established in the north of the island, while later colonisers established in the south.

_____

_____

3. Use the graphs to identify the following:

(a) The year the gull colony established: _____

(b) The most common method for new plant species to arrive on the island: _____

(c) The year of the arrival of the second wave of plant colonisers. Suggest a reason for this second wave of colonisers:

_____

_____

© 2017 **BIOZONE** International
ISBN: 978-1-927309-26-1
Photocopying Prohibited

LINK
173

KNOW

175 Secondary Succession

Key Idea: A secondary succession takes place after a land clearance events that do not remove the seedbank.

Events such as fire and logging do not involve the loss of the soil and seed and root stocks are often undamaged. As a result secondary succession tends to be more rapid than primary succession, although the time scale depends on the species involved and the climate and edaphic (soil) factors. Secondary succession events may occur over a wide area (such as after a forest fire), or in smaller areas where single trees have fallen.

Secondary succession in cleared land

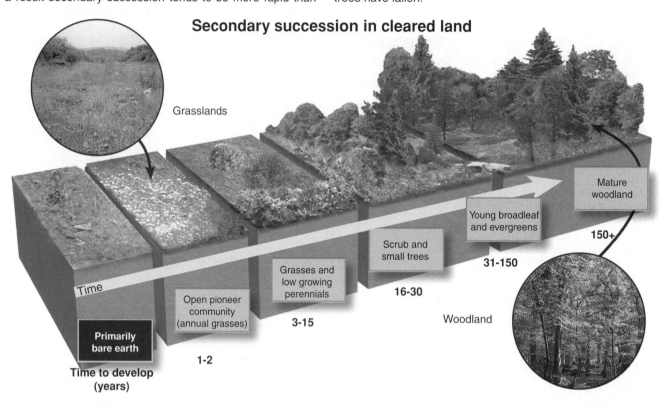

Grasslands

Time

Time to develop (years)

Primarily bare earth

Open pioneer community (annual grasses)

1-2

Grasses and low growing perennials

3-15

Scrub and small trees

16-30

Young broadleaf and evergreens

31-150

Mature woodland

150+

Woodland

Secondary succession: gap regeneration

Large canopy trees have a profound effect on the make-up of a forest community, reducing light penetration and impeding the growth of saplings. When a large tree falls, it opens a hole in the gap allowing far more light through to the forest floor than normal. This stimulates young trees below to start growing towards the light.

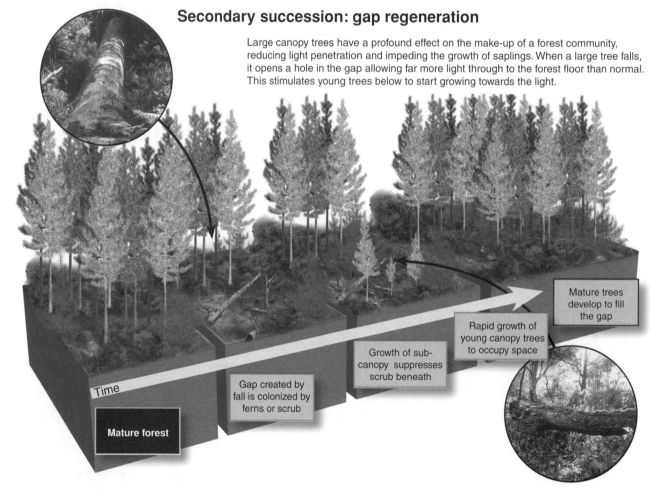

Time

Mature forest

Gap created by fall is colonized by ferns or scrub

Growth of sub-canopy suppresses scrub beneath

Rapid growth of young canopy trees to occupy space

Mature trees develop to fill the gap

KNOW

WEB
175

LINK
171

LINK
173

© 2017 **BIOZONE** International
ISBN: 978-1-927309-26-1
Photocopying Prohibited

Deflected succession

Humans (and sometimes nature) may deflect the natural course of succession (e.g. by mowing or fire) and the climax community that results will differ from the community that would occur if there had been no disturbance.

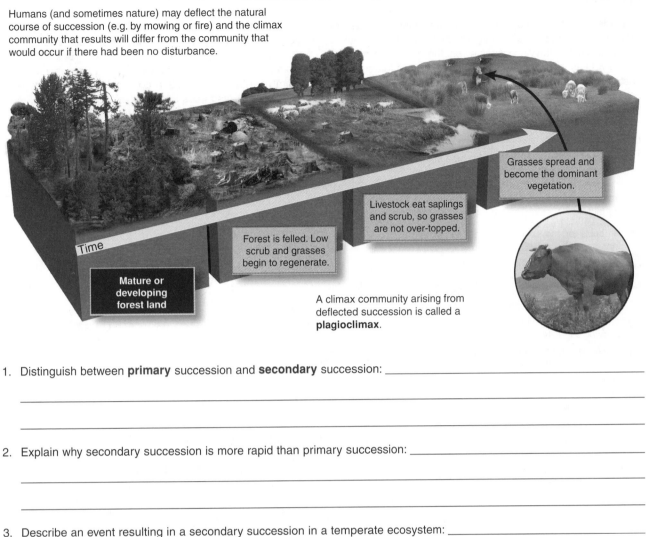

Grasses spread and become the dominant vegetation.

Livestock eat saplings and scrub, so grasses are not over-topped.

Forest is felled. Low scrub and grasses begin to regenerate.

Time

Mature or developing forest land

A climax community arising from deflected succession is called a **plagioclimax**.

1. Distinguish between **primary** succession and **secondary** succession: _____

_____

_____

2. Explain why secondary succession is more rapid than primary succession: _____

_____

_____

3. Describe an event resulting in a secondary succession in a temperate ecosystem: _____

_____

4. (a) Explain why forest felling results in a succession: _____

_____

_____

   (b) Selective logging is a practice in which individual trees (rather than an entire stand) are removed. What type of succession could this produce and why?

_____

_____

   (c) Why is selective logging considered to be less damaging to an existing ecosystem? _____

_____

5. (a) Explain what is meant by a **deflected succession**: _____

_____

_____

   (b) What role might deflected successions have in maintaining managed habitats: _____

_____

_____

_____

© 2017 **BIOZONE** International
ISBN: 978-1-927309-26-1
Photocopying Prohibited

176 Population Size and Carrying Capacity

Key Idea: Carrying capacity is the maximum number of organisms a particular environment can support.

An ecosystem's carrying capacity, i.e. the maximum number of individuals of a given species that the resources can sustain indefinitely, is limited by the ecosystem's resources. Factors affecting carrying capacity of an ecosystem can be biotic (e.g. food supply) or abiotic (e.g. water, climate, and available space). The carrying capacity of an ecosystem is determined by the most limiting factor and can change over time (e.g. as a result of seasonal changes). Below carrying capacity, population size increases because resources are not limiting. As the population approaches carrying capacity (or exceeds it) resources become limiting and environmental resistance increases, decreasing population growth.

Limiting factors

The effect of limiting factors and the type of factor that is limiting may change over time. The graph, right, shows how the carrying capacity of a forest-dwelling species changes based on changes to the limiting factors:

1. A population moves into the forest and rapidly increases in numbers due to abundant resources.

2. The population overshoots the carrying capacity.

3. The environment is damaged due to large numbers and food becomes more limited, lowering the original carrying capacity.

4. The population becomes stable at the new carrying capacity.

5. The forest experiences a drought and the carrying capacity is reduced as a result.

6. The drought breaks and the carrying capacity rises but is less than before because of habitat damage during the drought.

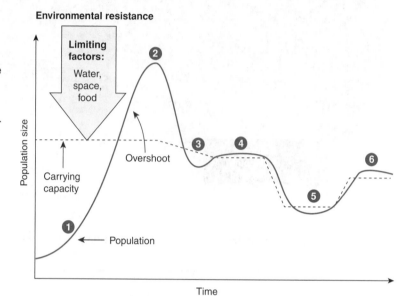

Factors affecting population size

Density dependent factors

The effect of these on population size is influenced by population density.

They include:

▶ Competition

▶ Predation

▶ Disease

Density dependent factors tend to be biotic and are less important when population density is low.

They regulate population size by decreasing birth rates and increasing death rates.

Density independent factors

The effect of these on population size does not depend on population density.

They include catastrophic events such as:

▶ Volcanic eruptions, fire

▶ Drought, flood, tsunamis

▶ Earthquakes

Density independent factors tend to be abiotic.

They regulate population size by increasing death rates.

1. What is carrying capacity? _____

_____

2. How does carrying capacity limit population numbers? _____

_____

_____

3. What limiting factors have changed at points 3, 5, and 6 in the graph above, and how have they changed?

(a) 3: _____

(b) 5: _____

(c) 6: _____

177 A Case Study in Carrying Capacity

Key Idea: Environmental factors influence predator-prey interactions so the outcomes are not always predictable. Environmental carrying capacity can be studied when an organism is introduced to a new environment. One such study involves the introduction of wolves to Coronation Island in Alaska in an attempt to control deer numbers.

When wolves were introduced to Coronation Island

Coronation Island is a small, 116 km² island off the coast of Alaska. In 1960, the Alaska Department of Fish and Game released two breeding pairs of wolves to the island. Their aim was to control the black-tailed deer that had been overgrazing the land. The results (below) were not what they expected. Introduction of the wolves initially appeared to have the desired effect. The wolves fed off the deer and successfully bred, and deer numbers fell. However, within a few years the deer numbers crashed. The wolves ran out of food (deer) and began eating each other, causing a drop in wolf numbers. Within eight years, only one wolf inhabited the island, and the deer were abundant. By 1983, there were no wolves on the island, and the deer numbers were high.

Black-tailed deer

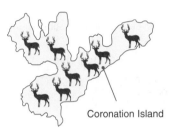

Coronation Island

Pre 1960
No wolves
Abundant deer

Two breeding
pairs of wolves
introduced

1960
Wolves introduced
Abundant deer

1964
13 wolves
Few deer

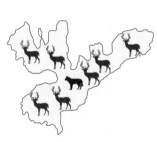

1968
1 wolf
Abundant deer

Grey wolf

What went wrong?

▶ The study showed Coronation Island was too small to sustain both the wolf and the deer populations.

▶ The deer could not easily find refuge from the wolves, so their numbers were quickly reduced.

▶ Reproductive rates in the deer may have been low because of poor quality forage following years of over-grazing. When wolves were introduced, predation and low reproductive rates caused deer numbers to fall.

▶ The deer were the only food source for the wolves. When deer became scarce the wolves ate each other because there was no other prey available.

1. Why were wolves introduced to Coronation Island? _____

_____

_____

2. (a) What were some of the factors that caused the unexpected result? _____

_____

_____

_____

(b) What do these results tell you about the carrying capacity of Coronation Island? _____

_____

_____

_____

178 Testing for Difference Using Chi-Squared

Key Idea: The chi-squared test for goodness of fit is used to compare sets of categorical data and evaluate if differences between them are statistically significant or due to chance.

The **chi-squared test** (χ^2) is used when you are working with frequencies (counts) rather than measurements. It is a simple test to perform but the data must meet the requirements of the test. Firstly, it can only be used for data that are raw counts (not measurements or transformed data such as percentages). Secondly, it is used to compare an experimental result with an expected theoretical outcome (e.g. an expected Mendelian ratio or a theoretical value indicating "no difference" between groups in a response such as habitat preference). Thirdly, it is not a valid test when sample sizes are small (<20). Like all statistical tests, it aims to test the null hypothesis. The following exercise is a worked example using the chi-squared test for goodness of fit to test habitat preference.

Pneumatophores

Using χ^2 in ecology

In an investigation of the ecological niche of the mangrove, *Avicennia marina var. resinifera*, the density of pneumatophores was measured in regions with different substrate. The mangrove trees were selected from four different areas: mostly sand, some sand, mostly mud, and some mud. Note that the variable, substrate type, is categorical in this case. Quadrats (1 m by 1 m) were placed around a large number of trees in each of these four areas and the numbers of pneumatophores were counted. Chi-squared was used to compare the observed results for pneumatophore density (as follows) to an expected outcome of no difference in density between substrates.

Mangrove pneumatophore density in different substrate areas			
Mostly sand	85	Mostly mud	130
Some sand	102	Some mud	123

Using χ^2, the probability of this result being consistent with the expected result could be tested. Worked example as follows:

Step 1: Calculate the expected value (E)

In this case, this is the sum of the observed values divided by the number of categories.

$$\frac{440}{4} = 110$$

Step 2: Calculate O – E

The difference between the observed and expected values is calculated as a measure of the deviation from a predicted result. Since some deviations are negative, they are all squared to give positive values. This step is usually performed as part of a tabulation (right, darker blue column).

Category	O	E	O - E	(O - E)^2	$\frac{(O - E)^2}{E}$
Mostly sand	85	110	-25	625	5.68
Some sand	102	110	-8	64	0.58
Mostly mud	130	110	20	400	3.64
Some mud	123	110	13	169	1.54

Total = 440 χ^2 → $\Sigma = 11.44$

Step 3: Calculate the value of χ^2

$$\chi^2 = \sum \frac{(O - E)^2}{E}$$

Where: O = the observed result
E = the expected result
Σ = sum of

The calculated χ^2 value is given at the bottom right of the last column in the tabulation.

Step 5a: Using the χ^2 table

On the χ^2 table (part reproduced in Table 1 below) with 3 degrees of freedom, the calculated value for χ^2 of 11.44 corresponds to a probability of between 0.01 and 0.001 (see arrow). *This means that by chance alone a χ^2 value of 11.44 could be expected between 1% and 0.1% of the time.*

Step 4: Calculating degrees of freedom

The probability that any particular χ^2 value could be exceeded by chance depends on the number of degrees of freedom. This is simply *one less than the total number of categories* (this is the number that could vary independently without affecting the last value). *In this case: 4–1 = 3.*

Step 5b: Using the χ^2 table

The probability of between 0.1 and 0.01 is lower than the 0.05 value which is generally regarded as significant. The null hypothesis can be rejected and we have reason to believe that the observed results differ significantly from the expected (at P = 0.05).

Table 1: Critical values of χ^2 at different levels of probability. By convention, the critical probability for rejecting the null hypothesis (H_0) is 5%. If the test statistic is less than the tabulated critical value for P = 0.05 we cannot reject H_0 and the result is not significant. If the test statistic is greater than the tabulated value for P = 0.05 we reject H_0 in favour of the alternative hypothesis.

Degrees of freedom	Level of probability (*P*)									
	0.98	0.95	0.80	0.50	0.20	0.10	0.05	0.02	0.01	0.001
1	0.001	0.004	0.064	0.455	1.64	2.71	3.84	5.41	6.64 χ^2	10.83
2	0.040	0.103	0.466	1.386	3.22	4.61	5.99	7.82	9.21 ↓	13.82
3	0.185	0.352	1.005	2.366	4.64	6.25	7.82	9.84	11.35 ↓	16.27
4	0.429	0.711	1.649	3.357	5.99	7.78	9.49	11.67	13.28	18.47
5	0.752	0.145	2.343	4.351	7.29	9.24	11.07	13.39	15.09	20.52

← Do not reject H_0 Reject H_0 →

179 Chi-Squared Exercise in Ecology

Key Idea: Chi-squared for goodness of fit can be used to study habitat preference using the counts of organisms.

This exercise illustrates the use of χ^2 for goodness of fit in ecological studies of habitat preference. In the first example, it is used for determining if the flat periwinkle *(Littorina littoralis)* shows significant preference for any of the four species of seaweeds with which it is found. Using quadrats, the numbers of periwinkles associated with each seaweed species were recorded. The data from this investigation are provided for you in Table 1. In the second example, the results of an investigation into habitat preference in woodlice (also called pillbugs, or slaters) are presented in Table 2.

1. (a) State your null hypothesis for this investigation (H_0):

_____

_____

_____

(b) State the alternative hypothesis (H_A): _____

_____

_____

Table 1: Number of periwinkles associated with different seaweed species

Seaweed species	Number of periwinkles
Spiral wrack	9
Bladder wrack	28
Toothed wrack	19
Knotted wrack	64

2. Use the chi-squared test to determine if the differences observed between the samples are significant or if they can be attributed to chance alone. The table of critical values of χ^2 is provided in *"The Chi-Squared Test"*.

(a) Enter the observed values (no. of periwinkles) and complete the table to calculate the c2 value:

(b) Calculate χ^2 value using the equation:

$$\chi^2 = \sum \frac{(O - E)^2}{E}$$

$\chi^2 =$ _____

(c) Calculate the degrees of freedom: _____

(d) Using the χ^2, state the P value corresponding to your calculated χ^2 value:

_____

(e) State whether or not you reject your null hypothesis:

reject H_0 / do not reject H_0 (*circle one*)

Category	O	E	O - E	(O - E)²	$\frac{(O - E)^2}{E}$
Spiral wrack					
Bladder wrack					
Toothed wrack					
Knotted wrack					
Σ					Σ

3. Students carried out an investigation into habitat preference in woodlice. In particular, they were wanting to know if the woodlice preferred a humid atmosphere to a dry one, as this may play a part in their choice of habitat. They designed a simple investigation to test this idea. The woodlice were randomly placed into a choice chamber for 5 minutes where they could choose between dry and humid conditions (atmosphere). The investigation consisted of five trials with ten woodlice used in each trial. Their results are shown on Table 2 (right):

(a) State the null and alternative hypotheses (H_0 and H_A) :

_____

_____

Table 2: Habitat preference in woodlice

Trial	Atmosphere	
	Dry	Humid
1	2	8
2	3	7
3	4	6
4	1	9
5	5	5

Use a separate piece of paper (or a spreadsheet) to calculate the chi-squared value and summarise your answers below:

(b) Calculate χ^2 value: _____

(c) Calculate the degrees of freedom and state the *P* value corresponding to your calculated χ^2 value: _____

(d) State whether or not you reject your null hypothesis: reject H_0 / do not reject H_0 (*circle one*)

LINK
178
WEB
179
DATA

180 Investigating Distribution and Abundance

Key Idea: Sampling populations *in-situ* can reveal patterns of distribution, which can be attributed to habitat preference. These investigations are common in ecological studies.

Use this activity to practise analysing data from a field study in which the aim was to describe and explain an existing pattern of species distribution.

The aim

To investigate the effect of humidity gradients associated with fallen tree logs on millipede distribution in a forest.

Background

Millipedes consume decaying vegetation and live in the damp conditions beneath logs and in leaf litter. The moist environment protects them from drying out as their cuticle is not a barrier to water loss.

Pill millipede
Glomeris marginata

Marshal Hedin cc 2.0

Experimental method

Students had previously made some readings of physical factors in and around the forest floor and established that areas close to fallen logs had higher relative humidity than areas more distant from logs. They then investigated the distribution of millipede populations in relation to fallen tree logs in a small forest reserve. Six logs of similar size were chosen from similar but separate regions of the forest. Logs with the same or similar surrounding environment were selected.

For each log, eight samples of leaf litter at varying distances from the fallen tree log were taken using 30 cm² quadrats. Samples were taken from two transects, one each side of the log. The sample distances were: directly below the log (0 m), 1.5 m, 2.5 m, and 3.5 m from the log. It was assumed that the conditions on each side of the log would be similar. The leaf litter was placed in Tullgren funnels and the invertebrates removed. The number of millipedes in each sample was counted. The raw data are shown below.

Experimental Setup

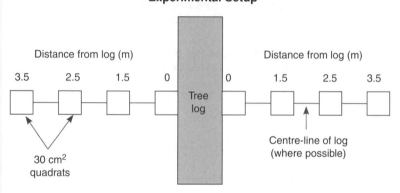

Distance from log (m): 3.5 2.5 1.5 0 | Tree log | 0 1.5 2.5 3.5 : Distance from log (m)

30 cm² quadrats

Centre-line of log (where possible)

Environmental conditions on either side of the log were assumed to be equal.

Raw data for tree log and millipede investigation

Tree log	Transect	\multicolumn{4}{c}{Distance from log (m)}
		0	1.5	2.5	3.5
1	1	12	11	3	2
	2	10	12	2	1
2	1	8	3	4	4
	2	9	5	2	1
3	1	14	6	3	3
	2	3	8	7	2

Tree log	Transect	\multicolumn{4}{c}{Distance from log (m)}
		0	1.5	2.5	3.5
4	1	2	4	1	6
	2	4	5	2	2
5	1	12	10	16	10
	2	6	3	2	5
6	1	10	9	7	2
	2	11	11	8	1

LINK
DATA 178

1. Complete the table below using the raw data on the previous page. Combine the values for each transect:

	Distance from log / m			
Tree log				
TOTAL				

2. Explain why a chi-squared test is the best statistical analysis of this data: _____

_____

_____

_____

_____

3. State the null hypothesis and alternative hypothesis for the statistical test: _____

_____

_____

4. Carry out the chi-squared test on the data by completing the table below. Combine the values of all the tree logs.

Distance / m	O	E	O-E	$(O-E)^2$	$\frac{(O-E)^2}{E}$
				$\sum \frac{(O-E)^2}{E}$	

5. Use the critical values table on page 262 to decide if the null hypothesis should be rejected or not rejected:

_____

_____

6. What could the students have done to relate their findings more conclusively to physical factors in the environment?

_____

_____

7. Discuss the result in relation to how millipedes live. Include the validity of the findings and any relevant biological ideas:

_____

_____

_____

_____

_____

_____

_____

181 Species Interactions

Key Idea: All species interact with other species. These interactions frequently regulate population growth.

Every organism interacts with others of its own and other species. These interactions are the result of coevolution, in which there is a reciprocal evolution of adaptations. A symbiosis describes a very close association between two or more parties, as occurs in mutualism and parasitism. A mutually beneficial relationship is called mutualism. If one party benefits but the other is unaffected, the relationship is commensal. If one party benefits at the expense of another, the relationship is an exploitation. In competitive interactions, resources are usually limited, so both parties are detrimentally affected. Interactions within and between species ultimately regulate population numbers.

Type of interaction between species				
Mutualism	**Exploitation**			**Competition**
	Predation	**Herbivory**	**Parasitism**	
A ⇄ B	A → B	A → B	A → B	A ⇄ B
Benefits / Benefits	Benefits / Harmed	Benefits / Harmed	Benefits / Harmed	Harmed / Harmed
Both species benefit from the association. **Examples**: Flowering plants and their insect pollinators have a mutalistic relationship. Flowers are pollinated and the insect gains food (below). **Population effects**: Flower population spreads by producing seeds. Bees use pollen to make honey and feed larvae, ensuring the hive's survival.	Predator kills the prey outright and eats it. **Examples**: Lion preying on wildebeest or praying mantis (below) consuming insect prey. Predators have adaptations to capture prey and prey have adaptations to avoid capture. These relationships are often the result of coevolution. **Population effects**: Predator numbers lag behind prey numbers.	Herbivore eats parts of a plant and usually does not kill it. Plants often have defences to limit the impact of herbivory. **Example**: Giraffes browsing acacia trees. Browsing stimulates the acacia to produce toxic alkaloids, which cause the giraffe to move on to another plant. **Population effects**: Browser damage is self limiting, so the plant is able to recover.	The parasite lives in or on the host, taking (usually all) its nutrition from it. The host is harmed but usually not killed. **Examples**: Pork tapeworm in a pig's gut. **Population effects**: High parasite loads make the host susceptible to diseases that may kill it. Parasite numbers generally stay at a level that is tolerated by the host.	Species, or individuals, compete for the same resources, with both parties suffering, especially when resources are limited. **Examples**: Plants growing close to each other compete for light and soil nutrients. **Population effects**: Competition reduces the maximum number of any one species in an area as resources are limited.

Honeybee and flower

Mantid eats cricket

Giraffe browses acacia

Pork tapeworm

Forest plants

1. For the purposes of this exercise, assume that species A in the diagram represents humans. Briefly describe an example of our interaction with another species (B in the diagram above) that matches each of the following interaction types:

    (a) Mutualism: _____

    _____

    (b) Exploitation: _____

    _____

    (c) Competition: _____

    _____

2. Plants are not defenceless against herbivores. They have evolved physical and chemical defences to deter herbivores. In some cases (as in grasses) grazing stimulates growth in the plant.

    (a) What is the acacia's response to giraffe browsing? _____

    (b) How might this response prevent over-browsing?_____

    _____

Examples of interactions between different species are illustrated below. For each example, identify the type of interaction, and explain how each species in the relationship is affected.

3. The European honey bee *Apis mellifera* collects pollen in pollen baskets on its back legs and in doing so spreads pollen from one flower to the next, pollinating the flowers it visits.

   (a) Identify this type of interaction: _____

   (b) Describe how each species is affected (benefits/harmed/no effect):

   _____

   _____

4. The squat anemone shrimp (or sexy shrimp), lives among the tentacles of sea anemones, where it gains protection and scavenges scraps of food from the anemone. The anemone is apparently neither harmed nor benefitted by the shrimp's presence although there is some evidence that ammonium released by the shrimp may benefit the anemone indirectly by supplying nutrients to the mutualistic photosynthetic algae that reside in the anemone's tissues.

   (a) Identify this type of interaction: _____

   (b) Describe how each species is affected (benefits/harmed/no effect):

   _____

   _____

   _____

5. Hyaenas will kill and scavenge a range of species. They form large groups and attack and kill large animals, such as wildebeest, but will also scavenge carrion or drive other animals off their kills.

   (a) Identify this type of interaction: _____

   (b) Describe how each species is affected (benefits/harmed/no effect):

   _____

   _____

6. Ticks are obligate haemtaophages and must obtain blood to pass from one life stage to the next. Ticks attach to the outside of hosts where they suck blood and fluids and cause irritation.

   (a) Identify this type of interaction: _____

   (b) Describe how each species is affected (benefits/harmed/no effect):

   _____

   _____

7. Large herbivores expose insects in the vegetation as they graze. The cattle egret, which is widespread in tropical and subtropical regions, follows the herbivores as they graze, feeding on the insects disturbed by the herbivore.

   (a) Identify this type of interaction: _____

   (b) Describe how each species is affected (benefits/harmed/no effect):

   _____

   _____

8. Explain the similarities and differences between a predator and a parasite: _____

_____

_____

182 Interpreting Predator-Prey Relationships

Key Idea: Predator and prey populations frequently show regular population cycles. The predator cycle is often based on the intrinsic population cycle of the prey species.

It was once thought that predators regulated the population numbers of their prey. However, we now know that this is not usually the case. Prey species are more likely to be regulated by other factors such as the availability of food. However, predator population cycles are often regulated by the availability of prey, especially when there is little opportunity for switching to alternative prey species.

A case study in predator-prey numbers

In some areas of Northeast India, a number of woolly aphid species colonise and feed off bamboo plants. The aphids can damage the bamboo so much that it is no longer able to be used by the local people for construction and the production of textiles.

Giant ladybird beetles (*Anisolemnia dilatata*) feed exclusively on the woolly aphids of bamboo plants. There is some interest in using them as biological control agents to reduce woolly aphid numbers, and limit the damage woolly aphids do to bamboo plants.

The graph below shows the relationship between the giant lady bird beetle and the woolly aphid when grown in controlled laboratory conditions.

Bamboo plants are home to many insect species, including ladybirds and aphids.

Aphids feed off the bamboo sap, and the ladybirds are predators of the aphids (below).

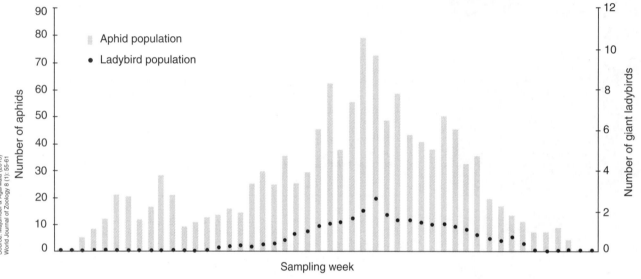

Source: Majumder & Agarwala (2013)
World Journal of Zoology 8 (1): 55-61

1. (a) On the graph above, mark (using different coloured pens) where the peak numbers of woolly aphids and giant ladybirds occurs:

   (b) Do the peak numbers for both species occur at the same time? _____

   (c) Why do you think this is? _____

   _____

   _____

   _____

2. (a) Is the trend between the giant ladybirds woolly aphids positive or negative (circle one).

   (b) Explain your answer: _____

   _____

   _____

   _____

   _____

   _____

183 Interspecific Competition

Key Idea: Interspecific competition occurs between individuals of different species for resources. It can affect the size and distribution of populations sharing the same environment.

Interspecific competition (competition between different species) is usually less intense than intraspecific (same species) competition because coexisting species have evolved slight differences in their realised niches. However, when two species with very similar niche requirements are brought into direct competition through the introduction of a foreign species, one usually benefits at the expense of the other, which is excluded (the **competitive exclusion principle**). The introduction of alien species is implicated in the competitive displacement and decline of many native species. Displacement of native species by introduced ones is more likely if the introduced competitor is adaptable and hardy, with high fertility. In Britain, introduction of the larger, more aggressive, grey squirrel in 1876 has contributed to a contraction in range of the native red squirrel (below), and on the Scottish coast, this phenomenon has been well documented in barnacle species (see next page)

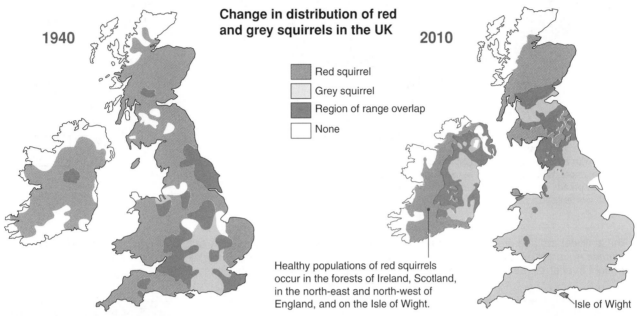

Change in distribution of red and grey squirrels in the UK

1940

2010

- Red squirrel
- Grey squirrel
- Region of range overlap
- None

Healthy populations of red squirrels occur in the forests of Ireland, Scotland, in the north-east and north-west of England, and on the Isle of Wight.

Isle of Wight

The European red squirrel was the only squirrel species in Britain until the introduction of the American gray squirrel in 1876. Regular distribution surveys (above) have recorded the range contraction of the reds, with the larger, more aggressive grey squirrel displacing populations of reds over much of England. Grey squirrels can exploit tannin-rich foods, which are unpalatable to reds. In mixed woodland and in competition with greys, reds may not gain enough food to survive the winter and breed. Reds are also very susceptible to several viral diseases, including squirrelpox, which is transmitted by greys.

Whereas red squirrels once occupied a range of forest types, they are now almost solely restricted to coniferous forest. The data suggest that the grey squirrel is probably responsible for the red squirrel decline, but other factors, such as habitat loss, are also likely to be important.

Red squirrel, *Sciurus vulgaris*

Gray squirrel, *Sciurus carolinesis*

Paul Whippey cc 3.0

BirdPhotos.com cc 3.0

1. Outline the evidence to support the view that the red-grey squirrel distributions in Britain are an example of the competitive exclusion principle:

_____

_____

_____

2. Some biologists believe that competition with grey squirrels is only one of the factors contributing to the decline in the red squirrels in Britain. Explain the evidence from the 2010 distribution map that might support this view:

_____

_____

_____

_____

_____

© 2017 **BIOZONE** International
ISBN: 978-1-927309-26-1
Photocopying Prohibited

LINK 184   LINK 181   WEB 183   **KNOW**

Competitive exclusion in barnacles

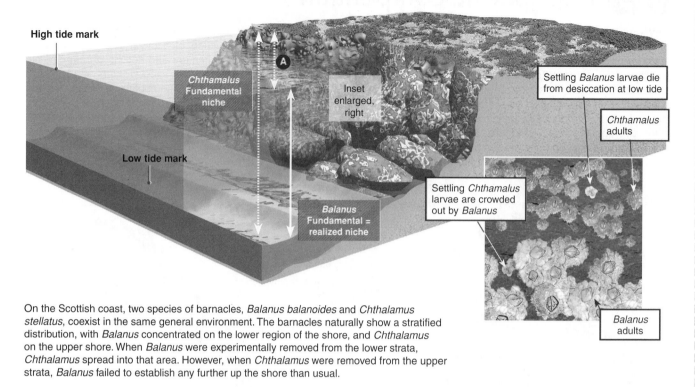

High tide mark

Low tide mark

Chthamalus Fundamental niche

Inset enlarged, right

A

Balanus Fundamental = realized niche

Settling *Balanus* larvae die from desiccation at low tide

Chthamalus adults

Settling *Chthamalus* larvae are crowded out by *Balanus*

Balanus adults

On the Scottish coast, two species of barnacles, *Balanus balanoides* and *Chthalamus stellatus*, coexist in the same general environment. The barnacles naturally show a stratified distribution, with *Balanus* concentrated on the lower region of the shore, and *Chthalamus* on the upper shore. When *Balanus* were experimentally removed from the lower strata, *Chthalamus* spread into that area. However, when *Chthalamus* were removed from the upper strata, *Balanus* failed to establish any further up the shore than usual.

3. The ability of red and grey squirrels to coexist appears to depend on the diversity of habitat type and availability of food sources (reds appear to be more successful in regions of coniferous forest). Suggest why careful habitat management is thought to offer the best hope for the long term survival of red squirrel populations in Britain:

_____

_____

_____

_____

_____

_____

_____

_____

4. Suggest other conservation methods that could possibly aid the survival of viability of red squirrel populations:

_____

_____

_____

5. (a) In the example of the barnacles (above), describe what is represented by the zone labeled with the arrow A:

_____

_____

_____

(b) Outline the evidence for the barnacle distribution being the result of competitive exclusion:

_____

_____

_____

184 Niche Differentiation

Key Idea: Competition between species for similar resources can be reduced if competing species have slightly different niches and exploit available resources in different ways.
Although Interspecific competition is usually less intense than competition between members of the same species, many species exploit at least some of the same resources. Different species with similar ecological requirements may reduce direct competition by exploiting the resources within different microhabitats or by exploiting the same resources at different times of the day or year. This is called niche differentiation.

Foraging behaviour of tits

Tits are omnivorous passerine (perching) birds, all belonging to same family. They feed on insects, fruits, nuts, and berries and are widespread throughout the UK, Europe, Africa, and North America. In the UK, tits are common in both coniferous forest and broadleaf forests. The feeding behaviours of a large number of tit species have been intensively studied. During most of the year there is plenty of food for coexisting species and they tend to forage in much the same way and in much the same parts of the forest. However during the winter when food is less abundant feeding behaviours change and species diverge in their foraging patterns, as illustrated for four tit species below.

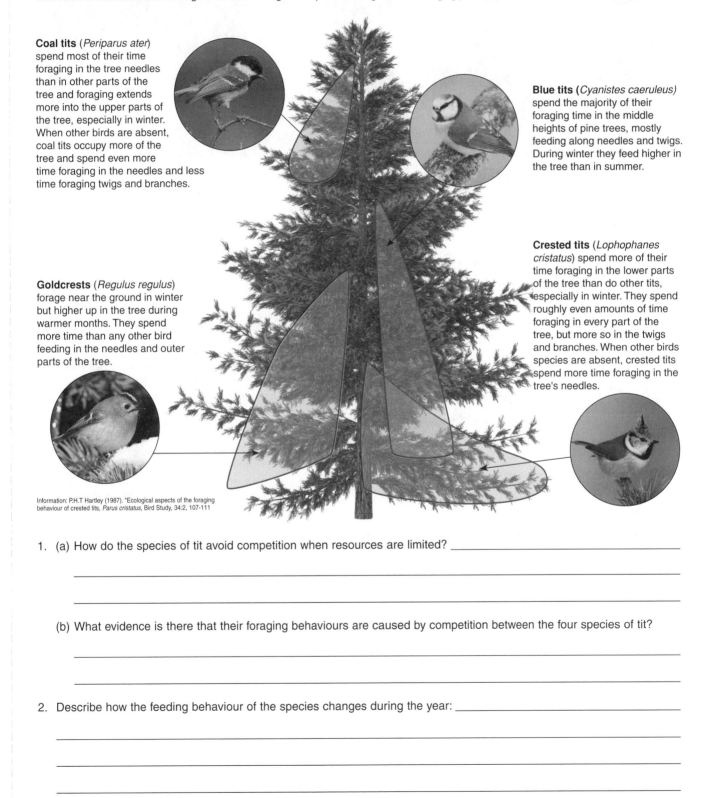

Coal tits (*Periparus ater*) spend most of their time foraging in the tree needles than in other parts of the tree and foraging extends more into the upper parts of the tree, especially in winter. When other birds are absent, coal tits occupy more of the tree and spend even more time foraging in the needles and less time foraging twigs and branches.

Blue tits (*Cyanistes caeruleus*) spend the majority of their foraging time in the middle heights of pine trees, mostly feeding along needles and twigs. During winter they feed higher in the tree than in summer.

Crested tits (*Lophophanes cristatus*) spend more of their time foraging in the lower parts of the tree than do other tits, especially in winter. They spend roughly even amounts of time foraging in every part of the tree, but more so in the twigs and branches. When other birds species are absent, crested tits spend more time foraging in the tree's needles.

Goldcrests (*Regulus regulus*) forage near the ground in winter but higher up in the tree during warmer months. They spend more time than any other bird feeding in the needles and outer parts of the tree.

Information: P.H.T Hartley (1987). "Ecological aspects of the foraging behaviour of crested tits, *Parus cristatus*, Bird Study, 34:2, 107-111

1. (a) How do the species of tit avoid competition when resources are limited? _____

    _____

    _____

    (b) What evidence is there that their foraging behaviours are caused by competition between the four species of tit?

    _____

    _____

2. Describe how the feeding behaviour of the species changes during the year: _____

    _____

    _____

    _____

185 Intraspecific Competition

Key Idea: Individuals of the same species exploit the same resources, so competition between them is usually intense and will act to limit population growth.

As a population grows, the resources available to each individual become fewer and **intraspecific competition** (competition between members of the same species) increases. When the demand for a resource (e.g. food or light) exceeds supply, that resource becomes a limiting factor to the number of individuals the environment can support (the **carrying capacity**). Populations respond to resource limitation by reducing growth rate (e.g. lower birth rates or higher mortality). The response of individuals to limited resources varies. In many invertebrates and some vertebrates, individuals reduce their growth rate and mature at a smaller size. In many vertebrates, territories space individuals apart according to resource availability and only those individuals able to secure a territory will have sufficient resources to breed.

Scramble competition in caterpillars

Direct competition for available food between members of the same species is called **scramble competition.** In some situations where scramble competition is intense, none of the competitors gets enough food to survive.

Contest competition in wolves

In some cases, competition is limited by hierarchies existing within a social group. Dominant individuals receive adequate food, but individuals low in the hierarchy must **contest** the remaining resources and may miss out.

Display of a male anole

Intraspecific competition may be for mates or breeding sites, or for food. In anole lizards (above), males have a bright red throat pouch and use much of their energy displaying to compete with other males for available mates.

Competition between tadpoles of *Rana tigrina*

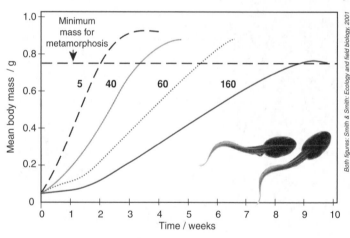

Both figures: Smith & Smith: Ecology and field biology, 2001

Food shortage reduces both individual growth rate and survival, and population growth. In some organisms, where there is a metamorphosis or a series of moults before adulthood (e.g. frogs, crustacean zooplankton, and butterflies), individuals may die before they mature. The graph (left) shows how the growth rate of tadpoles (*Rana tigrina*) declines as the density increases from 5 to 160 individuals (in the same sized space).

► At high densities, tadpoles grow more slowly, take longer to reach the minimum size for metamorphosis (0.75 g), and have less chance of metamorphosing into frogs.

► Tadpoles held at lower densities grow faster to a larger size, metamorphosing at an average size of 0.889 g.

► In some species, such as frogs and butterflies, the adults and juveniles reduce the intensity of intraspecific competition by exploiting different food resources.

1. Using an example, predict the likely effects of **intraspecific competition** on each of the following:

(a) Individual growth rate: _____

_____

_____

(b) Population growth rate: _____

_____

_____

(c) Final population size: _____

_____

_____

© 2017 **BIOZONE** International
ISBN: 978-1-927309-26-1
Photocopying Prohibited

Golden eagle breeding territories in Northern Scotland, 1967

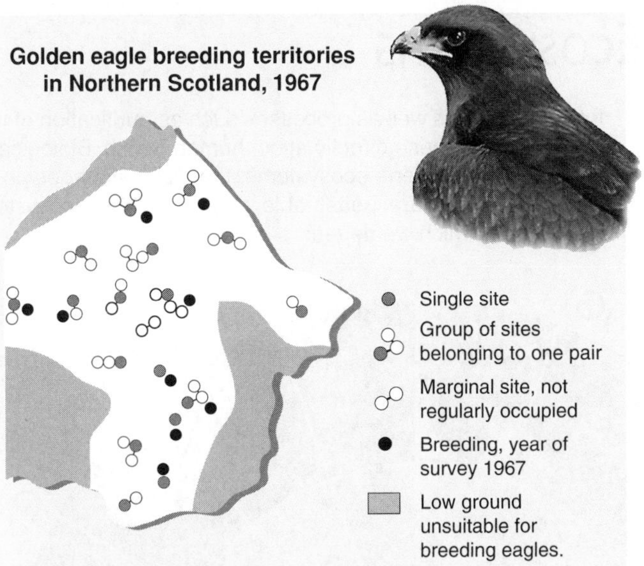

- ● Single site
- ● Group of sites belonging to one pair
- ● Marginal site, not regularly occupied
- ● Breeding, year of survey 1967
- ▨ Low ground unsuitable for breeding eagles.

Territoriality in birds and other animals is usually a result of intraspecific competition. It frequently produces a pattern of uniform distribution over an area of suitable habitat, although this depends somewhat on the distribution of resources. The diagram above shows the territories of golden eagles (*Aquila chrysaetos*) in Scotland. Note the relatively uniform distribution of the breeding sites.

Territoriality in great tits (*Parus major*)

Six breeding pairs of great tits were removed from an oak woodland (below). Within three days, four new pairs had moved into the unoccupied areas (below, right) and some residents had expanded their territories. The new birds moved in from territories in hedgerows, considered to be suboptimal habitat. This type of territorial behaviour limits the density of breeding animals in areas of optimal habitat.

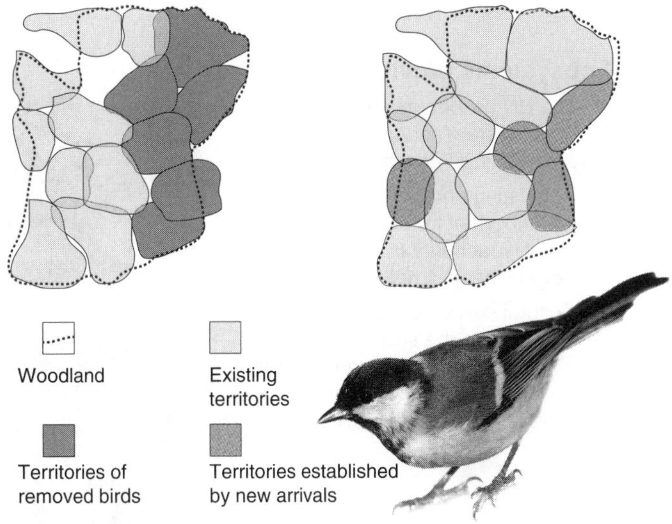

- ┈ Woodland
- ▨ Existing territories
- ■ Territories of removed birds
- ▨ Territories established by new arrivals

Source: Smith and Smith, 2001.

2. In the tank experiment with *Rana* (see previous page), the tadpoles were contained in a fixed volume with a set amount of food:

   (a) Describe how *Rana* tadpoles respond to resource limitation: _____

   _____

   (b) Categorise the effect on the tadpoles as density-dependent / density-independent (delete one).

   (c) Comment on how much the results of this experiment are likely to represent what happens in a natural population:

   _____

   _____

3. Identify two ways in which animals can reduce the intensity of intraspecific competition:

   (a) _____

   (b) _____

4. (a) Suggest why carrying capacity of an ecosystem might decline: _____

   _____

   (b) Predict how a decline in carrying capacity might affect final population size: _____

   _____

   _____

5. Using appropriate examples, discuss the role of territoriality in reducing intraspecific competition:

   _____

   _____

   _____

   _____

   _____

   _____

186 Humans Depend on Ecosystems

Key Idea: Humans rely on ecosystems and the services they provide for health, well being, and livelihood. The biodiversity of an ecosystem affects its ability to provide these services. Humans depend on Earth's ecosystems for the services they provide. These ecosystem services include resources such as food and fuel, as well as processes such as purification of the air and water. These directly affect human health. Biologically diverse and resilient ecosystems that are managed in a sustainable way are better able to provide the ecosystem services on which we depend.

Ecosystems provide services

▶ The UN has identified four categories of ecosystem services: supporting, provisioning, regulating, and cultural.

▶ Regulating and provisioning services are important for human health and security (security of resources and security against natural disasters).

▶ Cultural services are particularly important to the social fabric of human societies and contribute to well being. These are often things we cannot value in monetary terms.

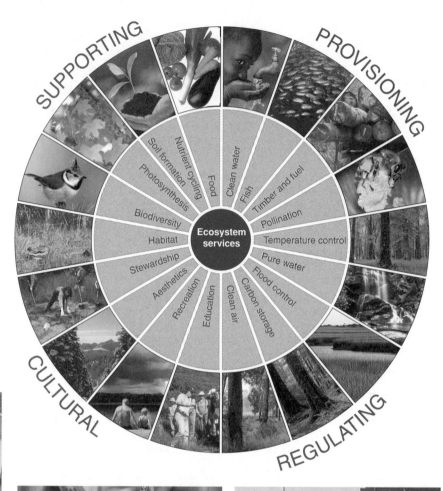

Ebola can be spread from infected bush meat to humans

High biodiversity creates buffers between humans and infectious diseases (e.g. Ebola) and increases the efficiency of processes such as water purification and nutrient cycling.

Rust on wheat stem

Biodiversity is important in crop development, e.g. promoting disease resistance. Many medical breakthroughs have come from understanding the biology of microbes and wild plants and animals.

Biodiversity and ecosystem health are essential for reducing the impact of human activities (e.g. pollution) and the effects of environmental disasters (e.g. eruptions and landslides).

1. What are ecosystem services and why are they important to humans? _____

_____

_____

_____

_____

275

Ecosystem services: a case study

▶ It is difficult fully quantify the value of ecosystem services. One way of doing so is to estimate what people would pay for the services the ecosystem provides as the following case study illustrates.

▶ The Peconic Estuary in Long Island has many wetlands and mudflats. Development of the area has caused these to degrade. Management programmes needed to estimate the benefits of rehabilitating the estuary. A study was carried out to estimate the contributions of the estuary to the production of wildlife (e.g. shellfish, fish, and birds).

▶ It was estimated that a hectare of eelgrass is worth $2631 per year, a hectare of saltmarsh is worth $835 per year, and a hectare of intertidal mudflat is worth $168 per year in terms of commercial values for the fish, viewing values for birds, and hunting values for waterfowl.

Doug Kerr

Human sustainability, resources, and biodiversity

▶ The sustainability (longevity) of human populations depends on the responsible management of the resources provided by the natural environment. Healthy, biodiverse ecosystems are essential to sustainability as these provide the essential services on which humans depend, e.g. clean air, fresh water, and carbon storage.

▶ If the quantity and quality of essential resources, such as water, are diminished, human sustainability is detrimentally affected. This also applies to biodiversity. If this decreases, the essential ecosystem services on which humans rely are negatively affected.

▶ We can express this relationship by saying that human sustainability (HS) is approximately equal to the resources available (RA) and the biodiversity (B) of the area. This could be written as a simple equation: HS ~ RA + B.

▶ Using this simple equation, we can see that any decrease in RA or B will cause a decrease in HS. However, human technology can compensate to a certain degree for reduction in resources or biodiversity. Technology (T) can help efficiency and reduce resource use, or it can help conservation programs to improve biodiversity. These factors can be put into our first equation so that now: HS ~ $(RA + T_1) + (B + T_2)$.

▶ Here the equation now shows HS can remain stable even if RA or B decrease, provided that T_1 or T_2 increase appropriately.

▶ It is important to remember that technological solutions to reduced resources or biodiversity require both effort and money. They come at a cost (C), so that C ~ $T_1 + T_2$. Benefits (Bt) from the system described are effectively equal to human sustainability (i.e. the benefit is that humans survive) so that HS ~ Bt.

▶ These simple equations by no means show the complexity of the human relationship with the environment but they do provide a way to visualise and compute the effects of simple changes to a system.

2. What is the relationship between biodiversity and the ability of an ecosystem to provide essential ecosystem services?

3. (a) Describe a way of putting a value on ecosystem services: _____

   (b) What is the purpose of putting a value on ecosystem services? _____

4. Use the equations above to describe what would need to happen in the following scenarios:

   (a) Keeping HS stable while allowing B to decrease: _____

   (b) Keeping HS stable while reducing the need for resources (RA): _____

   (c) The effect on cost (C) of allowing either (a) or (b) to occur: _____

   (d) The effect of reducing both B and RA on HS and C: _____

187 Human Sustainability

Key Idea: The key to humans living sustainably on this planet is finding a way to prolong the life of resources in the face of a continually growing population.

In the last 60 years, the human population has increased from fewer than 3 billion to over 7.4 billion. Since the 1950s, improvements in medicine and agriculture have allowed the world's population to grow at rate of almost 2% a year. Many scientists believe this growth is not sustainable and that the human population has already exceeded the planet's carrying capacity. They predict the inevitable collapse of food supplies and populations in the near future. Current predictions suggest the human population will reach at least 9.7 billion by 2050.

As the human population grows it uses more resources. Even with careful resource management and more efficient use the rate of resource use will continue to increase. This means that eventually either the resource will run out or it has to be replaced with another resource before that happens. In many countries, initiatives have been taken to lower birth rates in an attempt to relieve pressure on resources.

Year	Population / billions	Year	Population / billions
1850	1.26	1960	3.01
1900	1.65	1970	3.68
1910	1.75	1980	4.44
1920	1.86	1990	5.31
1930	2.07	2000	6.12
1940	2.30	2010	6.93
1950	2.52	2016	7.4

Population growth

▶ Births, deaths, immigrations (movements into the population) and emigrations (movements out of the population) are events that determine the number of individuals in a population.

▶ Population growth depends on the number of individuals being added to the population from births and immigration and the number being lost through deaths and emigration (right).

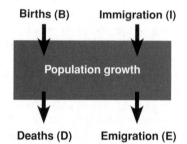

Resource use

▶ An example of the human population affecting resources is the consumption of coal in the last 200 years (right). The majority of the energy consumed by humanity originates from coal, either from using it directly for heat or using it to fuel power stations that produce electricity.

▶ As the human population has increased, so has the consumption of coal (and every other energy resource for that matter). Some of this comes from use of technology with high energy demands, but that technology has itself helped increase food supplies, living standards, life expectancy, and the human population itself.

Year	~ Coal consumption / x 10^{18} J	Year	~ Coal consumption / x 10^{18} J
1840	1	1940	41
1860	5	1960	50
1880	12	1980	70
1900	25	2000	100
1920	39	2015	150

1. What is the rate of the human population growth since 1950? _____

2. What will the human population be in 2050? _____

3. (a) Produce an equation that could be used to calculate the population growth of a certain population (e.g a country's population growth).

    _____

    (b) How would the equation for the entire global human population differ? _____

    _____

    (c) Write the equation for the entire global human population: _____

    _____

4. Discus some reasons for the rapid growth of the human population since 1950: _____

    _____

    _____

    _____

© 2017 **BIOZONE** International
ISBN: 978-1-927309-26-1
Photocopying Prohibited

5. Use the data on the opposite page to produce a graph to show the growth of the human population and the consumption of coal since 1840. You will need a left and right Y axis.

6. What type of growth curve do both human population and coal consumption show? _____

_____

7. Use your equation from question 3 to complete the following:

    (a) A town has a population of 70,230 in the year 2010. Over the next five years, 6556 people move into the town for work, but 4096 move to other parts of the country. A baby boom sees the birth of 5225 babies but there are also 4978 deaths. What is the population of the town in 2015?

    _____

    _____

    (b) What is the percentage growth over the 5 years? _____

    (c) The town uses water from a reservoir that holds 200 million L and is replenished at a rate of 60 million L a day. In 2010, the town used 46 million L per day. Calculate the average water use per person per day.

    _____

    (d) How much water would be used per day in 2015 if each person used the same amount of water as in 2010?

    _____

    (e) Assuming the town underwent the same rate of growth every 5 years into the future, when would the reservoir begin to fill more slowly than it was being used (i.e. the tipping point at which the water supply become unsustainable?)

    _____

    _____

    (f) At the end of 2025, the town introduces measures to extend the life of the water supply by asking people to cut their water use by 10%. Under these new measures, when will the water supply become unsustainable?

    _____

    _____

188 Human Impact on the Ocean

Key Idea: Humans have had a significant impact on the oceans, including the stocks of fish and the quality of the environment.

Less than two centuries ago the oceans must have seemed to people to be an inexhaustible resource. However, after years of exploiting this resource we are finally realising that even the ocean has its limits and that we, as a species, have begun to exceed them.

The decline of whales is an example of humans overexploiting a resource. During the 1700s-1900s the slaughter of whales became so efficient that ships were needing to sail further from land and for longer voyages to find any whales at all. By 1930, 50 000 whales were being killed a year. However whales breed very slowly and by 1980 many species were (and still are) on the brink of extinction. It is estimated that 90% of blue whales were killed by 1980 and over 2.9 million whales killed since 1900.

Fishing has provided food for people for thousands of years. However fish stocks have plummeted as the human population has increased and fishing has become a major global industry. Many fish species have been fished so intensively that they are no longer economic. Others are on the brink of collapse. Fishing techniques have become so sophisticated and efforts are on such a large scale that hundreds of tonnes of fish can be caught by one vessel on one fishing cruise. Fishing vessels can reach over 100 m long.

Pollution is a major problem in parts of the oceans. Activities causing pollution range from deliberate dumping of rubbish from ships, to runoff from the land and contaminated discharge into rivers that lead to the sea. An estimated 8 million tonnes of plastic finds its way into the sea each year. Plastic can have severe detrimental effects on marine life, especially those that mistake plastic bags for jellyfish or other prey species. Some areas are so polluted it is dangerous to eat fish caught there.

Cargo ships carry ballast water in their hulls to keep them stable when empty. As the cargo is loaded, the ballast water is pumped out to maintain stability and buoyancy. This has led to many marine organisms being unintentionally transported about the globe. This can be disastrous for the local marine environment when the organism is an invasive species. Newer ships are able to discharge ballast and replace it out at sea (where potentially invasive organisms would die in the open ocean).

Runoff from the land into the ocean has caused problems with eutrophication (nutrient enrichment). Combined with increasing surface water temperatures this has led to large algal blooms along coastlines. In some cases, these blooms make it dangerous for swimming. The algae often produce toxins that are concentrated by filter feeding organisms (e.g. clams). This makes them dangerous to eat and the public is often warned against collecting shellfish, taking away an important food resource.

Sea bed mining and drilling has had an impact on bottom dwelling marine organisms. Oil spills can affect the seabed and coastline for hundreds of kilometers. Although technology has made oil spills while drilling less likely, it is still a significant risk, and accidents can still occur, with catastrophic consequences, as the 2010 blowout of the oil well drilled by the Deepwater Horizon illustrated. Sea bed mining often uses dredges to vacuum up material from the sea floor, disturbing bottom dwelling organisms.

1. Describe three impacts of human activity on the ocean:

(a) _____

_____

(b) _____

_____

(c) _____

_____

189 Overfishing

Key Idea: Fisheries must be managed to ensure they are sustainable. Overfishing can severely deplete fish stocks.

Commercial fishing is a worldwide resource extraction industry. Decades of overfishing has pushed commercially important species into steep decline. Assessment of the world's fisheries have shown that the share of fish stocks with biologically sustainable levels decreased from 90% in 1970 to 68.6% in 2013. Thus over a third of fish stocks are unsustainable and overfished. The ten most productive species accounted for 27% of the marine capture production in 2013. Most of these are fully fished and therefore have no potential for a sustainable increase in capture in the future.

Lost fishing gear (particularly drift nets) threatens marine life. Comprehensive data on **ghost fishing** impacts is not available, but entanglement in, and or ingestion of, fishing debris has been reported for over 250 marine species.

Overfishing has resulted in many fish stocks at historic lows and fishing effort at unprecedented highs.

Over-capitalisation of the fishing industry has led to too many fleets, and too many large scale vessels. The fishing activities of these large vessels are unsustainable and, for every calorie of fish caught, a fishing vessel uses 15 calories of fuel.

Bottom trawls and dredges cause large scale physical damage to the seafloor. Non-commercial, bottom-dwelling species in the path of the net can be uprooted, damaged, or killed, turning the seafloor into a barren, unproductive wasteland unable to sustain marine life. An area equal to half the world's continental shelves is now trawled every year. In other words, the world's seabed is being scraped 150 times faster than the world's forests are being clear-cut.

The limited selectivity of fishing gear results in millions of marine organisms being discarded for economic, legal, or personal reasons. These organisms are defined as **by-catch** and include fish, invertebrates, protected marine mammals, sea turtles, and sea birds. Depending on the gear and handling techniques, some or all of the discarded organisms die. A recent estimation of the worldwide by-catch is approximately 30 million tons per year, which is about one third of the estimated 85 million tons of catch that is retained each year.

The orange roughy is a large deep sea fish found in Atlantic and Pacific waters. It is very long lived and was severely overfished during the decades after its discovery in the 1970s. In particular, Australian stocks dropped to just 10% of the original population.

Tuna are particularly prized fish species for consumption. Catches have more than doubled in the last decade. However species such as the bluefin tuna are slow breeding and heavily overfished and it is likely just a matter of time before the fishery collapses.

Swordfish are found throughout the world's oceans. They are overfished in many areas. In the Mediterranean, swordfish numbers have declined by 70% since the mid 1980s. More than two thirds of the fish landed are juvenile, so little breeding stock is left.

1. Explain how overfishing causes fisheries to collapse: _____

_____

_____

LINK 190 LINK 188 WEB 189 KNOW

North Sea cod

The stock of North Sea cod (*Gadus morhua*) is one of the world's six large populations of this economically important species. As one of the most intensively studied, monitored, and exploited fish stocks in the North Sea, it is considered a highly relevant indicator of how well sustainable fisheries policies are operating. Currently juvenile catch rates are much higher than adult catch rates. Recent figures show approximately 54 thousand tonnes are caught annually, vastly less than the 350 000 tonnes caught in the early 1970s.

The state of the fishery

▶ Fishing mortality (the chance of a fish being caught) reached its maximum in 2000 and has reduced sharply since then. However it has been above the theoretical maximum mortality rate due to fishing (F_{MSY}) since at least the 1960s (right middle).

▶ Recruitment has been generally poor since 1987 (right bottom).

▶ The number of spawning adults has fallen to levels below those required to recruit new individuals into the stock (bottom right).

▶ ICES (the International Council for the Exploration of the Sea) advised that the spawning stock biomass (an indicator of the number of breeding adults) reached a new historic low in 2006 and that the risk of stock collapse is high.

What has been done?

▶ With the cod fishery at imminent collapse, measures were taken to try to save the fishery. Depending on the fishing gear being used, fishing vessels were restricted to between 9 and 25 days at sea per month.

▶ If stock levels do not rise on track with recovery plans, quotas and fishing days are automatically cut by 20% each year.

▶ ICES has recommended a zero catch limit until the stock reaches at least 70 000 tonnes.

▶ Net mesh sizes were increased to reduce juvenile mortality.

There has been staunch opposition by fishing companies to these measures. They argue that livelihoods will be affected and that stock has been recovering.

Throughout its range, cod has been heavily exploited. In Canada's Grand Banks, where *Gadus morhua* is known as Atlantic cod, the fishery was closed in 1992 after the stock biomass fell to 1% of its historic levels. Nearly 22 000 jobs were lost.

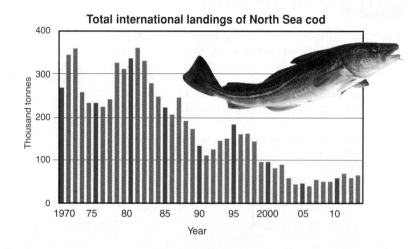

Total international landings of North Sea cod

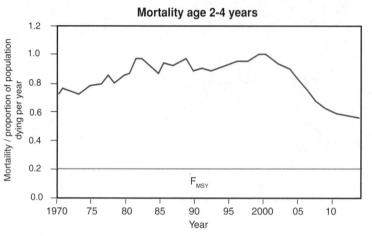

Mortality age 2-4 years

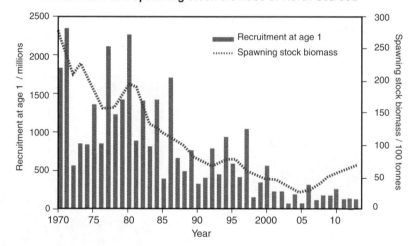

Recruitment and spawning stock biomass of North Sea cod

2. (a) Describe the trends in the North Sea cod fishery since 1970: _____

_____

_____

_____

_____

(b) The current recommended fisheries target for cod mortality is 0.4. Predict the effect of this on stock recovery:

_____

_____

_____

© 2017 **BIOZONE** International
ISBN: 978-1-927309-26-1
Photocopying Prohibited

190 Sustainable Fishing

Key Idea: Fisheries globally have a history of unsustainable stock management. The depletion of fish stocks has made it necessary to implement careful management strategies.

Fishing is an ancient human tradition. It provides food, and is economically, socially, and culturally important. Today, it is a worldwide resource extraction industry. Decades of overfishing in all of the world's oceans has pushed commercially important species (such as cod, right) into steep decline. According to the United Nation's Food and Agriculture Organisation (FAO) almost half the ocean's commercially targeted marine fish stocks are either heavily or over-exploited. Without drastic changes to the world's fishing operations, many fish stocks will soon be effectively lost.

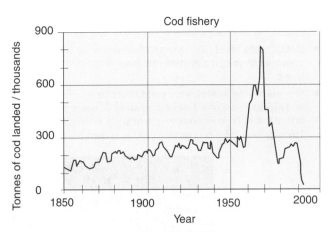

Cod fishery

Tonnes of cod landed / thousands vs *Year* (1850–2000)

Percentage of catch taken

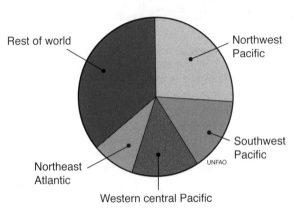

Rest of world, Northwest Pacific, Southwest Pacific, Western central Pacific, Northeast Atlantic

UNFAO

The single largest fishery is the Northwest Pacific, taking 26% of the total global catch.

Percentage exploitation of fisheries

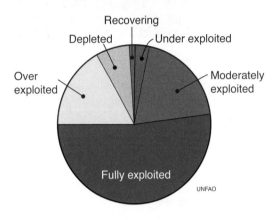

Recovering, Depleted, Under exploited, Over exploited, Moderately exploited, Fully exploited

UNFAO

52% of the world's fished species are already fully exploited. Any increase in catch from these species would result in over-exploitation. 7% of the fish species are already depleted and 17% are over-exploited.

NOAA

Part of the problem with fishing is by-catch, i.e. the fish that are not wanted. Even if thrown back, these fish or other marine organisms often don't survive. Techniques to reduce bycatch include changing hook design and attaching devices called pingers to the line or net that frighten away non-target organisms.

Peter Church

Different fish species are fished with different kinds of lines or nets. In particular, the mesh size of the net can be changed. This can be set so that small fish can swim through it and larger fish are caught. This can help to ensure that young fish survive to breeding age or that the wrong species of fish are not caught in the net.

Precision Seafood Harvesting

New types of net designs are constantly being tested. One of the newest net designs is called Precision Seafood Harvesting. It consists of a PVC liner towed by a trawler and forms a tunnel of water that reduces stress and damage to target fish, increasing catch efficiency. Holes allow unwanted fish to escape.

1. What percentage of fish stocks are depleted, overexploited, or fully exploited? _____

2. (a) What is bycatch? _____

_____

(b) Name two ways bycatch can be reduced: _____

_____

_____

LINK 189   LINK 187   WEB 190   KNOW

Calculating sustainable yields

▶ The sustainable harvesting of any food source requires that its rate of harvest is no more than its replacement rate. If the harvest rate is higher than the replacement rate then it follows that the food source will continually reduce at ever increasing percentages (assuming a constant harvest rate) and thus eventually be lost.

▶ **Sustainable yield** (SY) refers to the number or weight of fish that can be removed by fishing without reducing the stock biomass from year to year. It assumes that the environmental conditions remain the same and do not contribute to fluctuations in biomass levels.

▶ The **maximum sustainable yield** (MSY) is the maximum amount of fish that can be taken without affecting the stock biomass and replacement rate. Calculating an MSY relies on obtaining precise data about a population's age structure, size, and growth rate. If the MSY is incorrectly established, unsustainable quotas may be set, and the fish stock may become depleted. The equation for a sustainable yield is shown below:

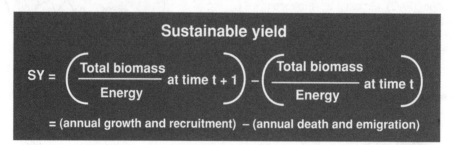

Sustainable yield

$$SY = \left(\frac{\text{Total biomass}}{\text{Energy}} \text{ at time } t+1 \right) - \left(\frac{\text{Total biomass}}{\text{Energy}} \text{ at time } t \right)$$

= (annual growth and recruitment) − (annual death and emigration)

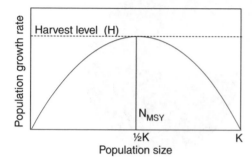

Harvest level (H)

N_{MSY}

½K   K

Population size

Population growth rate

▶ The theoretical maximum sustainable yield (N_{MSY}) occurs when a population is at half the carrying capacity (½K). At this point, the population growth rate will also be at its maximum.

▶ Under ideal conditions, harvesting at this rate (H) should be able to continue indefinitely. However, the growth rate of a population is likely to fluctuate from year to year.

▶ If a population has below-average growth for several years while the take remains the same, there is a high risk of population collapse because an ever-increasing proportion of the population will be taken with each harvest.

3. What is the maximum sustainable yield? _____

_____

_____

4. A fish population consists of about 3.5 million individuals. A study shows that about 1.8 million are of breeding age.

(a) Researchers want to know the maximum sustainable yield for the population so that it can be fished sustainably. What factors will they need to know to accurately determine the MSY?

_____

_____

_____

(b) Calculate the number of non-breeding individuals: _____

(c) Should these smaller non-breeding individuals be included in the catch? Explain your reasoning: _____

_____

_____

_____

(d) It is found that the larger a breeding individual is, the more fertile it is. What implications might this have on the harvesting method for these fish and the viability of the fishery?

_____

_____

_____

_____

Is fish farming a sustainable solution?

There is clear evidence that many of the world's most prized fisheries are being overfished. One of the solutions to reduce the number of wild fish caught while increasing the total number produced was to farm them. Aquaculture includes not just fish farming but the farming of any marine species, including mussels and prawns. It is a highly contentious issue, with arguments both for and against it (below).

Fish farming: A solution to the problem.

▶ Fish farming provides a way to produce fish and other marine products without the need to plunder wild populations. This is described for Atlantic salmon.

▶ Atlantic salmon have been so overfished that wild caught salmon is no longer a viable fishery. Instead, Atlantic salmon are farmed in large sea pens.

▶ Around 1.5 million tonnes of salmon are produced from farms a year, compared to less than three thousand tonnes caught in the wild. Returns like these from commercial fish farms help reduce the need to catch wild fish and so allow wild fish stocks to recover.

▶ Importantly, fish farming does not have to rely on specific locations. Atlantic salmon, native to the North Atlantic, are farmed in Chile, Canada, Norway, Russia, the UK, and Australia.

▶ Fish farming is highly efficient. In the wild, a salmon might need 10 kg of food for every 1 kg of body weight. Farmed fish require just 4 kg of food per kg of body weight. Much of this food includes fish meal.

▶ The increase in fish farming has not caused an increase in the catch of fish for fish meal. Instead, the fish meal required for fish farming has come from fish meal that was once fed to livestock such as pigs and poultry, which now use other feed types such as grain.

Fish farming: An unsustainable disaster.

▶ Most fish farming is carried out in sea cages rather than containment facilities. This means waste from the fish farm enters the local ecosystem directly.

▶ Fish in the pens can be subject to high stocking rates and thus produce a large and concentrated amount of waste, including faeces and food waste. In sites without adequate currents, these wastes can build up in the area and not only pollute the water but cause disease in the farmed fish and in local populations of marine animals.

▶ Disease can be a problem in such concentrated cages, quickly transferring between individuals. Various anti-fouling, antibacterial, and antiparasitic chemicals are used to reduce the incidence of disease.

▶ Escapes from the cages often occur, especially in high seas. If the fish being farmed are not native, they can compete with native fish. Because farmed fish have lower genetic diversity than wild fish, a large escape could decrease the overall genetic diversity of a wild population.

▶ Feeding the fish requires fish meal and fish oils. 50% of the world's fish oil production is fed to farmed fish.

▶ Most farmed fish are fed fish meal and a large percentage of the commercial catch is dedicated to catching small open-ocean fish such as anchovies specifically for fish meal.

5. Using an example, explain why a catch over the **maximum sustainable yield** will result in the collapse of a fishery:

_____

_____

_____

6. Use the graph showing the relationship between age, biomass, and stock numbers in a hypothetical commercially harvested fish population (below, right) to answer the following questions:

(a) What is the optimum age for harvest?

_____

(b) During which age range does the greatest increase in biomass occur?

_____

(c) What other life history data would be required by fisheries scientists when deciding on the management plan for this population?

_____

_____

_____

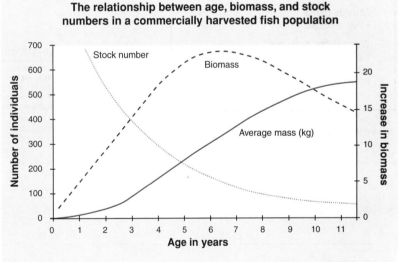

The relationship between age, biomass, and stock numbers in a commercially harvested fish population

7. Use the articles above and your own research to evaluate fish farming as a solution to overfishing. Write a short answer to the question "Can fish farming stop overfishing and produce a sustainable resource?" Include reasons and evidence to justify your answer. Staple any extra paper you have used to formulate your arguments to this page:

_____

_____

_____

191 The Greenhouse Effect

Key Idea: The greenhouse effect is the natural effect of having an atmosphere that retains heat received from the Sun. The Earth's atmosphere comprises a mix of gases including nitrogen, oxygen, and water vapour. Small quantities of carbon dioxide and methane are also present. These gases are called **greenhouse gases**. A natural process called the **greenhouse effect** describes how the atmosphere lets in sunlight, but traps the heat that would normally radiate back into space. This natural process results in the Earth having a mean surface temperature of about 15°C (33°C warmer than it would have without an atmosphere). Water vapour contributes the largest greenhouse effect, followed by CO_2. Methane has less effect as it is not as abundant in the atmosphere. Water is often ignored as a greenhouse gas because the amount in the atmosphere is related to temperature and therefore to the effect of other greenhouse gases. It is also subject to a positive feedback loop. More water vapour causes temperatures to increase and produce more water vapour. It is likely that the amount of human generated water vapour has not increased as much as other human-generated greenhouse gases.

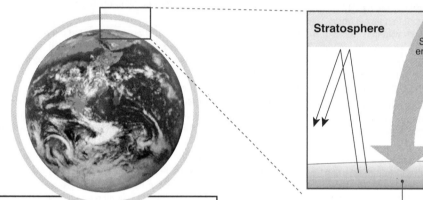

Solar energy is absorbed as heat by Earth, where it is radiated back into the atmosphere

Most heat is absorbed by CO_2 in the troposphere and radiated back to Earth

Sources of 'greenhouse gases'

Carbon dioxide
• Exhaust from cars
• Combustion of coal, wood, oil
• Burning rainforests

Methane
• Plant debris and growing vegetation
• Belching and flatus of cows

Chloro-fluoro-carbons (CFCs)
• Leaking coolant from refrigerators
• Leaking coolant from air conditioners

Nitrous oxide
• Car exhaust

Tropospheric ozone*
• Triggered by car exhaust (smog)

*Tropospheric ozone is found in the lower atmosphere (not to be confused with ozone in the stratosphere)

Greenhouse gas (excluding water vapour)	Tropospheric conc.		Global warming potential (compared to CO_2)¶	Atmospheric lifetime (years)§
	Pre-industrial 1750	Present day (2012*)		
Carbon dioxide	280 ppm	395.4 ppm	1	120
Methane	700 ppb	1796 ppb	25	12
Nitrous oxide	270 ppb	324 ppb	310	120
CFCs	0 ppb	0.39 ppbb	4000+	50-100
HFCs‡	0 ppb	0.045 ppb	1430	14
Tropospheric ozone	25 ppb	34 ppb	17	hours

ppm = parts per million; **ppb** = parts per billion; ‡Hydrofluorcarbons were introduced in the last decade to replace CFCs as refrigerants; * Data from 2012-2013. ¶ Figures contrast the radiative effect of different greenhouse gases relative to CO_2 over 100 years, e.g. over 100 years, methane is 25 times more potent as a greenhouse gas than CO_2 § How long the gas persists in the atmosphere. *Data compiled from the Carbon dioxide Information Centre http://cdiac.ornl.gov/pns/current_ghg.html*

1. What is a greenhouse gas? _____

_____

_____

2. What is the greenhouse effect? _____

_____

_____

3. Calculate the increase (as a %) in the 'greenhouse gases' between the pre-industrial era and the 2012 measurements using the data from the table above. **HINT**: The calculation for carbon dioxide is: (395.4 - 280) ÷ 280 x 100 =

   (a) Carbon dioxide: _____   (b) Methane: _____   (c) Nitrous oxide: _____

4. Why is the effect of water vapour often not included in greenhouse gas tables? _____

_____

_____

192 Climate Change

Key Idea: Global warming refers to the continuing rise in the average temperature of the Earth's surface.

Since the mid 20th century, the Earth's surface temperature has been steadily increasing. The consensus scientific view (97% of publishing climate scientists) is that this phenomenon, called **global warming**, is attributable to the increase in atmospheric levels of CO_2 and other greenhouse gases emitted as a result of human activity.

Changes in near-surface temperature

This graph right shows how the mean temperature for each year from 1860-2010 (bars) compares with the average temperature between 1961 and 1990. The blue line represents the fitted curve and shows the general trend indicated by the annual data.

Most anomalies since 1977 have been above normal and warmer than the long term mean, indicating that global temperatures are tracking upwards. The last ten years have been some of the warmest on record.

Source: Hadley Centre for Prediction and Research

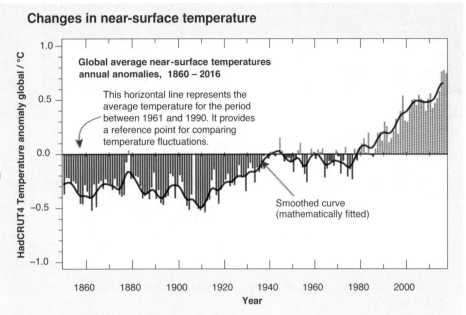

Global average near-surface temperatures annual anomalies, 1860 – 2016

This horizontal line represents the average temperature for the period between 1961 and 1990. It provides a reference point for comparing temperature fluctuations.

Smoothed curve (mathematically fitted)

Changes in atmospheric CO_2

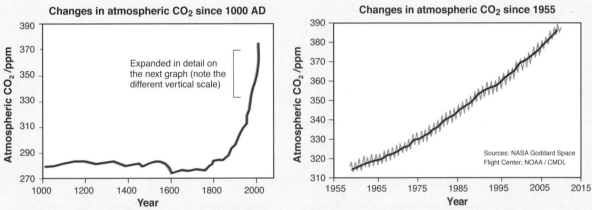

Changes in atmospheric CO_2 since 1000 AD

Expanded in detail on the next graph (note the different vertical scale)

Changes in atmospheric CO_2 since 1955

Sources: NASA Goddard Space Flight Center; NOAA / CMDL

Atmospheric CO_2 has been rapidly increasing since the 1800s. In 2012, the world emitted a record (till then) 34.5 billion tonnes of CO_2 from fossil fuels. In total, humans have emitted 545 billion tonnes of CO_2. CO_2 levels fluctuate seasonally, especially in the northern hemisphere because of its much larger landmass and forests.

During the Industrial Revolution (1760-1840), coal was burned in huge quantities to power machinery. The increase in CO_2 released is attributed to an increase in average global temperatures. The combustion of fossil fuels (coal, oil, and natural gas) continues to pump CO_2 into the atmosphere and contribute to the current global warming.

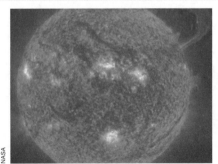

The Earth receives energy from the Sun (above) as UV, visible, and near-infrared radiation. Some is absorbed by the Earth's surface and the rest is reflected away as long-wavelength thermal radiation (heat). Much of this is trapped by the greenhouse gases and directed back to Earth, further increasing the mean surface temperature.

The oceans act as a carbon sink, absorbing the CO_2 produced from burning fossil fuels. The CO_2 reacts in the water, forming carbonic acid, lowering ocean pH, and reducing the availability of carbonate ions. This makes it harder for corals (above) to build their calcium carbonate exoskeletons and is causing significant coral reef damage.

LINK 194 LINK 191 WEB 192 KNOW

Confusing the debate

Media coverage

Global warming is a complex issue and most people obtain their information from the popular media. Despite the scientific consensus on the role of human activity in global warming, some media sources still provide biased or inaccurate information. In order to make an informed decision, people must read or listen to a wide range of media, or read scientific documents and make their own decision.

Lobby groups

Lobby groups with specific interests strive constantly to influence policy makers. Reducing CO_2 emissions by restricting coal and oil use will help reduce global warming. However, fossil fuel consumption generates billions of dollars of revenue for coal and oil companies, so they lobby against legislation that penalises fossil fuel use. If successful, lobbying could result in less effective climate change policies.

Controversy

All scientific bodies of international standing agree that human activity has contributed disproportionately to global warming. However, there are still some in the political, scientific, and commercial community who claim that global warming is not occurring. These people often command media attention and engage a poorly informed public audience, who are often suspicious of the scientific community.

1. Explain the relationship between the rise in concentrations of atmospheric CO_2, methane, and oxides of nitrogen, and global warming:

_____

_____

_____

_____

_____

2. (a) What effect did the Industrial Revolution have on atmospheric CO_2 levels? _____

(b) Explain why this occurred: _____

_____

_____

3. Explain why models of climate change are constantly revised: _____

_____

_____

_____

4. Evaluate claims by climate change sceptics that human activities are not causing climate change. Summarise your arguments below:

_____

_____

_____

_____

_____

_____

_____

© 2017 **BIOZONE** International
ISBN: 978-1-927309-26-1
Photocopying Prohibited

193 The History of Climate Modelling

Key Idea: Climate models have become more complicated and sophisticated over time, allowing scientists to better predict climate change.

Climate models have been in use since the 1950s, but these very early versions really only modeled the weather in a particular region. The sophistication and accuracy of climate models has increased over time (below). This is because

our knowledge about factors contributing to climate has increased and also because developments in computing and mathematics have allowed the more accurate prediction of more complicated scenarios. In 1988, the Intergovernmental Panel on Climate Change (IPCC) was established. Its role is to analyse published climate data and inform the international community about their findings.

Climate models have become more sophisticated over time

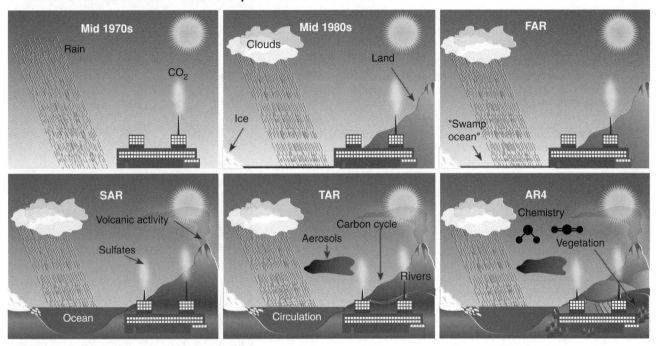

▶ The diagrams above show how the sophistication of climate models has changed over time. Note how the complexity has increased as more elements are incorporated into the models. Early models in the 1970s were very simple and factored in only a few components (incoming sunlight, rainfall, and CO_2 concentration).

▶ By the 1980s, the models were becoming more complex and other features were added such as clouds, land surface features, and ice. After the establishment of the IPCC, several climate models were developed in relatively quick succession.

▶ The First Assessment Report (FAR) in the early 1990s, the Second Assessment Report (SAR) in 1995, the Third Assessment Report (TAR) in 2001, and the Fourth Assessment Report (AR4) in 2007. FAR included the ocean's effect for the first time, and subsequent models became more sophisticated, including adding the effect of atmospheric constituents such as sulfates and aerosols, the role of the carbon cycle, atmospheric chemistry, and vegetation.

How are climate models tested?

To see how well models work, scientists enter past data and see how accurately they predict the climate changes that have already occurred. If the models recreate historical trends accurately, we can have confidence that they will also accurately predict future trends in climate change.

The graph on the right shows an example of how climate models are tested. The grey band represents data from 14 models and 58 different simulations. The black line represents the average of all 58 simulations. The gray line represents the average actual (observed) data for the same period. The gray vertical lines represent large volcanic eruptions during the period.

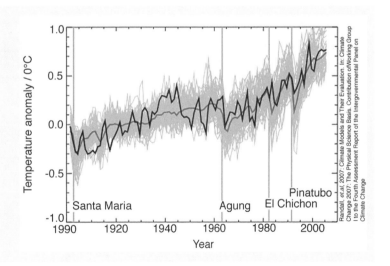

1. When were the effects of the ocean first included in climate models? _____

2. What effect do eruptions have on the observed temperatures? _____

_____

LINK 194 LINK 192 WEB 193 **KNOW**

What should a climate model include?

Climate models predict climate change more accurately when the model incorporates all the factors contributing to climate change. Some components influencing climate (e.g. the ocean and atmosphere) have their own models to better understand how the individual components can be influenced. Data from these separate models can provide more detailed information about the climate model as a whole. As we have already seen, climate models have become more complicated over time. Most now incorporate the following components:

Sea ice

- **Atmosphere**: This includes cloud cover, air pressure, water vapor, and gas concentrations.

- **Oceans**: Oceans have a key role in climate regulation. They help to buffer (neutralize) the effects of increasing levels of greenhouse gases in the atmosphere by acting as a carbon sink. They also act as a heat store, preventing rapid rises in global atmospheric temperature.

- **Ice sheets and sea ice (the cryosphere)**: These factors influence how much of the Sun's heat is reflected or retained. Increased ice levels reflect more heat away from Earth. Less ice allows more heat to be retained.

Carbon emissions

- **Biogeochemical cycles**: Levels of some atmospheric compounds can greatly influence climate change. Carbon is the most significant, but others such as nitrogen, phosphorus, and sulfur can also influence climate.

- **Biosphere**: The level of plant cover on Earth has a significant impact on the amount of carbon in the atmosphere. During photosynthesis, plants utilize carbon dioxide from the atmosphere to produce carbohydrates, effectively removing a major greenhouse gas from the atmosphere.

- **Human activity**: Human activity has increased the rate of global warming, especially through the actions of deforestation and carbon emissions into the atmosphere. The addition of greenhouse gases into the atmosphere through human activity is driving current climate change.

Deforestation

- **External influences**: These include energy variations from the Sun (e.g. through sunspot cycles) and levels of carbon dioxide and other aerosols released during volcanic eruptions.

3. (a) How has the complexity of climate models changed over time? _____

_____

_____

(b) What has been the significance of this? _____

_____

_____

4. (a) How do scientists check the accuracy of their models? _____

_____

(b) Why is it important that they do this? _____

_____

_____

(c) Study the testing results on the previous page. Do you think the average data from the models accurately reflects the historical data? Why or why not?

_____

_____

_____

5. (a) Working in pairs or small groups, select one component of a climate model and research its significance to climate change. Summarise your findings and report back to the class.

(b) Once all the presentations have been made, determine if any factor(s) has a larger influence than another.

© 2017 **BIOZONE** International
ISBN: 978-1-927309-26-1
Photocopying Prohibited

194 Models of Climate Change

Key Idea: Climate change models provide best-case and worst-case scenarios. The models can be used to predict the likely effects on Earth's systems.

There are elements of uncertainty even in well tested models. The major source of uncertainty is human activity and, in particular, how much the consumption of fossil fuels will

change in the future. The level of greenhouse gases in the atmosphere will have a significant impact on future climate change. The IPCC often run a number of different scenarios to predict climate change. Between them, the results provide best-case and worst-case scenarios.

Using climate models to predict change

▶ The major scenarios are presented below, but there are subcategories (e.g. A1B) to help make them more accurate:

- **A1** assumes rapid economic and technological growth, a low rate of population growth, and a very high level of energy use. Differences between "rich" and "poor" countries narrow.

- **A2** assumes high population growth, slower technological change and economic growth, and a larger difference between countries and regions than in other scenarios. Energy use is high.

- **B1** assumes a high level of environmental and social consciousness and sustainable development. There is low population growth, high economic and technological advancement, and low energy use. The area devoted to agriculture decreases and reforestation increases.

- **B2** has similar assumptions to B1. However, there are more disparities between industrialised and developing nations, technological and economic growth is slower than in B1, and population growth is greater (but less than A2). Energy use is midway between B1 and A2. Changes in land use are less dramatic than in B1.

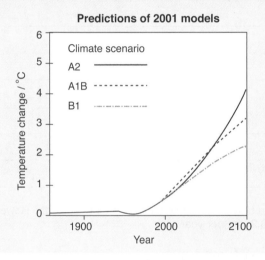

Predictions of 2001 models

Climate scenario
A2
A1B
B1

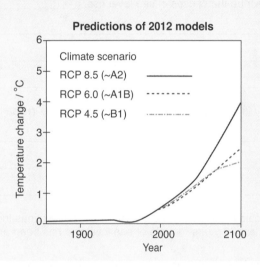

Predictions of 2012 models

Climate scenario
RCP 8.5 (~A2)
RCP 6.0 (~A1B)
RCP 4.5 (~B1)

1. Why do scientists simulate a number of different scenarios when they run a climate model? _____

_____

_____

2. Study the 2001 and 2012 models of climate change predictions (above).

(a) In the 2001 model, identify which scenario was predicted to produce the highest temperature change by 2100:

_____

(b) What factors are likely to contribute to this? _____

_____

(c) Why would scenario B1 produce the lowest temperature increase? _____

_____

_____

(d) How do the predictions between the 2001 and 2012 models differ? _____

_____

_____

_____

LINK   WEB
193   194

KNOW

What causes sea level rise?

The increase in global temperature is linked to a rise in global sea level. Sea level rise occurs because of two main factors, thermal expansion and melting ice. When water heats up it expands and takes up more space. Around 24 million km³ of water is stored in permanent snow, glaciers, and ice caps. When these melt, they add to the volume of water in the oceans. Sea level rise will not only affect people living in coastal communities, but also Earth's systems. Many models have been developed to predict sea level rise under different scenarios in order to determine its effect.

What effect will sea level rise have in the US and UK?

In 2010, around 39% of the US population (around 123 million people) lived in counties directly on the shoreline. This population is expected to increase by 8% by 2020. Rising sea levels therefore represent a significant hazard to the US. Large cities such as New York (right) are in danger of becoming inundated (flooded) as sea levels rise. Other large cities, such as San Francisco and Los Angeles, are at sea level, or close to it. In New York, a sea level rise of only a few metres would inundate thousands of hectares of highly developed land. Airports, ports, railroads, housing developments, highways, factories and industry would be damaged. In the UK, London would be the worst affected city, with inundation north and south of the Thames. Coastal areas in the south and east of England would also be inundated.

NASA

3. (a) Describe the causes of sea level rise: _____

_____

_____

_____

   (b) Why is the US particularly vulnerable to a rise in sea level? _____

_____

_____

_____

4. Some calculations estimate global mean sea level has increased between 10-20 cm over the last 100 years. However, for the last 20 years the rate of sea level rise has been around 3.2 mm per year.

   (a) Calculate the average rate of sea level change per year for the last 100 years: _____

   (b) How does this compare to the mean sea level change over the last 20 years: _____

_____

_____

   (c) What factor could be contributing to the change observed in 4(b)? _____

   _____

   _____

5. (a) Study the graph on the right. What does it show?

   _____

   _____

   _____

   _____

   (b) What is the worst case scenario? _____

   _____

   (c) What is the best case scenario? _____

   _____

Predicted global sea level rise under a number of scenarios

Global sea level rise (cm above 1992) — Year axis from 1900 to 2100. Observed (to ~2005) and Scenarios (after). Y-axis values: -40, 0, 40, 80, 120, 160, 200.

Global Sea Level Rise Scenarios for the United States National Climate Assessment. NOAA (2012)

195 Climate Change and Effects on Biodiversity

Key Idea: Climate change is causing shifts in the distribution, behaviour, and even viability of plant and animal species.
A warming climate is changing the habitats of organisms and this may have profound effects on the biodiversity of specific regions as well as on the planet overall. As temperatures rise, organisms may be forced to move to areas better suited to their temperature tolerances. Those that cannot move or tolerate the temperature change may face extinction. Changes in precipitation as a result of climate change will also affect where organisms can live. Long term changes in climate will ultimately result in a shift in vegetation zones as some habitats contract and others expand.

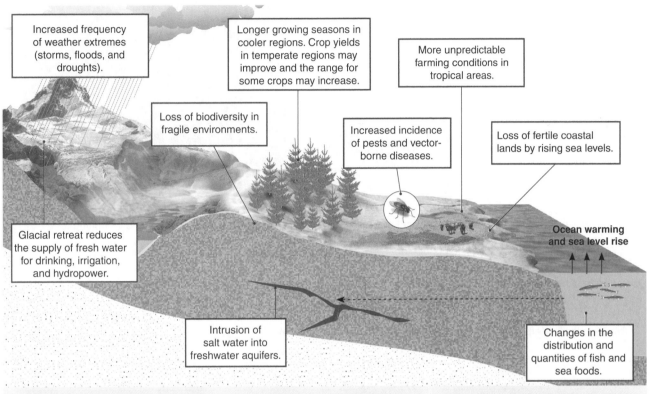

Increased frequency of weather extremes (storms, floods, and droughts).

Longer growing seasons in cooler regions. Crop yields in temperate regions may improve and the range for some crops may increase.

More unpredictable farming conditions in tropical areas.

Loss of biodiversity in fragile environments.

Increased incidence of pests and vector-borne diseases.

Loss of fertile coastal lands by rising sea levels.

Glacial retreat reduces the supply of fresh water for drinking, irrigation, and hydropower.

Ocean warming and sea level rise

Intrusion of salt water into freshwater aquifers.

Changes in the distribution and quantities of fish and sea foods.

Studies of forests in the United States have shown that although there will be increases and decreases in the distribution ranges of various tree species, overall there will be an 11% decrease in forest cover, with an increase in savanna and arid woodland. Communities of oak/pine and oak/hickory are predicted to increase in range while spruce/fir and maple/beech/birch communities will decrease.

Photo: Walter Siegmund

Studies of the distributions of butterfly species in many countries show their populations are shifting. Surveys of Edith's checkerspot butterfly (*Euphydryas editha*) in western North America have shown it to be moving north and to higher altitudes.

An Australian study in 2004 found the centre of distribution for the AdhS gene in *Drosophila*, which helps survival in hot and dry conditions, had shifted 400 kilometers south in the last twenty years.

Sex ratios of reptiles are affected by the temperature. In turtles males are produced at low incubation temperatures with females being produced at higher temperatures. Any rises in global temperatures could significantly affect these reptile populations.

A 2009 study of 200 million year old plant fossils from Greenland provided evidence that a sudden collapse in biodiversity was correlated with, and appeared to be caused by, a very slight rise in CO_2 levels.

LINK 198   LINK 192   WEB 195   KNOW

Effects of increases in temperature on animal populations

Change in centre of abundance in 305 widespread North American birds

Distance moved north (km)

72
64
56
48
40
32
24
16
8
0
-8

1969/70 1973/74 1977/78 1981/82 1985/86 1989/90 1993/94 1997/98 2001/02 2005/06

Source: Birds and climate change, Aububon Society 2009

Animals living at altitude are also affected by warming climates and are being forced to shift their normal range. As temperatures increase, the snow line increases in altitude pushing alpine animals to higher altitudes. In some areas of North America this has resulted in the local extinction of the North American pika (*Ochotona princeps*).

Wiki Commons

A number of studies indicate that animals are beginning to be affected by increases in global temperatures. Data sets from around the world show that birds are migrating up to two weeks earlier to summer feeding grounds and are often not migrating as far south in winter.

1. Global warming is likely to affect the physical environment as well as both the plants and animals inhabiting it:

   (a) Describe some of the likely effects of global warming on physical aspects of the environment: _____

   _____

   _____

   (b) Describe the effects that global warming may have on plant crops: _____

   _____

   _____

   (c) Suggest how farmers might be able to adjust to these changes: _____

   _____

   _____

   (d) Describe how increases in global temperatures have affected some migratory birds: _____

   _____

   (e) Explain how these changes in migratory patterns might affect food availability for these populations:_____

   _____

   _____

   (f) Explain how global warming could lead to the local extinction of some alpine species: _____

   _____

   _____

   _____

2. Discuss the historical evidence that insect populations are affected by global temperature: _____

   _____

   _____

   _____

   _____

196 Climate Change and Agriculture

Key Idea: Climate change may alter the types of crops that can be grown and where they can be grown.

The global impacts of climate change on agriculture and horticulture will vary depending on location. In some regions, temperature changes will increase the growing season for existing crops, or enable a wider variety of crops to be grown. Changes in temperature or precipitation patterns may benefit some crops, but have negative effects on others. Increasing atmospheric CO_2 levels will enhance the growth of some crops (e.g. wheat, rice, and soybeans).

Effects of increases in temperature on crop yields

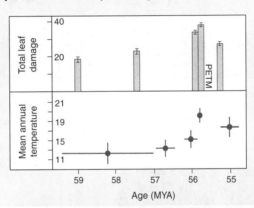

Studies on the grain production of rice have shown that maximum daytime temperatures have little effect on crop yield. However minimum night time temperatures lower crop yield by as much as 5% for every 0.5°C increase in temperature.

Possible effects of increases in temperature on crop damage

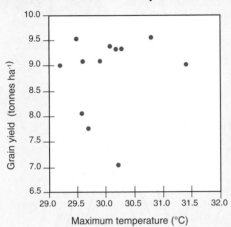

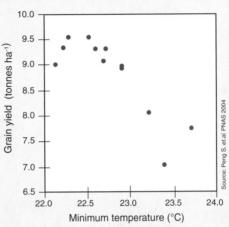

The fossil record shows that global temperatures rose sharply around 56 million years ago. Studies of fossil leaves with insect browse damage indicate that leaf damage peaked at the same time as the Paleocene Eocene Thermal Maximum (PETM). This gives some historical evidence that as temperatures increase, plant damage caused by insects also rises. This could have implications for agricultural crops.

Growing regions for crops currently produced in middle latitudes will likely shift towards the poles as temperatures increase.

Grain crops (such as wheat, above)are at higher risk of crop failures if precipitation decreases.

Corn rootworm beetle

Milder winters and longer growing seasons may see the distribution of agricultural pest species spread.

1. Why will a warming climate benefit some agricultural crops, while disadvantaging others? _____

_____

_____

_____

2. Explain how climate change can influence the distribution of pest species, and in turn affect agriculture: _____

_____

_____

LINK 198   LINK 192   WEB 196

KNOW

197 Climate Change and Effects on the Arctic

Key Idea: Higher average temperatures melt sea-ice. Less heat is reflected back to space, warming sea temperature and promoting further melting of the ice.

The surface temperature of the Earth is in part regulated by the amount of ice on its surface, which reflects a large amount of heat into space. However, the area and thickness of the polar sea-ice has almost halved since 1980. This melting of sea-ice can trigger a cycle where less heat is reflected into space during summer, warming seawater and reducing the area and thickness of ice forming in the winter.

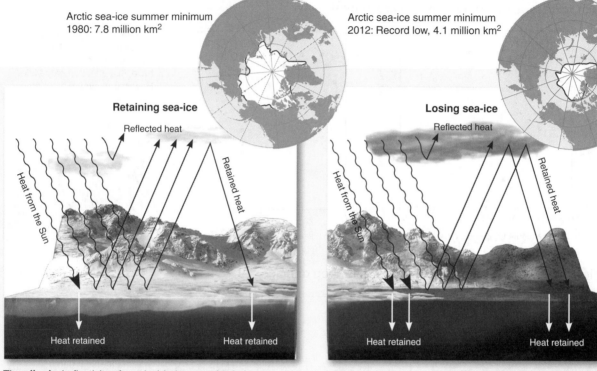

Arctic sea-ice summer minimum
1980: 7.8 million km²

Retaining sea-ice

Reflected heat

Heat from the Sun

Retained heat

Heat retained

Heat retained

Arctic sea-ice summer minimum
2012: Record low, 4.1 million km²

Losing sea-ice

Reflected heat

Heat from the Sun

Retained heat

Heat retained

Heat retained

The **albedo** (reflectivity of sea-ice) helps to maintain its presence. Thin sea-ice has a lower albedo than thick sea-ice. More heat is reflected when sea-ice is thick and covers a greater area. This helps to regulate the temperature of the sea, keeping it cool.

As sea-ice retreats, more non-reflective surface is exposed. Heat is retained instead of being reflected, warming both the air and water and causing sea-ice to form later in the autumn than usual. Thinner and less reflective ice forms and perpetuates the cycle.

The temperature in the Arctic has been above average every year since 1988. Coupled with the reduction in summer sea-ice, this is having dire effects on Arctic wildlife such as polar bears, which hunt out on the ice. The reduction in sea-ice reduces their hunting range and forces them to swim longer distances to firm ice. Studies have already shown an increase in drowning deaths of polar bears.

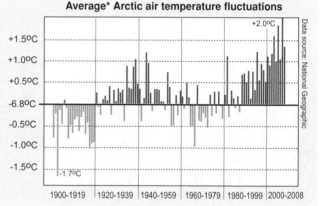

Average* Arctic air temperature fluctuations

Data source: National Geographic

+2.0°C

+1.5°C
+1.0°C
+0.5°C
-6.8°C
-0.5°C
-1.0°C
-1.5°C
-1.7°C

1900-1919 | 1920-1939 | 1940-1959 | 1960-1979 | 1980-1999 | 2000-2008

*Figure shows deviation from the average annual surface air temperature over land. Average calculated on the years 1961-2000.

1. Explain how low sea-ice albedo and volume affects the next year's sea-ice cover: _____

_____

_____

2. Discuss the effects of decreasing summer sea-ice on polar wildlife: _____

_____

_____

_____

198 Temperature and the Distribution of Species

Key Idea: Global warming will have important implications for the development, distribution, and survival of many species. Similar species avoid competition by breeding at different times and under different conditions. Temperature shifts may force similar species into competition within overlapping ranges. Many habitats will change in a warmer climate. Climatic zones will shift and some species will need to relocate or adapt to the new conditions in order to survive.

Distribution and breeding of leopard frogs in North America

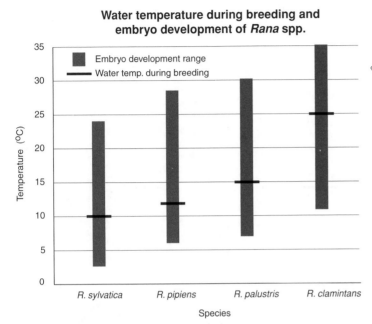

Water temperature during breeding and embryo development of *Rana* spp.

- Embryo development range
- Water temp. during breeding

Species: R. sylvatica, R. pipiens, R. palustris, R. clamintans

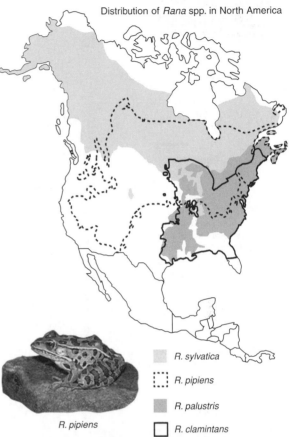

Distribution of *Rana* spp. in North America

The frog genus *Rana* is relatively common and widely distributed in North America (top right). The graph above shows the preferred water temperature for breeding in four common species of *Rana*, as well as the temperature tolerance range for embryonic development. Outside these ranges, embryonic development rate decreases or the embryos die. Increases in temperature could reduce the available breeding habitat for some species (e.g. *Rana sylvatica* requires low temperature to breed). Another likely outcome would be a change to the timing of breeding or a shift in the distribution patterns of populations.

R. pipiens

- R. sylvatica
- R. pipiens
- R. palustris
- R. clamintans

The spread of a pathogenic fungal species *Batrachochytrium dendrobatidis* has been linked with global warming and the extinction of the golden toad *Bufo periglenes*.

Dragonflies thrive in warm temperatures. Studies of UK dragonfly populations have found that since 1980, 34 of the 37 species have expanded their range northwards.

Between 1931 and 1996, shoreline ocean temperatures along the Californian coast increased by 0.79°C. Populations of invertebrates including sea stars, limpets and snails moved northward in their distributions.

1. Discuss the potential effects of a rise in global temperature on the North American distribution of the frog genus *Rana*:

2. Discuss how an increase in gobal temperature affects species distribution:

KNOW

199 Ocean Acidification

Key Idea: Carbon dioxide reacts with water to reduce its pH. The oceans act as a carbon sink, absorbing much of the CO_2 produced from burning fossil fuels. When CO_2 reacts with water it forms carbonic acid, which decreases the pH of the oceans. This could have major effects on marine life, especially shell making organisms. Ocean acidification is relative term, referring to the oceans becoming less basic as the pH decreases. Ocean pH is still above pH 7.0

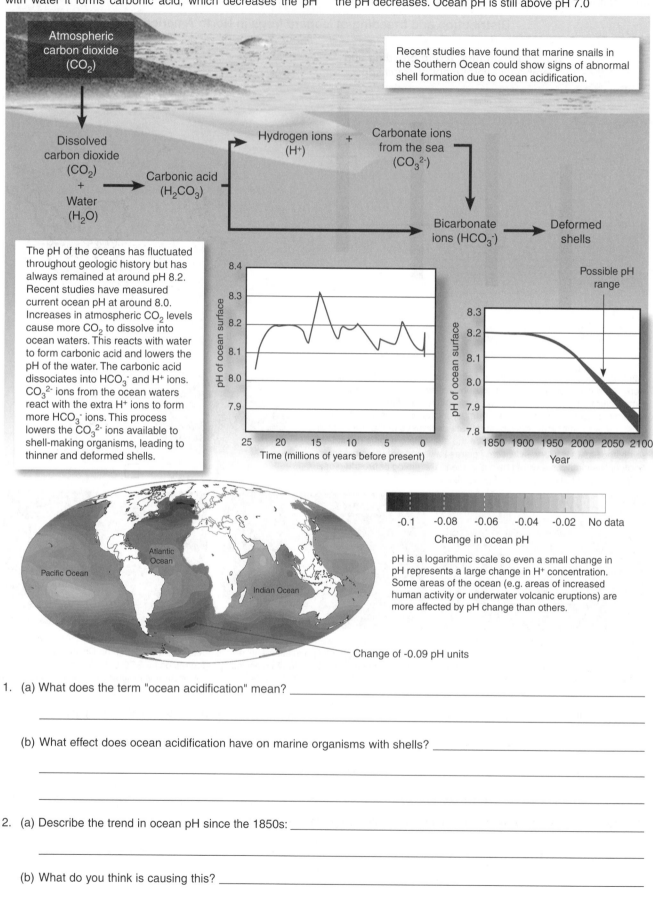

Atmospheric carbon dioxide (CO_2)

Recent studies have found that marine snails in the Southern Ocean could show signs of abnormal shell formation due to ocean acidification.

Dissolved carbon dioxide (CO_2) + Water (H_2O) → Carbonic acid (H_2CO_3) → Hydrogen ions (H^+) + Carbonate ions from the sea (CO_3^{2-})

Bicarbonate ions (HCO_3^-) → Deformed shells

The pH of the oceans has fluctuated throughout geologic history but has always remained at around pH 8.2. Recent studies have measured current ocean pH at around 8.0. Increases in atmospheric CO_2 levels cause more CO_2 to dissolve into ocean waters. This reacts with water to form carbonic acid and lowers the pH of the water. The carbonic acid dissociates into HCO_3^- and H^+ ions. CO_3^{2-} ions from the ocean waters react with the extra H^+ ions to form more HCO_3^- ions. This process lowers the CO_3^{2-} ions available to shell-making organisms, leading to thinner and deformed shells.

pH of ocean surface — Time (millions of years before present)

Possible pH range

pH of ocean surface — Year

Change in ocean pH: -0.1 -0.08 -0.06 -0.04 -0.02 No data

pH is a logarithmic scale so even a small change in pH represents a large change in H^+ concentration. Some areas of the ocean (e.g. areas of increased human activity or underwater volcanic eruptions) are more affected by pH change than others.

Atlantic Ocean
Pacific Ocean
Indian Ocean
Change of -0.09 pH units

1. (a) What does the term "ocean acidification" mean? _____

_____

(b) What effect does ocean acidification have on marine organisms with shells? _____

_____

_____

2. (a) Describe the trend in ocean pH since the 1850s: _____

_____

(b) What do you think is causing this? _____

_____

200 Technological Solutions to Climate Change

Key Idea: New technologies are aiming to reduce carbon dioxide emissions and so help slow climate change.

Burning fossil fuels in power stations for electricity accounts for about 40% of global carbon dioxide emissions. The transport industry accounts for at least another 30%. Even power stations using high quality coal and oil release huge volumes of CO_2. Systems that capture the CO_2 produced so that it can be stored or used for other purposes are beginning address this problem (below). Another important source of CO_2 emissions is often overlooked, probably because it is so common we don't stop to consider its effects. The manufacture of cement and concrete account for 5-10% of all CO_2 emissions. New types of cement and techniques for manufacture are aiming to reduce this amount.

Schematics of possible carbon capture systems

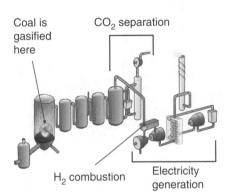
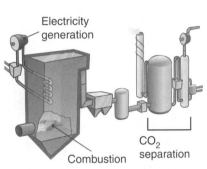
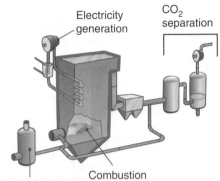

Pre-combustion capture: The coal is converted to CO_2 and H_2 using a gasification process. The CO_2 is recovered while the H_2 gas is combusted.

Post combustion capture: CO_2 is washed from the flue gas after combustion. It is then passed to a desorber to re-gasify the CO_2, where it is then compressed for storage.

Oxyfuel combustion: Concentrated O_2 is used in the furnace, producing only CO_2 gas in the flue gas. This is then compressed for storage. Compressed CO_2 is useful as a inexpensive, nonflammable pressurized gas, e.g. for inflation and for carbonated water.

Storing captured CO_2

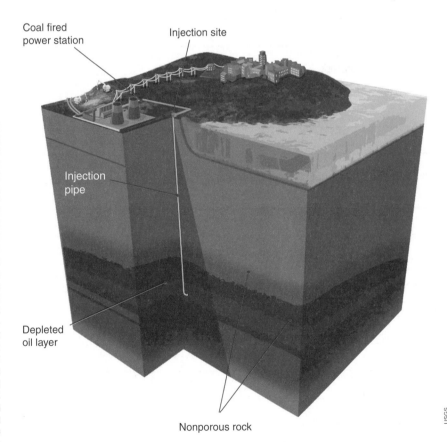

CO_2 can be stored by injecting it into depleted oil wells or other deep geological formations, releasing it into deep ocean waters, or reacting it with minerals to form solid carbonates. The CO_2 can also be used as a starting point for the production of synthetic fuels.

Deep ocean storage of CO_2 risks lowering ocean pH, and storing CO_2 in geological formations risks sudden release of large quantities of CO_2 if the rock proves unstable. The sudden release of CO_2 can kill animal life in the area (above).

Captured CO_2 can be injected into porous strata between nonporous layers. Power stations near to injection sites can pipe the recovered CO_2 to the injected well. Other stations will need to transport the CO_2 to the site. The transportation of the CO_2 will produce less CO_2 than is captured by the power station, making the option viable.

Lowering emissions in the cement industry

▶ Cement and concrete (the final cured product of cement mixed with water and gravel) are essential to the building industry and the global economy. 4.1 billion tonnes of cement were produced in 2015. This is expected to increase to 4.8 billion tonnes by 2030. This is important to the global climate because producing one tonne of cement also produces about one tonne of CO_2 (and uses the equivalent of 200 kg of coal).

▶ The most common cement used is called Portland cement, which is very strong when set. Its manufacture is highly energy intensive. 40% of the CO_2 emissions come from the burning of fossil fuels to heat limestone ($CaCO_3$) and other minerals to around 1400 °C. At this temperature, the limestone degrades and releases CO_2. This step accounts for about 50% of the CO_2 emissions. Portland cement reabsorbs about half of this CO_2 as it hardens and over the life time of the cement.

▶ Reducing the CO_2 emissions for cement manufacture can be done at three steps in the process: Reducing the amount of fossil fuels needed to heat the raw materials, reducing the amount of CO_2 released by the raw materials, and increasing the amount of CO_2 absorbed when setting.

▶ New types of cement using magnesium silicates instead of limestone are under trial. These do not need to be heated to such high temperatures and also release no CO_2 when heated. This leads to total CO_2 emissions of up to 0.5 tonnes of CO_2 per tonne of cement produced (half that of Portland cement). Additionally, during setting, CO_2 is absorbed at a greater rate than in traditional cement (about 1.1 tonnes per tonne of cement produced). This type of cement is often called carbon negative cement as it actually absorbs more CO_2 than is produced in its manufacture (about 0.6 tonnes of CO_2 absorbed for every tonne of cement produced).

1. Describe the differences and similarities in the three types of carbon dioxide capture systems:

_____

_____

_____

_____

_____

_____

2. Describe how captured carbon dioxide might be used or stored: _____

_____

_____

_____

3. Discuss some of the potential problems with capturing and storing carbon dioxide: _____

_____

_____

_____

4. (a) Approximately how many tonnes of CO_2 were produced by the cement industry in 2015? _____

(b) Where is this CO_2 produced in the manufacture of cement? _____

_____

_____

(c) Explain why carbon negative cement is carbon negative: _____

_____

_____

(d) Based on the 2015 figures, how much carbon would carbon negative cement absorb?

_____

© 2017 **BIOZONE** International
ISBN: 978-1-927309-26-1
Photocopying Prohibited

201 Supporting Conservation Through Legislation

Key Idea: There are several global conservation agreements designed specifically to protect wildlife and habitats.

One of the greatest concerns facing conservationists today is the rapidly accelerating rate at which species are being lost. To help combat this, conservation agreements have been established which typically deal with environmental and conservation issues and are designed to provide long-term protection and conservation priorities for wildlife species and their habitats. Failure to comply with the conditions of the agreement can carry legal or trading implications. The UK has signed up to several European and international conservation agreements, but also has national conservation agreements in place, such as the Countryside Stewardship Scheme, which focusses on arable environments.

International agreements

There are several international treaties and conservation agreements between governments designed to conserve biodiversity. Two such agreements are the Rio Convention on Biological Diversity and the Convention of International Trade in Endangered Species (CITES).

Rio Convention on Biological Diversity

The Convention on Biological Diversity became active in 1993. It aims to develop strategies for the conservation and sustainable use of resources while maintaining biodiversity. It has three main goals:

- ▶ Conservation of biodiversity
- ▶ use of its (biodiversity's) components
- ▶ Fair and equitable sharing of the benefits arising from genetic resources.

CITES

CITES aims to ensure that trade in species animals and plants does not threaten their survival in the wild. Trade on products are controlled or prohibited depending upon the level of threat to each species. More than 35 000 species are protected under the agreement.

CITES banned trading in ivory (right) or ivory products in 1989. However poaching is still prevalent and large seizures of ivory by authorities still occur.

World Wide Fund for Nature

The World Wide Fund for Nature (WWF) is a non-governmental organisation focussed on the conservation of biodiversity and reduction of humanity's ecological footprint. It is the world's largest conservation organisation and operates in more than 100 countries. Its work currently focusses on six areas, centred around linking people with nature. The areas are climate, food, forests, fresh water, oceans, and policy influence.

One of the approaches the WWF and other NGOs use in conservation efforts is to convince governments to adopt and enforce environmentally friendly policies. One way to do this is to publicly release details when a government proposes a course of action with negative effects on the environment. For example, in 2012, WWF spoke out against the use of shale gas in the UK, saying the UK government needed to reaffirm its commitment to tackling climate change.

Domestic agreements

Most countries have a system of reserved lands focused on ecosystem conservation. These areas aim to protect and restore habitats of special importance and they may be intensively managed through pest and weed control, revegetation, reintroduction of threatened species, and site specific management practices.

1. State the main objectives of the following conservation agreements:

   (a) Rio Convention on Biological Diversity: _____

   _____

   _____

   (b) CITES: _____

   _____

   _____

2. Describe the aims of the WWF and explain its strategies for achieving these: _____

   _____

   _____

   _____

LINK 187 LINK 186

KNOW

202 Chapter Review

Summarise what you know about this topic under the headings and sub-headings provided. You can draw diagrams or mind maps, or write short notes to organise your thoughts. Use the images and hints to help you and refer back to the introduction to check the points covered:

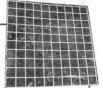

Ecological sampling

HINT: Describe sampling methods and examples of when they should be used.

Ecosystem structure

HINT: Describe components of ecosystems and trophic structures.

Energy transfers and nutrient cycles

HINT: Detail how energy is transferred through ecosystems including ecological pyramids. Describe the cycling of nitrogen and carbon.

© 2017 **BIOZONE** International
ISBN: 978-1-927309-26-1

Changes in ecosystems

HINT: Differences between primary and secondary
succession. Describe the effect of biotic and abiotic
factors on populations.

Human impact on ecosystems

HINT: Give examples of human impact on ecosystems,
including overfishing and climate change.

203 KEY TERMS: Did You Get It?

1. Test your vocabulary by matching each term to its definition, as identified by its preceding letter code.

abiotic factor

biotic factor

carbon cycle

competition

conservation

ecological pyramid

nitrogen cycle

nutrient cycle

primary succession

quadrat

secondary succession

transect

trophic level

A A line across a habitat along which organisms are sampled at set intervals to determine changes in community composition.

B The position an organism occupies on the food chain.

C A measured and marked region used to isolate a sample area for study.

D A term for any non-living part of the environment, e.g. rainfall, temperature.

E The processes by which nitrogen circulates between the atmosphere and the biosphere. Ammonification, denitrification and nitrification are all part of this cycle.

F An interaction between organisms exploiting the same resource.

G Biogeochemical cycle by which carbon is exchanged among the biotic and abiotic components of the Earth.

H The term used in ecology for any contribution to the environment by a living organism.

I A graphical representation of the numbers, energy, or biomass at each trophic level in an ecosystem. Pyramidal in shape, but sometimes inversely so.

J A succession sequence that takes place after a land clearance event (e.g. forest fire or landslide). It does not involve the loss of soil, seeds, or root stock.

K The act of protecting a resource so that it will be available in the future.

L A succession sequence that occurs on land that has not had plants or soil in the past or has been cleared of its vegetation by volcanic eruption or uplift.

M Cycle in which inorganic nutrients move between the abiotic and biotic environments.

2. (a) The graph (right) shows primary production in the oceans. Explain the shape of the curves:

_____

_____

(b) About 90% of all marine life lives in the photic zone (the depth to which light penetrates). Suggest why this is so:

_____

_____

_____

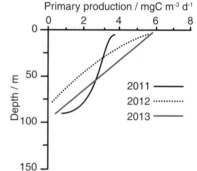

Primary production / mgC m^{-3} d^{-1}

2011 ——
2012 ········
2013 ——

Depth / m

3. A simple food chain for a cropland ecosystem is pictured below. Label the organisms with their trophic status (e.g. primary consumer).

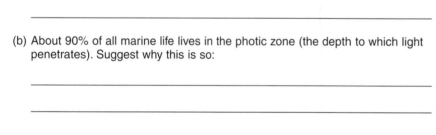

Corn   Mouse   Corn snake   Hawk

_____   _____   _____   _____

4. Increasing levels of atmospheric CO_2 and climate changes have been attributed to human activities such as the burning of fossil fuels (i.e. the changes are anthropogenic). Some people disagree with this viewpoint. Investigate the evidence for anthropogenic climate change, state whether you agree or disagree, and state the reasons for your opinion:

_____

_____

_____

REVISE

© 2017 **BIOZONE** International
ISBN: 978-1-927309-26-1
Photocopying Prohibited

Image credits

The writing team would like to thank the following people and organisations who have kindly provided photographs or illustrations for this edition:

• Dartmouth college for the electron micrograph images of the chloroplast • Louisa Howard Dartmouth college for the electron micrograph of the mitochondria • Wintec for the sports testing image • Dr David Wells, AgResearch • BioRad • Don Horne for the photo of the snails • Marc King for the photos of the chicken combs • Dr Frankhauser, University of Cincinatti, Clermont College for the photo of the Pacinian corpuscle • C Gemmil for the transect sampling photo • Jonathan Wright Bernard Field Station, Claremont College.

We also acknowledge the photographers who have made images available through Wikimedia Commons under Creative Commons Licences 2.0, 2.5, 3.0, or 4.0: • Kristian Peters • Masur • Tomoaki Horie • Madprime • CDC: Janice Haney Carr • Ute Frevert • Cesar Calderon: USDA, • Liang Qu IAEA • Greg Webb IAEA • Helena Paffen • C Beard • Obli • Volker Brinkmann PLOS • Maggie Bartlett, NHGRI • IRRI • Dr Graham Beards • 25kartika • Zephyris • NIMH • Lexicon genetics/HGRI • KTBN • Olaf Leillinger • Menna Jones • Mike Lehmann • Tangopaso • Ildar Sagdejev • Ragesoss • IGEM:Cambridge/2008/Turing Pattern Formation/Experiments/ Bacillus subtilis transfomation • Woutergroen • Dan Ferber • Roadnottaken • UC Regents David campus • Dr Frankhauser, University of Cincinatti, Clermont College • Mikael Haggstrom • Pollo • Dr D. Cooper: University of California San Francisco • Adorabutton • Iidar Sagdejev • RM Hunt • Graham Crumb • Sagt • Andreas Trepte • Stemonitis • Shirley Owens MSU • Wojsyl • Sharon Loxton • Janke • Rasbak • Mikrolit • Daderot • Marshal Hedin • Luc Viatour www.Lucnix.be • Paul Whippey • BirdPhotos. com • Edwin S • Doug Kerr • Peter Church • Precision Seafood Harvesting • Walter Siegmund • US Fish and Wildlife Service

Contributors identified by coded credits are:

BH: Brendan Hicks (Uni. of Waikato), CDC: Centers for Disease Control and Prevention, Atlanta, USA, EII: Education Interactive Imaging, MSU: Michigan State University, NASA: National Aeronautics and Space Administration, NIH: National Institute of Health, NOAA: National Oceanic and Atmospheric Administration , RA: Richard Allan, RCN: Ralph Cocklin, USDA: United States Department of Agriculture, USGS: United States Geological Survey, WBS: Warwick Silvester (Uni. of Waikato), WMU: Waikato Microscope Unit.

Royalty free images, purchased by Biozone International Ltd, are used throughout this workbook and have been obtained from the following sources: iStock, Corel Corporation from their Professional Photos CD-ROM collection; IMSI (Intl Microcomputer Software Inc.) images from IMSI's MasterClips® and MasterPhotos™ Collection, 1895 Francisco Blvd. East, San Rafael, CA 94901-5506, USA; ©1996 Digital Stock, Medicine and Health Care collection; © 2005 JupiterImages Corporation www.clipart.com; ©Hemera Technologies Inc, 1997-2001; ©Click Art, ©T/Maker Company; ©1994., ©Digital Vision; Gazelle Technologies Inc.; PhotoDisc®, Inc. USA, www.photodisc.com • TechPool Studios, for their clipart collection of human anatomy: Copyright ©1994, TechPool Studios Corp. USA (some of these images were modified by Biozone) • Totem Graphics, for their clipart collection • Corel Corporation, for use of their clipart from the Corel MEGAGALLERY collection • 3D images created using Bryce, Vue 6, Poser, and Pymol

Index